THROUGH A CITY ARCHWAY

By D. Chapman-Huston

DAISY, PRINCESS OF PLESS
FROM MY PRIVATE DIARY
    With Daisy, Princess of Pless

SIR SIDNEY LOW: A MEMOIR

By E. C. Cripps
PLOUGH COURT

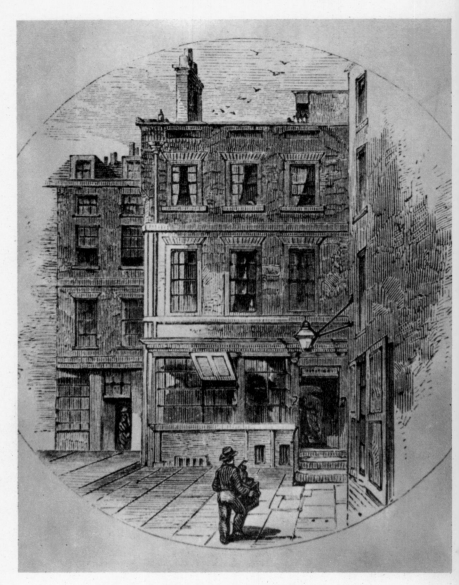

THE OLD PLOUGH COURT PHARMACY, 1715

THROUGH
A CITY ARCHWAY

The Story of Allen and Hanburys
1715–1954

By

DESMOND CHAPMAN-HUSTON

AND

ERNEST C. CRIPPS

Author of 'Plough Court'

LONDON
JOHN MURRAY, ALBEMARLE STREET

First Edition . . . 1954

Made and Printed in Great Britain by Butler & Tanner Ltd., Frome and London
and Published by John Murray (Publishers) Ltd.

CONTENTS

BOOK ONE: FOUNDATION

THE BEVAN PERIOD 1691–1814

BOOK TWO: EXPANSION

THE ALLEN PERIOD 1770–1843

v

CONTENTS

BOOK THREE: CONSOLIDATION

THE HANBURY PERIOD 1794–1893

CONTENTS

BOOK FOUR: REALIZATION

THE MODERN PERIOD 1894–1954

ILLUSTRATIONS

ILLUSTRATIONS

x

ILLUSTRATIONS

PREFACE

*T*HROUGH A CITY ARCHWAY—*The story of Allen &
Hanburys Ltd.* is a new book on the subject which was
dealt with in *Plough Court—The Story of a Notable
Pharmacy*, published in 1927. Since *Plough Court* was written,
research has been continuously carried on, not only with the old
records of Allen & Hanburys but more particularly with fresh
historical material which has come to hand during the intervening
years. In addition, and in spite of the vast upheaval of a second
World War, the last thirty years have seen a revolution in the
practice of medicine and pharmacy more profound than anything
previously seen in the whole history of mankind. The older
story has therefore been revised and added to, while more recent
events have been chronicled for the first time.

It is fortunate indeed that Mr. E. C. Cripps, the compiler of
Plough Court, has been able to act as joint author of the present
volume. In this work his fellow author has been Major Desmond
Chapman-Huston, an historical writer of grace and charm, whose
untimely death while his work was still uncompleted broke a
partnership which was a happy one on both sides.

The story here told begins in 1715 in Old Plough Court,
Lombard Street in the City of London, when one Silvanus Bevan,
an apothecary and Quaker, opened his shop in the house where
twenty-seven years or so earlier Alexander Pope, the poet, was
born. The business prospered and Timothy Bevan came from
Wales and joined his brother Silvanus in partnership : William
Allen became proprietor at the close of the eighteenth century
and forged a link with the Hanburys by marrying as his second
wife Charlotte Hanbury and taking her nephews into partnership.
The story touches throughout upon the history of the times ; the
rise of the Quakers in business and in those professions open to
them, the social life of the City of London in the eighteenth and
nineteenth centuries, the commercial and cultural ties between

PREFACE

Great Britain and North America both before and after the War
of Independence; the Napoleonic Wars, and the Industrial Revolution and the vast changes that it brought about in the life of
the country. The story is told of the metamorphosis of the
apothecary's shop into a great industrial organization with world-
wide ramifications.

The warmest thanks of the Company are given to all who in
any way have contributed to the production of this book.

These include the many correspondents, members of the Staff
of Allen & Hanburys and of the public who, for a period extending over many years, have supplied historical information relating
to the past history of the Firm and to the lives of the partners.
It is not possible here to give a list of the names of these, but we
feel that mention should be made of the valuable assistance given
by Mr. Whitfield J. Bell, Jr., of Dickinson College, Carlisle, Pa.,
U.S.A., who, having access to historical material not available in
this country, very kindly placed this at our disposal. This related
to the connection of the Bevans with medical men and hospitals
in North America and to their help in the eighteenth century
in founding the Pennsylvania Hospital, the first of its kind in
that country.

Many public libraries and those of educational and scientific
institutions have rendered invaluable assistance, for which grateful
thanks are given. The Librarians of the Society of Friends and
of the Pharmaceutical Society particularly, have always shown
a willing and courteous attention to requests for information
which often involved lengthy and protracted research. Without
such help, given in such a friendly spirit, the work of the authors
would have been considerably increased.

The Bibliography will be found on page 325 and quotations
from other books of reference have been freely used. Although
every effort has been made to give the source of such quotations,
it has not been found possible to do so in every case. The authors
offer their sincere apologies to those concerned for any such
omissions.

Finally, the Company wishes to express its deep appreciation
of the invaluable contribution of the late Major Chapman-Huston

and of the untiring labours of Mr. E. C. Cripps, most of whose
work was carried out during and after his eightieth year.

F. CAPEL HANBURY,
[Chairman of Allen & Hanburys Ltd.]

BETHNAL GREEN,
LONDON, E.2.
June, 1954.

Postscript. Frederick Capel Hanbury retired from the chairmanship of the Company on the 30th June, 1954, and was
succeeded in that position by his son, John Capel Hanbury.

BOOK ONE : FOUNDATION

THE BEVAN PERIOD

THE ART OF THE APOTHECARY

And the Lord said unto Moses, Take unto thee sweet spices, stacte, and onycha, and galbanum ; these sweet spices with pure frankincense : of each shall there be a like weight : and thou shalt make it a perfume, a confection after *the art of the apothecary*, tempered together, pure and holy.

EXODUS xxx. 34.

CHAPTER 1

THE ROMANCE OF PHARMACY

JOHN KEATS, whom Kipling—forgetting George Crabbe, Dante and some others—described as ' the only poet who was ever a druggist', was by no means the only druggist who was a poet. Indeed it might not be putting it too high to say that to be a good druggist or, as we say now, a good pharmacist, you must be something of a poet because it is one of the oldest, most far-reaching and most romantic professions or, if preferred, trades or crafts, in the world, and outside its sworn practitioners, it has fascinated men and women, lay and professional, all down the ages. Until the middle of the nineteenth century when some Darwinians—not Darwin—began to preach that man was merely an animal, the priest, the physician and the metaphysician often walked hand in hand, and it is arguable from the investigations of Freud, Jung, and Whitehead that we shall have little sound health, little bodily or mental wholeness, either individually or collectively, until their respective functions are reunited ; perhaps unavoidably, specialization and sectionalism now spread their dangerously segregating influence everywhere.

As the priests were the earliest known pharmacists it is worth while glancing at what some eminent ecclesiastics thought and did about the subject within comparatively recent times.

Few names in literature are more attractive than that of Mary, sister of the famous Sir Philip Sidney, who became Countess of Pembroke. Aubrey says that ' her genius lay as much towards Chymestrie as poetry ' ; one of her many attendant swains, Adrian Gilbert, half-brother of Sir Walter Raleigh, went even farther and roundly declared that she was ' more of an alchemist than a poet '. Another of Mary's close friends was Gerarde, the noted herbalist. George Herbert, a kinsman of Mary's husband, was Rector of Bemerton, which is close to Wilton, the magnificent Pembroke home near Salisbury. An authentic poet and considered by many a saint, George Herbert loved dabbling in medicaments, and in his wise book *The Country Parson* set it down as an axiom that an efficient rural clergyman must have knowledge of simples, asserting that :

> hyssope, valerian mercury, adder's tongue, yerrow melict and Saint John's wort made into a salve, and elder, camomell, mallowes, comphrey and smallage made into a poultis, have done great and rare cures.

Some hundred years after the Rector of Bemerton another divine, John Wesley, proved himself an equally keen and perhaps more dangerous amateur physician. In his *Primitive Physic* he mentions the occasional administration of half an ounce of mercury and even more for certain ailments !

With that great wit, master of irony, and brilliant prose writer, Sydney Smith (who lived to be Canon of Saint Paul's), we are almost in our own times. Completely captivated by the art of the apothecary, he confesses that he had ' a lifelong fancy for dabbling in medicine ' ; adding that wherever his clerical duties led him he assumed some of the functions of village doctor. When his six-months-old daughter was seized with cramp he says he gave her in twenty-four hours thirty-two grains of calomel besides bleeding, blistering and emetics. Having, apparently, an iron constitution, the infant survived. He wrote :

> I am performing miracles in my parish with garlic for whooping-cough. . . . We conquered the whooping-cough here with a pennyworth of Salts of Tartar, after having filled them with the expensive poisons of Holford. . . . I attended two of my children through a good stout fever of the typhus kind without ever calling in an apothecary, but for one day. . . . Douglas alarmed us the other night with the Croup. I darted into him all the mineral and vegetable resources of my shop, cravatted his throat with blisters and fringed it with leeches, and set him in five or six hours to playing marbles, breathing gently and

4

inaudibly. . . . Our evils have been want of water and scarlet fever in our village ; where, in three-quarters of a year, we have buried fifteen, instead of one per annum. You will naturally suppose that I have killed all these people by doctoring them. . . .

A master of dialectic, the great Sydney could ignore relevant fact with the best of us. He conveniently forgot that those suffering from whooping-cough had already been filled with ' the expensive poisons of the eminent Dr. Holford ' ; and that an apothecary had already been called in—if only for one day. On another occasion he asserted : ' The Sixth commandment is suspended, by one medical diploma, from the North of England to the South.' As we shall see, Sydney Smith confidently advised William Allen on farming and small holdings.

In those days parents had a firm belief in home-made nostrums ; addressing a Mrs. Henry Howard in a long metrical effusion entitled *The Poetical Medicine Chest* the author (or authoress) has, like Sydney Smith, small mercy for youthful sufferers :

> Spare not in Eastern blasts, when babies die,
> The wholesome rigour of the Spanish Fly.
> From timely torture seek thy infant's rest,
> And spread the poison on his labouring breast.
> And so, fair lady, when in evil hour
> Less prudent mothers mourn some faded flower,
> Six Howards valiant, and six Howards fair,
> Shall live, and love thee, and reward thy care.

Writing as late as 1870, Lady Burton, the remarkable wife of old ' Pack-pay-and-follow ' Burton, had no doubts of her own ability as a quack, Sir Richard's position as Her Britannic Majesty's Consul in Damascus giving her ample opportunities of inflicting herself and her nostrums upon the afflicted. She was of course right about the faith :

> . . . I found that with more natural instinct about medicine, and a few good herbs . . . that I managed to do a great deal of good . . . Our garden presented the strangest scene

in the afternoon—fever patients making wry faces over quinine wine, squalling babies guzzling oil, paralytic and rheumatic Bedouins being shampooed, and gouty old women having joints painted with iodine . . . they fancied my hands were blessed, and that no doctor could have done as well. Certainly there is a great deal in faith.[1]

[1] Quoted by Jean Burton in *Sir Richard Burton's Wife* (London, 1942. George G. Harrap & Co.).

CHAPTER 2

SILVANUS BEVAN

BEHIND every worth-while human achievement there are human beings, and this book will deal with the succession of knowledgeable men who, generously supported by their womenkind, founded, cherished, served and brought to lasting success a notable and far-flung business adventure. In the older meaning of the words a merchant venturer was one who, like Queen Elizabeth I, risked other people's money, a merchant adventurer, one who risked his own. For a period of some two hundred and forty years the worthies whose inspiring stories we are about to retell were each, in the true sense, Merchant Adventurers, their world-wide activities covering the innumerable developments of our social progress from the reign of George I to that of Elizabeth II. By them and their like in every trade and profession the greatness of England and the British Commonwealth and Empire was founded stone by stone, often painfully and in hardship ; and it is only by them and their like that the best of the old traditions can be perpetuated in the modern world.

To be born a Quaker was in many ways a piece of good fortune for anyone belonging to a commercial people such as the British. In any business community integrity, reliability, industry and craftsmanship are essential to success, and they are qualities ordained and nurtured by the Quaker way of life.

In 1715, the year after George I ascended the throne, Silvanus Bevan, then aged twenty-four, opened an apothecary's shop in Old Plough Court, off famous Lombard Street, within that square mile historically known as the City of London, the premises being leased to him by the Quaker merchant, Salem Osgood. That Silvanus had ability, industry, courage and enterprise is proved by the fact that he had only just been admitted to the

7

Freedom of the Society of Apothecaries ; this official Society was founded in 1617, and in its Minute Book Bevan's admission is thus recorded :

> 1715. July 5th Silvanus Bevan. Apprentice of Thomas Mayleigh having served 7 years and paid a fine of £6.9 for ye remainder of his time according to Ye Order of Court of Assists., was examined, approved, sworne, and made free.

Research in the Archives of the City of London reveals nothing about Thomas Mayleigh who so thoroughly taught Silvanus his trade, but there is presumptive evidence that his apothecary's shop may have been in Cheapside.

Unfortunately little is known about the forbears of the self-reliant Silvanus except that he came of good Welsh Quaker stock. His grandfather, William Bevan, who was born in 1627, was an alderman and merchant of Swansea ; he married, and all we know of his wife is that she was named Priscilla. William is remembered in his native city to this day as the donor of the Quaker meeting-house and the large plot of ground on which it stands.

William and Priscilla had a son named Silvanus (Silvanus I) who married Jane Phillips ; it was their second son, also named Silvanus (Silvanus II), who became in due course Thomas Mayleigh's likeable apprentice.

Apart from faithfully serving his master and thoroughly learning his craft young Silvanus went courting early, suitably and successfully. Before the end of the year in which he became a fully qualified apothecary he married. His choice was Elizabeth, the daughter of Daniel Quare, a noteworthy person in his own right. Daniel invented and made the first repeating watches and, in 1695, obtained a patent for a portable weather-glass. He was by Royal Appointment clockmaker to George I ; [1] examples of his craftmanship are sought after by connoisseurs to this day.

The marriage of Silvanus Bevan to Elizabeth Quare took place at the Friends' Meeting House, White Hart Court, Gracechurch Street, in the City of London, on November 9th, 1715. A copy of the marriage certificate is preserved in the British Museum and,

[1] Appendix One.

as was the fashion amongst Quakers then and for long afterwards, it bears the signatures of a large number of witnesses, in this instance more than one hundred. As a Quaker, Daniel Quare had at first refused to take the oath of allegiance, but this difficulty was eventually overcome, and, that he was highly thought of in Royal circles, is proved by the fact that amongst the many notabilities present at the marriage of Silvanus and Elizabeth was ' a large party from the Court '.

Before he married at the age of twenty-four, Silvanus had been through a strenuous training and served, as have so many pharmaceutical apprentices since his time, seven laborious years. We do not know exactly what urged him to become an apothecary, or why he moved to London ; there were apothecaries in Swansea where he could have served his apprenticeship outside the jurisdiction of the Society of Apothecaries which controlled only those practising the ' art and mystery ' within the City of London and seven miles thereof. However, from our subsequent knowledge of the man we may assume that a right ambition, and the desire to excel amongst his peers, inspired him and then, as now, London was the Mecca of the eager and adventurous.

Before Silvanus was bound apprentice to Thomas Mayleigh he must have given to the Society proof of a fairly liberal education and, in particular, that he had acquired a sound knowledge of elementary Latin. We know from the Minutes of the Society that as early as 1683 a boy who desired to be bound apprentice was rejected for insufficiency in the Latin tongue. Silvanus satisfied the authorities and began his specialized or, as we would say, vocational training for his profession. Let us, in these days when everything educational is made sweet and easy, briefly survey what the lad had to go through.

His examination (after serving his apprenticeship) was concerning his knowledge and Election of Simples, and concerning the preparing, dispensing, handling, commixing and compounding of medicines. When he had satisfied the examiners in these matters he was at liberty :

to have, keep or furnish an Apothecary's Shop, or to prepare, make, mingle, work, compound, give, apply, minister, utter, put forth, sell or set on sale, any medicines or otherwise by any other ways or means exercise the Art of an Apothecary, or any part thereof within the City of London and Liberties and Suburbs of the same, or within seven miles of the same City.

The greater part of his knowledge would have been gained from his practical work in the shop where he was apprenticed. There he would have opportunities for examining a large number of drugs and animal substances. He would also have to visit the markets and shops where such goods were sold, and the gardens where many were grown, such as the Chelsea physic garden. Then he would take part in the 'herbarizings and simplings' of the Society. These excursions took place in the summer on set days and were in the nature of botanical walks or rambles in the country which in those days meant a mere mile or two from the City. The Master, wardens, and other officials of the Society of Apothecaries participated, as well as the members and apprentices. On June 21st, 1627, it is recorded that a 'simpling' started at five in the morning at 'Graies Inne in Holborne to make acquaintance with all the vegetable tribes'.

Valuable practical knowledge of manufacturing on a substantial scale, which he put to good purpose afterwards, was probably obtained by Silvanus from visits to the Laboratory of the Society of Apothecaries, set up in 1671 for the purpose of making reliable preparations, both chemical and galenical.[1]

[1] The word galenical means a medicine compounded of a mixture of chemical and/or vegetable drugs. It is derived from the name Galen, a distinguished Arabian physician of the second century A.D.

CHAPTER 3

THE APOTHECARIES AND
THE DISPENSARIES

AT this point it will be well to look back to the formation of the Society of Apothecaries which then, and for many years afterwards, controlled the entire professional life of Silvanus Bevan, and of every chartered apothecary. In very early times the sale of drugs was in the hands of the grocers. The Grocers' Company is first heard of in 1373, but it seems to have had its origin in the Guild of Pepperers, which was not new in 1180, for it is on record that the Pepperers of Soper Lane were allied with the Spicers of Cheap. The grocers in those days had very little in common with our modern conception of a grocer. They were men who dealt wholesale in contradistinction to the shopkeeper or retailer.

The apothecary was in ancient times a grocer, as were also some herbalists and sellers of drugs. Many of them had been assistants to the Physicians, whose College was founded in 1518, and subsequently they had opened their own shops. In 1606 the apothecaries had, in the first instance, been incorporated with the grocers, but the partnership was not satisfactory, and in 1617 they were separated from them by Royal Charter and the grocers were forbidden to keep an apothecary's shop. In 1624 King James I declared to the Civic Authorities of the City of London that 'he had passed the patent to the Society of Apothecaries from his own judgment for the health of his people, knowing that grocers were not competent judges of the practice of medicine'. It should be noted that the chartered apothecaries were from the first something more than mere dispensers of the medicines ordered by the physician. By their Charter of 1617 they were authorized to give and apply medicines, and as a consequence appear to have had the right of entry to the houses of their customers to an extent denied to those who merely sold or dispensed medicines.

Upon its foundation the Society, its Master and wardens were invested with considerable powers, and in 1694 apothecaries were exempted from serving the offices of constable or scavenger, and from other parish duties and attendance on juries. The apothecaries were in fact becoming a powerful, influential and wealthy body ; their number had increased from the original one hundred and fourteen to nearly one thousand ; as assistants to the physicians they were beginning to practise medicine as well as pharmacy and the physicians, growing jealous of them, suggested legislation to confine them to their original condition of grocers and vendors of drugs. The contest became heated ; pamphlets with long and involved titles were published from both sides. For the apothecaries it was claimed that their improved status had been of great benefit to the public, and that the physicians were trying to undo the good work their predecessors had done in forming themselves into a chartered company. The physicians argued that the apothecaries made extortionate charges for their wares and in many instances a person of slender means could not afford to pay both the physician and the apothecary : in proof of this statement amounts charged by some of the apothecaries were published which, if correct, were certainly on the heavy side.

The outcome of this agitation was that the physicians, in order to help poor patients who could not afford to pay the charges for medicines made by the apothecaries, united and set up dispensaries where they supplied medicines on reasonable terms, employing assistants to dispense them under their own supervision. There were three of these establishments in London ; coming into operation about the beginning of 1697 they not only dispensed physicians' prescriptions or ' bills ' as they were called, but sold drugs as well.

It can easily be imagined that these doctors' dispensaries gave great offence to the apothecaries. A violent paper contest again started and more pamphlets were published on both sides of the question. The apothecaries argued that the drugs used in the dispensaries were of poor or bad quality and the assistants employed were unqualified. The physicians retorted that, among other things, the medicines supplied were of the best, that in their dispensaries there were many excellent remedies ' which have never yet been trusted in the apothecaries' shops ' and that the patient could be served : ' quantity for quantity and quality for quality, fifteen shillings in the pound cheaper than anywhere else, which is a thrift the greatest man that does not love to be cheated need not be ashamed of '.

It was stated that in the three London dispensaries some twenty thousand prescriptions were made up yearly, and that : ' the doses of the electuaries, juleps, pills, etc., one with the other, may be about a penny apiece, though even the most useful drug, though of the highest prices, is in every composition '. It will be seen later that the physicians from one of these dispensaries were successful for a time in obtaining the business of supplying the Navy with drugs.

As pointed out in Bell and Redwood's *Progress of Pharmacy*, it is not easy amidst the rival claims of physicians and apothecaries to arrive at the truth, but it seems clear that the dispensaries set up by the physicians flourished, and, state the authors :

we have reason to believe that the Assistants employed and instructed by the Physicians at these institutions, became dispensing chemists on their own account ; and that some of the Apothecaries who found their craft in danger, followed the example, *from which source we may date the origin of the Chemists and Druggists.*

CHAPTER 4

THE OLD PLOUGH COURT
PHARMACY

MUCH of all this was common knowledge when Silvanus
Bevan started the Plough Court Pharmacy in 1715,
and no doubt echoes of the controversies reached him
while he was serving his apprenticeship. As a Quaker his business policy was summed up in his determination to sell good
drugs at fair prices, to make as many preparations as he could
on his own premises, and as opportunity offered to extend his
business beyond the confines of Plough Court.

Competition is one of the many ways to excellence and Silvanus
Bevan had to meet plenty of it. It is evident that in the reign
of George I not only grocers but several classes of traders sold
drugs and chemicals. The grocers had long been not only the
wholesalers but the retailers of crude drugs as well, such as
roots, barks, herbs and other vegetable and animal substances,
but, although by 1715 much of this trade had passed to the
druggists, the grocers, clinging to their perquisites, still sold
drugs, particularly in the provinces where there was more
freedom ; they even occasionally still dispensed medicines.

The druggists, already a considerable body, obtained and sold
both wholesale and retail such drugs as were once the monopoly
of the grocers, and, like them, did not scruple to compound
and dispense medicines when they had the opportunity.

But there now comes into the picture still another body, the
chymists, who, originally, specialized in the preparation of
medicines of mineral origin and who were about this time
beginning to keep shops in which they sold both drugs and
chemicals and got any business they could from the compounding of medicines generally and the making-up of physicians'
prescriptions.

THE OLD PLOUGH COURT PHARMACY, ABOUT 1856

THE OLD PLOUGH COURT PHARMACY, ABOUT 1870

The extent of the competition to which young Silvanus had to face when he began business at Plough Court can be estimated from the fact that while there were then only nine apothecaries between Holborn and Aldgate, shortly after there were within the area no less than thirty-nine druggists' and two chymists' shops ; eighteen of these were within half a mile of Plough Court and three in adjoining Lombard Street.

Plough Court was, in those days, a cul-de-sac ; modern Plough Court is a passage from famous Lombard Street, to Lombard Court, which runs from Clement's Lane to Gracechurch Street. Plough Court, as late as 1870, was entered from Lombard Street through the archway, which gives this book its title, and which is shown in the woodcut on the title-page. The residence of Silvanus Bevan, number two, faced this passage and could be seen by those passing down Lombard Street ; in front of it was a forecourt or yard common to all the houses in the court. From this yard ingress could be obtained to the spacious cellars below the buildings.

The houses in the Court were numbered one, two and three and dated back to 1668, occupying the site of earlier buildings destroyed in the Great Fire of London in 1666. Number two appears to have been well suited for the calling of an apothecary. It was a lofty three-storeyed building with offices, with good-sized rooms, in one of which Alexander Pope, the poet, was born in May or June, 1688.[1]

An old writer says :

The Apothecary's house, when in a city or town, should be in an appropriate and lucid place. It must be ample and high that such simples as should be kept dry may be reposed in its highest room and such as should be moist in its cellar.

Numbers two and three Plough Court had commodious cellars in which the moist ' simples ' could be kept. Whether Elizabeth Bevan allowed her husband to keep the dry ones in the attics or upper rooms is not known, but the shop of the apothecary was always redolent of its contents, and there are allusions to

[1] Appendix Two.

this by the poets and dramatists. Shakespeare, in *The Merry Wives of Windsor*, makes Falstaff refer to the lisping hawthorn buds that come like women in men's apparel, and smell like Bucklersbury in simple time. In Charles the Second's reign a writer speaks of Bucklersbury, the street of the apothecaries and perfumers, being replete with physic drugs and spicery, he says it was so perfumed at the time with the pounding of spices, melting of gums, and making of perfumes, that it escaped the great plague.

Unfortunately no illustration exists that would give a true idea of the appearance of the interior of the Bevan shop in the eighteenth century and particularly of its fittings. The writer quoted above, after speaking of the apothecary's shop and house, goes on to say :

> And that his medicaments may be duly disposed in his pharmacopoly, many shelves must be classically collocated therein from the bottom upwards, upon wooden and iron nails fastened in the walls, and the partition betwixt the kitchen (or laboratory) and the shop, so that some of their rows may include the lesser, some greater boxes, some earthen pots, some glasses, some tin vessels and some wooden vessels. The names also of the medicaments must be inscribed upon every vessel and bag wherein they are included, that the medicaments to be exhibited may soon be seen and not mistaken for another.

There seems no doubt that Bevan, quite early in his career, possessed a laboratory for making many of the preparations used in his business. We have some proof of this in the statement by William Cookworthy, one of his assistants of whom we shall hear later, writing of the necessity for using a certain large still head for the evaporation of sea-water, said that ' Silvanus Bevan has such a still '.

To complete this slight sketch of the house and shop we need some idea of the contents of the boxes, earthen pots, glasses, tin vessels, wooden vessels, and other containers. It should be remembered that it was still the empirical age in medicine. The science of chemistry, for instance, was so little advanced that the

real composition of articles used as medicines was seldom understood and in many instances different virtues were attributed to
the same substance, according to the source from whence it was
obtained. Crab's eyes, prepared pearls and oyster shells, for
example, were severally recommended as specifics in certain
ailments, although the qualities of these remedies were supposed
to be essentially different. A good idea of the pharmacy, or
poly-pharmacy of the early eighteenth century, can be obtained
from a study of the Pharmacopoeia actually used by the Bevans
and still in existence ; this was a copy of *Pharmacopoeia Londinensis
(The New London Dispensatory)*, published in 1677 and annotated
by the owner or his assistants. It is claimed that in this Pharmacopoeia, in six sections, is the whole art of healing, ' with the
preparations, virtues and uses of all simple medicaments, vegetable, animal and mineral—together with some choice medicines
by the Author '. It is a reformed edition (the preceding one
is dated 1650), the inference being that many of the absurd and
unverified remedies of earlier editions were omitted. Even so,
there are lists of substances such as earthworms, woodlice, the
slough of a snake, the dung of various animals, as well as some
others, which must have been difficult to obtain and more
difficult to swallow, such as the fat of a man, the horn of a
unicorn, and moss growing on a human skull. Reading this
book and noting the astrological reference to the collection and
prescribing of some of its contents one seems :

> To catch the far-off murmurs of generations of mediaeval
> doctors, prescribing for their unhappy patient with their
> eyes on the midnight horizon and cupping him at the bidding
> of the stars.

Some time before 1730 Silvanus was joined by his brother
Timothy Bevan ; they soon issued a wholesale list entitled :
*A Catalogue of Druggs, and of Chemical and Galenical Medicines,
Prepared and sold by Silvanus and Timothy Bevan in Plow Court,
in Lombard Street, London.* From a perusal of its pages it is
evident that the more disgusting of the remedies mentioned in
the 1677 Pharmacopoeia were apparently not stocked, or at any

rate they did not appear in the list ; but there are others listed which, because of their historical interest and empirical composition, deserve notice.[1]

The ' catalogue ' was divided into three sections : ' Druggs ', Galenicals, Chemicals. In the list of the first named many chemicals, as now understood, are included, and in the list of chemicals many galenical preparations appear. It is noteworthy that a number of these are in use to-day and are to be found in the *British Pharmacopœia*, although the methods of making them may have been changed and the formulæ of many have been simplified.

The few chemicals listed show the preponderance of herbs, roots, barks, leaves and preparations made from them over the comparatively few ' chemical medicines ' which were not very popular as remedies : amongst those in the Bevan list are alum, arsenic, antimony and several of its salts, borax, calomel, cream of tartar, calamine, liquid ammonia and carbonate, magnesia, mercury and several salts, sugar of lead, sal ammoniac, sulphur, black and precipitated, white vitriol, tartar emetic ; the acids were nitric, sulphuric and hydrochloric.

There is no mention of any of the large number of medicinal specifics, many of which were patented and were called then and for many years afterwards patent medicines. The first patent for such was granted in 1711 to Timothy Byfield for his ' sal oleosum volatile '. By the year 1748 a list of more than two hundred was published in the *Gentleman's Magazine* under the title of Pharmacopoeia Empirical. The trade carried on in such articles became so extensive that in 1783 the Government considered them to be ' very proper subjects in taxation ' and the Patent Medicine Stamp Duty was imposed by Act of Parliament. Vendors other than those who had served a regular apprenticeship to a surgeon, apothecary, druggist, or chemist, were required to take out an annual licence to sell these articles.

No doubt many of Silvanus Bevan's customers were the friends and acquaintances of Daniel Quare, his father-in-law, who was quite a popular character with influence extending as far as Court

[1] Appendix Three.

circles. It should be noted that in 1715 London, even in the City, was then rural in character; shopkeepers and merchants lived over their places of business; and many of the houses had spacious gardens attached. From such dwellers in the neighbourhood, as is proved by the Plough Court prescription and account books of one hundred years or so later, the shop drew a considerable number of customers.

It was not long before Silvanus Bevan was able to leave the routine of the business to his assistants, and travel, no doubt with the idea of extending it on the wholesale side. He achieved considerable success and by 1725, only ten years after starting at Plough Court, at the early age of thirty-nine, he achieved the highest possible professional status by becoming a Fellow of the Royal Society, being nominated for that honour by Henry Heathcote, F.R.S.

Silvanus had a son by his first wife Elizabeth Quare. The infant died within a few hours of birth, and Elizabeth did not long survive it. He married as his second wife, Martha, daughter of Gilbert Heathcote of Calthorpe, Derby; they had no children.

In his later years Silvanus practised as a physician, as was the custom with many apothecaries, and was known by courtesy as Dr. Bevan. That he possessed considerable knowledge of anatomy and similar subjects is shown by the fact that in May, 1743, he sent a letter to the Royal Society which was printed in *Philosophical Transactions* that year. Entitled *An Account of an Extraordinary Case of the Bones of a Woman Growing Soft and Flexible, communicated to the Royal Society by Mr. Silvanus Bevan*, it describes how he had the curiosity to make a post-mortem examination, and gave a summary of his findings.

The second letter was sent to Dr. James Jurin, F.R.S., a well-known physician of his day, who obtained considerable publicity through the part he played in supporting the practice of inoculation for small-pox.[1] He published annually accounts of the *Success of Inoculating the Small-pox in Great Britain*, and it was Bevan's wish that his letter to Jurin should be included in the account for the year 1725.

---

[1] Letter to Dr. Jurin. Appendix Four.

Two years later Silvanus was corresponding with James Logan, deputy in Pennsylvania to William Penn, and Secretary to the Colony. Elsewhere will be found an account of the relations of Silvanus and his brother, Timothy, with the Pennsylvania Hospital.

A Quaker Post Bag, by Mrs. Godfrey Locker Lampson, published in 1910, contains a number of letters written from 1693 to 1742 by prominent Quakers to Sir John Rodes, the Quaker baronet of Barlborough Hall, Derbyshire; amongst them are two from Silvanus Bevan. The one dated August 16th, 1719, was written to his brother-in-law, Cornelius Heathcote, whose sister, Martha, second wife of Silvanus, was a niece of Sir John Rodes. The purpose of the letter was to announce the sad news that Dr. Gilbert Heathcote, the writer's father-in-law, had been thrown from his ' chariott' near Highgate ' about ten o'clock fifth day night last, on his return from seeing a patient by which he received a violent contusion of the brain and died in about half an hour '.

This letter has some Bevan family interest as it shows that when he wrote it Silvanus had not been long married to Martha, as he begins : ' I am sorry the first occasion of my writing to thee since my being in your family should be on so melancholy an occasion.'

The second letter was written to Sir John Rodes and is dated March 15th, 1742. It is a gossipy epistle evidently meant to cheer up the worthy baronet after ' an extreme fitt of sickness '. Bevan, although a Quaker, was, it would seem, no ascetic :

I hope thou received the hamper of wine safe, the Clarett Hermitage, Burgundy, and Champagne I had of a French wine March^t, who engaged to put in the best. The old Madeira 30 years old, the Canary and Cyprus 18 years old, were out of my own cellar and the Usquebach is a present of Dr. Mead's and is very old and the best, which he recommended as a good remedy for those constant vomitings thou wast then attended with.

A footnote seems to show that at times Bevan acted as an

agent for his former father-in-law, Daniel Quare, the clock-maker :

> I intend to send thy watch (which has been ready some time) by Joseph Broadbent, there has been a great deal done to it and the repeating part is repaired.

The phrase ' there has been a great deal done to it ' became an axiom in the watchmaking trade, and so remains !

In the *Morris Letters*, edited by J. H. Davies, M.A., 1907, we get a glimpse of Bevan at the age of seventy. A free transcription of the extract says :

> Last Sunday of all Sundays, the atmosphere sultry and airless, early that day I travelled to the village of Hackney and was introduced to the famous Sylvanus Bevan,[1] the Quaker F.R.S. Very great welcome by him, living well on good food and drinks. Walked in the beautiful garden where there is in the earth every kind of flowers, plants and vegetables, also fruit trees and flowering shrubs, etc., the noble statue of the Gladiator, mentioned by Pliny to have been found in Britain and other curious figures. An area by the garden with variety of poultry, mostly foreign, two shells from India to hold water for them, weighing each about 300 pounds. In the house a variety of curious paintings and rich old china, and a large library containing books on most subjects, several of the first printed ones in ethics, Latin folios exactly imitating the written characters of those days : can speak Welsh fluently.
>
> Greatly desirous of being acquainted with British antiquities, but never saw British MSS., was surprised we had any. Wished he could be fairly convinced that the Saxons borrowed their letters from us. A hundred of other subjects we talked about—I am to see him again and to get him Powell's Caradog if possible.

He says his intellects are as strong as ever and that he has pleasure in reading a book now as he was when a young man. He was bred a chymist and apothecary, but has practised as a physician for many years. Now he is retired

---

[1] He spelt his Christian name Silvanus.

from all business. He is a batchelor (widower ?) and his brother who has a family of children keeps on the trade at the old shop in Lombard Street. He is visited by most great men of taste, also by the Ministry, being one of the leading men among the Quakers. . . . I wish I had known him sooner !

Silvanus was skilful in carving ivory, and several miniature busts of well-known men of the time, carved by him, are still to be found in private collections ; a well-known one was that of William Penn ; the circumstances of its origin are given in *William Penn*, by John W. Graham, accompanied by a photographic illustration.

When Lord Cobham was setting up the statues of famous men in his garden at Stowe, he made enquiries of a likeness of Penn, but could find none. Sylvanus Bevan, a Quaker, who had a great talent for cutting likenesses of persons whom he had known, hearing of Lord Cobham's desire, set himself to recollect Penn's face with which he had been well acquainted. From his accurate memory he cut this very ivory medallion and sent it to Lord Cobham without any letter or information. On receiving it, my Lord, who had personally known Penn, immediately exclaimed, ' Whence came this ? It is William Penn himself.'

So we leave Silvanus Bevan II in his spacious house at Hackney amongst his works of art, furnished with good food and drink, surrounded by his own flowers and fruit ; honoured, learned, paid court to by the great and distinguished but, in spite of all, perhaps a little lonely.

CHAPTER 5

TIMOTHY BEVAN

W E are now concerned with Timothy Bevan, the fourth son of Silvanus I of Swansea, and his wife Jane Phillips. He seems to have arrived at Plough Court in 1724 or 1725 about the time his eldest brother Silvanus took over the lease of number three ; tradition says that, before doing so, Timothy had completed his medical studies at Leyden. The following extract is from the Register of the Society of Apothecaries :

> London, March 11, 1730. Mr. Timothy Bevan, who as he says has been bred an Apothecary, in the country, and has been some time with his brother, Mr. Silvanus Bevan, a Member of this Company, desires his Freedom of this Society by Redemption ; ordered—that on payment of £25, and 40/– to the Garden and the usual Fees, and passing an Examination, he be made free. He was admitted to the Freedom accordingly on April 6th, 1731.

It is probable that soon after Timothy became a Freeman of the Society the brothers entered into a formal business partnership as in the *London Directory* for 1731 appears the entry : Silvanus and Timothy Bevan, Apothecaries, Lombard Street.

And now took place one of those marriages that change the course of family history. In 1735 Timothy married Elizabeth Barclay at the Bull and Mouth Meeting House in Aldersgate in the City of London. She bore him five children, four sons and one daughter. Three of the four sons were by a curious and perplexing persistency named Silvanus—perhaps, as in anticipation, the heir of their childless uncle. Two, however, dying in infancy, the third Silvanus baby reigned alone and lived to become one of the early pillars of the notable banking family

23

of Barclay ; he was also a partner in what was afterwards known as the Barclay and Perkins brewery once owned by Henry Thrale, the great friend of Dr. Johnson. Ten years after the marriage Elizabeth died, their entire married life having been spent at Plough Court in that part of the business premises once occupied by Silvanus.

Timothy remained a widower for seven years and, in 1752, married Hannah, widow of Nathaniel Springall of Norwich. A daughter of Joseph and Hannah Gurney of Norwich, this marriage connected the remarkable and happily still flourishing families of Barclay, Gurney and Bevan. Timothy brought Hannah to Hackney where, near brother Silvanus, he by then owned a large house and grounds the site of which is now covered by Mare Street and Loddidge Street ; [1] a description of the place and its owners survives :

> One of those sound Georgian villas with plenty of well-kept flower beds and shrubberies, where solid and expensive comfort was joined with the Quaker dread of worldly show. When we look back into the lives of our ancestors who lived in the eighteenth century, we must make due allowance for their peculiar environments, for the Quaker world was aloof, and aloft, and somewhat detached from the general structure of life. They were distinguished from the world, they were unlike other people, they were Friends.

Timothy's person is :

> . . . thin, as to height of the middle size, and of complexion uncommonly sallow ; he wore a white wig, and as it was the custom of each Plain Friend in those days to choose a colour and stick to it, he always appeared in light drab. He was of a temper the very opposite to cheerfulness and affability, in all his deportment, you seemed to hear the language of ' stand off '.

Timothy, in fact, enjoyed bad health which would largely account for the sallow complexion, austere person, and low spirits. This

[1] Appendix Five.

TIMOTHY BEVAN, 1704–1786

is borne out by a letter of one of the sons of a contemporary preserved in the Library of the Society of Friends :

> My Father, you must know, was a drug grinder, and we often had dealings with him, Timothy Bevan, Thos. Corbyn and several other Quakers, and although we deemed them good customers with respect to pay, yet they were generally cross and difficult to please. When I lived with my Father I was young, and used to collect in our bills ; if any of them did not happen to agree with their books, when I called for payment, I was sure to be huffed, or the bill of parcels flung at me with ' Make that amount right before thee comest here for the money '. The mistake was sometimes a half-penny or a penny too much or too little charged, and sometimes a day wrong in the date, yet they would growl and be ready to snap my head off. ' Whenever I see a person snappish, cross or surly,' once said a friend of mine, ' conclude that they are with respect to health unwell, or they could not behave so.' Now admitting the hypothesis, we may with propriety exclaim, ' How poorly our ancestors always were ! '

A year after the death of Silvanus Bevan II at Hackney on June 8th, 1765, at the age of seventy-four, the style of the Firm was changed to Timothy Bevan and Sons, Druggists and Chemists, Plough Court, Lombard Street, Timothy having by then taken into partnership his two elder sons, Timothy II and Silvanus III ; two years later, however, when Silvanus III abandoned the Plough Court business to become a partner in Barclay's Bank, the ' s ' was dropped from sons.

In 1773 Timothy II predeceased his father, who for two following years appears to have carried on the business alone and lived mainly at Plough Court. In 1775 Timothy I retired to Hackney, having handed over the business to his younger son, Joseph Gurney Bevan, the child of his second marriage, sometimes visiting Plough Court to see how things were going on without him. On June 12th, 1786, he died at Hackney aged eighty-two years.

What sort of a private life did these plain Quakers live as

they prospered and advanced in the world ? Of course not all Quakers moved into large suburban houses on the outskirts of London—although a surprising number of them did. The majority, however :

. . . lived over their business premises ; at the end of the eighteenth century London was still a place of green fields and gardens. Mrs. Elizabeth Hanbury, who died in 1901 at the age of one hundred and eight, used to speak of her home in Leadenhall Street with its large gardens and a summerhouse ! Dr. Hingston Fox, in *Dr. John Fothergill and His Friends*, writes of the ' best Quaker Society in the city, then full of the residence of merchants '.

The Fothergills visited David Barclay in his fine house in Cheapside with his consort and lovely daughter Agatha ; the Gurneys, the Bevans of Plough Court, John Eliot of Bartholomew Close, Abraham Gray of Newgate Street, the Capel Hanburys of Mark Lane, the Corbyns of Bartholomew Square, the Fosters of Bromley, and the Beaufoys of Cupers Bridge were among their friends. . . .

That is the first mention we have in this story of the Capel Hanburys ; later the name will become very familiar. St. Fond, the distinguished French geologist, painted what some may be disposed to regard as an exaggerated picture of Quaker social life towards the end of the eighteenth century :

Where women in other ranks of society were wearing great erections on their heads of powdered artificial hair so high as to be cumbersome and, in addition, were smothering their faces with paint tricked out with black patches of varying shapes, and scenting themselves heavily because baths were not considered healthy, the Quaker women wore their beautiful hair free and floating with becoming gracefulness on handkerchiefs uncommonly white and fine.

St. Fond also speaks of supping one evening with Dr. Lettson, the Quaker physician, when some of the most amiable women in London were of the party :

One of their chief attractions was their elegant but simple dress made from stuffs of beauty and excellent quality and above all the charming faces and the grace of those who wore it.

The meal was on a table of the finest mahogany and the exquisitely flavoured meat and choice vegetables were served up in dishes of an elegant form. Dessert and comfits followed, with other delicacies and a variety of wines in crystal decanters.

A lively but decorous gaiety with the frankest good nature animated the scene although judged by the standards of other classes of 18th century society the topics discussed in the candle-lit drawing-rooms might be regarded as tepid and uninteresting.

There was perhaps an absence of literary, sporting, artistic and dramatic small talk ; gambling was unknown and visits to the theatre where the genius of Garrick and Mrs. Siddons was attracting all classes were alien to the Quaker way of life. Even such a simple relaxation as the enjoyment of music, whether vocal or instrumental—in spite of the great popularity of such great composers as Bach, Handel, Haydn and Mozart—was frowned upon ; indeed one hundred years later a warning against ‘ indulging in music especially what goes by the name of sacred music ’ was issued from one of the Yearly Meetings of the Society of Friends.

The conversation at such gatherings would be on family matters and the thees and thous would be heard from small groups who might be discussing the business of the last Monthly Meeting or of that to be discussed at the next. Perhaps a Friend who had recently returned from missionary work abroad would give a talk on his experiences, or some method of giving practical help to a deserving cause or movement would be discussed. There was plenty of cheerful and even witty talk, but scandal was rightly frowned upon.

CHAPTER 6

JOSEPH GURNEY BEVAN

ROM 1775, when Joseph Priestley began his *Experiments and Observations on Different Kinds of Air* and Joseph Gurney Bevan took over control of the Plough Court business from his father Timothy, the Firm's records, being from then onward much more extensive and complete, its uninterrupted and fascinating progress can be followed with greater ease, Joseph's letters with his highly individual signature being particularly noticeable.

At the age of seventeen he ceased using the ' heathen names of the months ' and in his letter-books the month is always designated numerically. This custom was continued by the Firm for another sixty years or so, although occasionally, in correspondence, the expression was used ' the month called January ', in place of ' 1st month '.

The letter-books, the first of which covers the period 1775–8, and continue uninterruptedly until 1885, constitute a unique record of the history of the Firm for the period ; always written and signed by a partner, the letters in the letter-books were regarded as the original document, and the letter sent to the correspondent as the copy. Those were leisurely days and frequently not more than one letter was recorded in a day, although sometimes it might well occupy two foolscap pages.

These books were carefully indexed ; the ink has not faded sufficiently to render the writing illegible ; some volumes show signs of fires which broke out at Plough Court ; many of them were soaked with water in the bombing of the Bethnal Green Factory of 1940, but careful drying, and in some cases re-binding, have restored them to a condition in which they will remain serviceable for many years yet.

The earliest ledger dates from 1780 ; the earliest ' waste ' books from 1773, these being books in which both wholesale and overseas' sales were entered and then transferred to other volumes.

In reading the letter books, particularly those of the earlier years of the James Gurney Bevan régime, there is abundant evidence that he took over from his father a flourishing overseas business ; many of the letters were to overseas customers, principally in British Colonies ; as executor to his father's estate he also carried on a very considerable correspondence regarding property in South Wales.

*   *   *

It cannot be emphasized too often that every business or profession fails or flourishes because of the quality of the recruits it attracts, and the foresight, skill and judgment of those who select them.   Therefore anything throwing light on the sort of assistants the Bevans and their successors took pains to secure has not only historic interest, but social, economic and commercial value.   In 1720 Silvanus was journeying on business through Cornwall and at Kingsbridge in Devon made the acquaintance of a poor woman named Edith Cookworthy who a year before had lost her husband, William Cookworthy I, a highly respected Quaker and weaver of that town.   She was in great distress having since his death lost her slender monetary resources through the bursting of the South Sea Bubble,[1] and was trying to support her family by dressmaking.

There were six children, the eldest, William, aged fifteen. Anxious to help, and struck with the intelligence shown by William, Bevan offered to take him into his business.   The offer was accepted and in due course William journeyed on foot from Kingsbridge to London, his only coat being one made of camlet for Sunday wear.   He was not bound an apothecary's apprentice to Bevan ; quite likely he could not afford to pay the necessary fees which, considering the value of money in those days, were somewhat heavy.   Few details are available of the

[1] The South Sea Company, established in 1710, exploded in 1720 ruining thousands of families.

work done at Plough Court by William Cookworthy, although his mastery of Latin and Greek and his facility in the French language were probably obtained there in his lecture hours with the help of Silvanus Bevan.

After leaving Plough Court, and before his marriage, Cookworthy began business as a wholesale chemist and druggist in Plymouth. Not later than 1735, the year of his marriage to Sarah Berry, Silvanus and Timothy Bevan took him into partnership under the title of Bevan and Cookworthy. The Bevans withdrew in 1746 and Cookworthy was then joined by his brother, Philip, and the Plymouth firm was known as William Cookworthy & Company.

Cookworthy, after many journeys into Devon and Cornwall in search of English materials similar to those used by the Chinese, discovered at Tregonin Hill, Tregonning near Breage, and later in the parish of St. Stephens near St. Austell in Cornwall, on the property of Lord Camelford, large beds of half-decomposed kaolinic clay, specimens of a similar substance from Virginia having been examined by him in 1745. These beds, and similar ones discovered later in Devonshire, have ever since produced large quantities of material for manufacturing china at home and abroad.[1] In March, 1768, Camelford and Cookworthy took out a patent and soon opened the Plymouth China Factory in High Street, where, with the aid of workmen from Sèvres, they succeeded in producing the first fine hard porcelain to be made in England. The business was afterwards transferred to Bristol, the patent rights being subsequently acquired by a firm in the Potteries ; neither Cookworthy nor his family ever received any benefit from this industry.

In the memorial windows of the Town Hall at Plymouth, unfortunately destroyed by bombing in the Second World War, was this inscription :

William Cookworthy, Chemist and Potter, the discoverer of the English China-clay and the first maker in England of true Porcelain.

[1] China-clay exports for 1951 earned £2,633,698 in foreign currency, a record.

WILLIAM COOKWORTHY, 1705–1780

Cookworthy's experience at Plough Court doubtless enabled him to follow an even more illustrious Devonian, Sir Walter Raleigh, in designing a method of obtaining fresh water at sea : he was also the author of a memoir on the use of the *Virgula divinatoria*, or dowsing fork, still used in the mining districts of Cornwall and the limestone regions of Somersetshire for discovering underground water, a practice considered by some to be mere superstition, but by others to be scientifically proven.

Cookworthy had many friends in all ranks of life, but he was specially drawn to those of a naval type. He hospitably entertained Captain Cook and his companions Sir Joseph Banks and Dr. Daniel Solander before they sailed in the *Endeavour* to Otaheite in 1769 to observe the transit of Venus ; John Smeaton, the engineer, was also his guest during part of the time he was building the old Eddystone Lighthouse. Cookworthy was also acquainted with the Swedish scientist and mystic, Emanuel Swedenborg, whose *Doctrine of Life* translated from the Latin by Cookworthy was first published in English in 1763.

Cookworthy died in 1780 at the age of seventy-five years, leaving to us lasting moral, spiritual and commercial legacies.

Another of the assistants at Plough Court was Gilbert Thompson, a Quaker and an M.D. of Edinburgh. We hear of him through Dr. J. C. Lettsom, F.R.S., the well-known Quaker physician, philanthropist, and man of letters, who was at one time a pupil at the Quaker school of Penketh, near Warrington in Lancashire, while Thompson was an usher there : he was a distant relative of John Fothergill, already mentioned. After graduating in 1758 Thompson came to London, to succeed, it was suggested, to his relative's extensive practice. He appears to have had considerable ability, but he was shy and, meeting with very little encouragement, he attended a boarding-school at Tottenham as a writing master, afterwards becoming 'a dispensing assistant to Bevan, an eminent chemist'. Eventually his uncle at Penketh died, leaving him a fortune, and with this started in practice, lodging at 40 Gracechurch Street with his old pupil Lettsom, and Peter Collinson, F.R.S., the

Quaker botanist. Thompson published a Life of Fothergill in 1782.

A different type of assistant from either Thompson or Cookworthy was Joseph Jewell, who began at Plough Court as a porter to Joseph Gurney Bevan, and who ended his career as a partner with Luke Howard.

Jewell was an extraordinary character. Born in 1763, he started work as a farmer's boy in Berkshire at the age of eight. After considerable farming experience, and several years as an ostler at a famous hostelry in the Bath Road, he gravitated to London. He had joined the Society of Friends in the meantime and was anxious to obtain a situation with Joseph Gurney Bevan, whose high reputation was already well known.

Eventually, leaving his better-paid job as porter with a sheet-glass maker, Jewell secured the post as a laboratory assistant at the Old Plough Court pharmacy at a date unknown, but probably about 1790. His wage was £15 a year, indoors, and his native shrewdness and intelligence were appreciated and put to use by his new master.

The work of the laboratory at the time was supervised by a German, assisted by a junior, and when the German went back to his own country, Jewell took his place and very quickly began to make chemicals which Bevan had hitherto bought from other manufacturers in the locality.

*   *   *

The abolition of the Slave Trade owed more to England than to any other country, and far more to the Quakers than to any other influential section of the community. The attitude of Joseph Gurney Bevan towards the problem was characteristically shown in a letter given in the appendix.[1] He was an earnest worker for the cause of Abolition, although it was not till 1807 that the General Abolition Bill, which applied to all British possessions, was passed.

The Dictionary of National Biography states that Joseph Gurney

[1] Appendix Six.

Bevan was of a lively and affectionate disposition and very quick to learn. From an uncle who was an artist and naturalist he derived much information. His literary studies were pursued for some years under a physician who was a classical scholar with a taste for poetry. He had a natural liking for gay apparel and twice changed the style of his dress, but returned to the sober colours of the plain Quakers out of filial regard for his mother.

In later years he was regarded as the 'Ablest of the Quaker Apologists' and is known in Quaker history as the 'sober, solid Friend'. One of his contemporaries called him 'our chief disciplinarian'. His literary output was considerable. He wrote lives of Isaac Penington, Robert Barclay and other worthies, and was editor of a small Quaker journal entitled *Piety Promoted*.

In a conversation with Daniel Hanbury, Paul Bevan described Joseph Gurney as doing duty in the City as special constable and having to sit up at the station house one night a week, described the early supper on those evenings and the huge white greatcoat Joseph Gurney used to wear. He was extremely particular in fulfilling all the disagreeable duties of the post, even to the attendance at executions, which it appears was sometimes required. He used to pursue his classical studies at the station house, many Greek books being sent there for midnight reading.

Joseph Gurney retired from the business in July, 1794, at the early age of forty 'with a diminuation of capital' and, it would seem, impaired health. His retirement ended the Bevan reign, a period rich in fulfilment and promise. The foundations of a lasting business were well, truly and, above all, honestly laid. The name of Bevan, it is true, disappeared from the Plough Court Pharmacy and the great and widespread business of which it was the precursor, but, as we have seen, it survives in honour to this day in several great national activities, notably banking.

Two years before retiring Joseph Gurney had taken into his business William Allen, a youth of twenty-two, and could not have made a wiser or better choice. Although his remaining years were clouded with illness and much suffering, Joseph remained the firm friend and acute adviser of young Allen who in his diary frequently mentions the kindness of Bevan and his wife ; three years after their business relations formally ended Allen recorded : ' After meeting, dear J. G. B. came as usual. He possesses the faculty of sympathy in an eminent degree.'

Let that be his epitaph.

He died in September, 1814, aged sixty-one.

CHAPTER 7

A RETROSPECT

THE one hundred and twenty-three years which elapsed from the birth of Silvanus Bevan II until the retirement of Joseph Gurney Bevan, constituting what is here called the Bevan period, connected the seventeenth with the nineteenth century ; it showed notable developments in the British way of life in social, literary and scientific activities, the latter contributing directly to the advance of pharmacy. A brief reminder of the most outstanding events may help to set the period in perspective against its historic background, and to remind us that nothing happens in isolation.

Between 1691, the year in which Silvanus Bevan was born, and the arrival of William Allen in 1792 at the Old Plough Court Pharmacy at the age of twenty-two, Great Britain and the world were successively enriched by the publication of George Fox's *Journal* and Newton's *Optics* ; St. Paul's Cathedral in London, Wren's masterpiece, was completed, and *Robinson Crusoe* published. Gabriel Daniel Fahrenheit invented the mercurial thermometer and fixed the freezing point of water. Ultra-Protestant John Wesley translated the peerless *Imitatio Christi* of Thomas à Kempis, Carl Linnæus published his *Philosophia Botanica* which systemized and summed up the results of the labours of his predecessors in botany.

In the year Joseph Gurney Bevan retired, John Hunter, ' the greatest surgeon of his times ', published his epoch-making *Treatise on the Blood*. In 1808 John Dalton, Quaker, chemist and friend of William Allen, published his *New System of Chemical Philosophy*, reviving the atomic theory of matter as an explanation of the facts of chemical combination.

In the year Joseph Gurney Bevan died (1814) Jane Austen published *Mansfield Park*, Byron *Lara* and *The Corsair*, Scott

Waverley and Wordsworth *The Excursion* ; George Stephenson constructed the first locomotive ; and London was first lit by gas. With steam and gas we are at the beginning of modern times.

CHAPTER 8

EARLY TRADE WITH AMERICA

WHETHER trade follows the flag or the flag follows trade is disputed ; there can be no disputing the fact that trade conducted on honest and equitable principles is one of the cements of civilization and foundations of peace. Amongst many thousands of individual and co-operative overseas business enterprises Allen and Hanburys has, almost from its beginning, played an honourable and continuously extending part. Indeed it might be said that its commercial activities had, in due course, a real, if modest, place in helping to heal the wounds left by the American War of Independence.

About 1725, some ten years after Silvanus Bevan opened his apothecary's shop in Old Plough Court, he turned his attention to the supply of drugs and other goods to surgeons, apothecaries and traders in countries overseas. Many of these were Quakers, and with the clannishness of members of the Society they naturally preferred to do business with one of their kind ; there were probably also very few Quaker apothecaries in London in the early years of the eighteenth century.

Supplies of goods were soon being sent regularly to European buyers in Seville, Cadiz, Bremen and Hamburg ; in the West Indies there were customers at Kingston in Jamaica and on Antigua and Barbados.

There was business with British North America but it was not extensive, although it was important to the American colonies at a time when the medical profession there was establishing itself and the first hospitals were being opened. Silvanus Bevan and his brother Timothy supplied their customers with reliable drugs, assisted them with credit, gave them advice, and often performed small but helpful personal services : this is illustrated by Silvanus Bevan's contacts with Philadelphia, an association which was the closer because that city was the capital of the Quaker's Holy Experiment in the New World.

From 1727 onwards Silvanus was in regular correspondence with James Logan, one of Pennsylvania's most distinguished public men and scholars ; through Logan Bevan got in touch with other men of scientific and humanitarian interests in the Quaker colony, such as John Bartram, the botanist. To Logan Bevan sent drugs and news of learned publications—there was a scholarly exchange on Newton's *Principia* ; and from the Pennsylvanians he received in return specimens of American plants such as ginseng, and copper ore for assay.

Bevan's name was thus favourably known to many Philadelphians when, in 1751, under the leadership of Benjamin Franklin and Dr. Thomas Bond (whom Bevan met in London in 1738), they resolved to establish the first hospital in British America ; Dr. Bond was one of three physicians who gave their services gratuitously for a period of three years.

The first need was a site ; the second a stock of medicines ; and in both matters they turned to Silvanus Bevan. They named him and Thomas Hyam, a Quaker merchant, agents of the Hospital in London and charged them with securing from Thomas Penn, the principal proprietor of Pennsylvania, then living in London, the grant of a site. Bevan and Hyam represented the Hospital project before Penn with energy and succeeded in securing from him the grant of several city lots ; but the conditions Penn attached to the grant made it unacceptable to the Managers. Throughout these tedious negotiations, which lasted from 1751 to 1755, the Managers and their London agents corresponded, as their letters show, with complete confidence ; and the Philadelphians gladly testified to the ' cheerful concurrence with us, in the foundation of the Pennsylvania Hospital '.

Meanwhile, in 1752, the Managers opened a small hospital in a rented dwelling-house in Philadelphia and ordered a stock of medicines from Bevan. The bill for this first supply of medicines for the first hospital in the British American colonies amounted to £112 15s. 2½d ; to pay it, a special solicitation was made among ' the rich widows and other single Women in

Town ', the widows contributed one hundred and eleven pounds odd out of the total collection of one hundred and twenty-six pounds. The Bevans continued to supply drugs to the Hospital at least until the outbreak of the war of the American Revolution, extending credit when the Hospital's resources were low, repeatedly assuring the Managers that they ' sincerely wish so beneficial an Establishment may flourish and increase. . . .' Timothy Bevan made the Hospital a gift of one hundred pounds Pennsylvania, about sixty-six pounds sterling, in 1766 : he was also instrumental, in 1771, in engaging William Smith, a London apothecary, as resident apothecary to the Hospital for three years at a salary of one hundred pounds a year, Philadelphia currency, the Hospital to provide ' good and sufficient meat, drink, washing and lodging '.

Silvanus and Timothy Bevan appeared most prominently to the Americans as firm and generous friends of America and Americans. When he first visited London as the agent of the Pennsylvania legislature in 1757, Benjamin Franklin carried an introduction to Silvanus Bevan who was one of those who introduced Franklin to the influential dissenting circles of London which were so useful to him. Many young Americans, especially Pennsylvanians, going abroad to study medicine in London and Edinburgh, carried letters to the Bevans. Among those who as students received the Bevans' hospitality and advice one of the most important was John Morgan of Philadelphia. Bevan was one of those who sponsored Morgan for the Fellowship of the Royal Society ; and when Morgan returned to Philadelphia in 1765 with a project designed to effect the separation of medical practice from the sale of drugs, he was accompanied by a trained apothecary, David Leighton, with a large stock of drugs prepared by Silvanus and Timothy Bevan. Nor did the Americans, once returned home, hesitate to ask the Bevans to make purchases for them of a private nature, like the latest books on medicine or a chimneypiece and some window glass for a new house building !

The death of Silvanus Bevan in 1765 and the retirement of Timothy Bevan ten years later put the management of the Firm's affairs in the hands of Joseph Gurney Bevan. The Americans assumed that he would regard their accounts with the same friendly tolerance his father and uncle had shown ; but Joseph Gurney Bevan was of another mind.

In 1775 the American War of Independence broke out and brought trade to America virtually to a close. For eight years there was scarcely any legal commerce between England and the Thirteen States. As insurance rates increased and supplies of American drugs dwindled in England, the cost of drugs rose. The Firm's letter-books give some indication of the nature and extent of Bevan's American trade at this period, as well as of the burdens and irritations under which it was carried on.

Only with New York (which was in British hands from 1776 until the end of the War) was there any prospect that trade could be carried on. During most of this period, however, trade was generally forbidden, although special licences were sometimes granted. The interdict was evaded by some British merchants by shipping their goods to Halifax whence they were at once sent on to New York. If this was not exactly illegal, it seemed to Joseph Gurney Bevan at least a doubtful practice ; as he wrote to a New York customer :

> To enter outgoods for Halifax, and to have no other intention than that of sending them to another place is too incompatible with my notions of truth for me to comply with . . .

He did, however, make use of the licensed ships and, when the trade was open in 1779-80, he sent large supplies of drugs to William Stewart, Donald McLean, and William Brownjohn, who appear to have been his principal agents in New York at that time.

The war ended in 1781 and normal trading conditions were resumed by 1783. Many of Timothy Bevan's American friends, not knowing he had retired from business, wrote in the summer of that year to renew their friendship and their business relations. Joseph Gurney Bevan replied to these letters, noting that the price of drugs was higher than before the war, explaining the terms on which he extended credit, and, sometimes, expressing the hope that he would not be thought 'a degenerate successor' to his father. Charles and Christopher Marshall, druggists of

Philadelphia, immediately ordered drugs to the amount of £340 0s. 7½d; and orders came in the same year from Dr. Thomas Bond, Dr. John Morgan, and, in 1786, the very distinguished Dr. Benjamin Rush who, two years previously, had established along with James Pemberton the first anti-slavery society in America. Rush, who wrote to inquire about prices, was assured that Bevan would be happy to deal with one whose 'obliging behaviour to me, then a boy', he gratefully remembered. During the next few years Bevan fulfilled orders from such men as Dr. Isaac Chanler, of Charleston, S.C., Dr. George Stevenson, of Carlisle, Pa., Dr. Samuel Stringer, of Albany, N.Y., Edward Stabler, of Alexandria, Va., Robert Mackay and John Thomson of Peterburg, Va., and Thomas Tomlinson, of New Bern, N.C. To New York City alone he sent in 1784 drugs to John Price, John Stites, Francis Lanton, Oliver Hull, Pearsall and Glover, and William Lowther.

Although he received and executed these orders in his own grave friendly manner, Joseph Gurney Bevan was not really anxious to have most of this American business. It might be too harsh to say that in that post-war period the Americans' credit was dubious; it is certainly true that they were not prompt in payment. More than this, times were hard and money scarce in America; although Bevan observed pointedly to one dilatory customer that those who alleged the hardness of the times as an excuse for non-payment were, generally speaking, those whose pre-war payments had been dilatory also.

One example of an American customer's post-war relations with Bevan will illustrate the position. Morgan, in 1783, purchased drugs to the amount of £219 9s. 7d. The following year he sent Bevan a bill of exchange for twenty-two pounds and a quantity of tobacco worth about forty-five pounds. Bevan was reluctant to accept the tobacco and asked that no more be sent as he was required to sign various Customs' House bonds to the King, who was called by several titles 'which I, not thinking true, do not chuse to subscribe—such as King of France, Defender of the Faith, etc.' In 1785 Morgan sent Bevan a bill of exchange on Brussels for one hundred pounds, but the bill was protested and, though Bevan urged him to find an alternative means of payment, he did nothing. However, in response to Bevan's reminders, he sent fifty pounds in 1786. Not another word did Bevan receive until, in the winter of 1789–90, he read in the *Gentleman's Magazine* that Morgan had died at Philadelphia. With interest, the unpaid balance of the account amounted to about one hundred and twenty-five pounds. Not until 1797, eight years after Morgan's death and fourteen years after the drugs were sold, was the debt finally discharged by Morgan's executors. Business on such terms as these was hardly desirable.

To the business man's caution in extending credit was added Joseph Gurney Bevan's Quaker principles against over-reaching. Repeatedly, when merchants wrote from America to order drugs, he suggested that they should make their purchases through the established agents. When the price of drugs was high, he generally cut down the quantity ordered. He peremptorily refused to deal in what he considered second-best, though his customers might order it. The business he accepted he wished to carry on well and when he retired he wanted to be able to close his affairs speedily and simply.

On this basis the American business continued throughout Joseph Gurney Bevan's control of the Firm. The conditions of trade during the War of Independence were repeated in the 1790's, when the general European war broke out.

European events during the early years of the nineteenth century were even more productive of difficulties in the shipment of goods for foreign trade than they had been in the eighteenth century. The renewal of the war with France in May, 1803, is noted by William Allen in his diary : ' Hostilities are now going on—this is an additional load on my spirits.' In July he wrote : ' In public affairs the cloud thickens.'

Throughout the year 1804 and well into the year 1805 the danger of invasion hung heavy over England, and it was not until September 1805 that Allen was able to write to a correspondent :

With respect to public affairs the apprehensions of invasion are for the present nearly over. The combined fleets of

France and Spain are blockaded in Cadiz and there appears great probability that the flames of war will be rekindled on the continent. Russia and Austria have made such preparations that Bonaparte has withdrawn great part of his troops from Boulogne and sent them to the interior.

But new difficulties which affected shipment of goods to and from America had meanwhile arisen. Continental warfare had led to an inevitable increase in American commerce, and as a result British Orders in Council and French Imperial Decrees declared a blockade of European ports and of those of Great Britain. The commerce of the United States was thus threatened with disabilities comparable with those of the belligerent powers. President Jefferson, supported by the Republican Party, adhered to strict neutrality. The Federalist Party desired alliance with Great Britain to secure the privileges incident to the freedom of the seas. Neutral policy, however, for the moment was almost impossible. 'The alarm in this nation among American merchants has been so great since thy letter came to hand', William Allen wrote in June, 1808, to Edward Stabler, one of his American customers :

. . . and especially since the issuing of our orders in council which took place soon after, that it was generally reckoned highly imprudent to make any shipment to your country, and the only reason I did not write sooner, was the constant hope, week after week, that some favourable intelligence might arrive from America which would justify the execution of thy order. Down to the present moment, however, it does not appear but that the embargo and non-importation acts continue in force and we are not certain but that stronger measures might be taken by your government before the goods could arrive.

On June 18th, 1812, the United States declared war against Great Britain, and the far-ranging operations of American privateers, characteristic of the three years during which this war lasted, determined the impracticability of any attempt to increase the foreign trade of the Plough Court Pharmacy. 'William Allen's trade lies more in the line of Pharmaceutical preparations than dealing very largely in Drugs ', John Thomas Barry wrote to a Bristol correspondent in 1813, adding later in his letter that for years past Allen had ' concluded not to increase the list of connexions abroad '.

The type of business carried on with overseas' customers during the first half of the nineteenth century was not of quite such a varied character as that of fifty years earlier shown in the Appendix,[1] but from the correspondence in the letter-books it is evident that articles other than drugs and chemicals were sometimes ordered.

Perhaps the most extraordinary quotation to an overseas' customer ever given in William Allen's time was one for horses.[2] The letter is given in full : it is addressed to a well-known customer, T. C. Whitfield, Buenos Ayres.

[1] Appendix Seven.   [2] Appendix Eight.

THE ALLEN PERIOD

1770–1843

Friend, parent, neighbour, first it will embrace,
His country next, and next all human race;
Wide and more wide the o'erflowings of the mind
Take every creature in, of every kind.

POPE : Essay on Man.

CHAPTER 1

EARLY YEARS AT PLOUGH COURT

WHEN on Wednesday, August 29th, 1770, William, the eldest of three sons was born to Job Allen, at his house in Stewart Street, Spitalfields, within that world-famous square mile known as the City of London, the English silk trade, in which Job was engaged as a manufacturer, was still flourishing : George III had been ten years on the throne, and Lord North of dubious fame was his Prime Minister.

Job Allen came from Scrooby in the west of Nottinghamshire not far from Sheffield ; his wife, Margaret Stafford, from an Irish family resident in Cork. Comfortably off, the Allens adhered firmly to the Society of Friends. William and his brothers grew up in a loving, peace-filled home and this background of affection, security and sound religion gave him an excellent start in life. As was fitting, he received his earliest religious teaching from a mother to whom he was all his life passionately devoted. Having herself but modest interest in anything outside her religion and home, she always feared that her eldest son's ever-expanding intellect and interests tended to wean him from spiritual realities as she saw them, and to which she would have had him dedicate himself entirely. Again and again she tried to dissuade William from following paths obviously indicated for him by character, temperament and inclination and, with ignorant love, often added inhibiting elements of uncertainty to his natural apprehensiveness. As things turned out, few Englishmen in any station have lived as useful, varied, devoted and influential a life as did William Allen.

William received his earliest secular instruction from an unnamed schoolmistress who gained his lasting affection and esteem ; something winning in the lad's nature bespoke him love from low and high wherever he went. He spent a short but happy time at a boarding-school kept by William Alexander at Boley Hill, Rochester, Kent, but, being delicate, it cannot be said that he received anything but a scanty formal education.[1]   Job Allen naturally looked upon his eldest son as his heir and business successor and, upon leaving school at the age of fifteen, William entered the silk trade, remaining in it three years, all the while living at home.   Probably the years spent in his father's business did him no harm.   Always diligent, attentive and, by nature, conscientious, he learned habits of order, system, and application to uncongenial tasks, which afterwards proved invaluable : moreoever, the experience strengthened and confirmed his inner beliefs as to his life work.

By the time William was fourteen he was already displaying his life-long interest and happiness in the stimulating science of astronomy and—fortunately for himself and for us—had personally to find the wherewithal to gratify his inborn tastes.   Not, as he put it, being strong in cash he got hold of some cardboard, bought an eyepiece and an object-glass and constructed for himself a little telescope through which he could see the moon and even the satellites of Jupiter.   This significant toy cost him one shilling and twopence which, we may be sure, was no small part of his strictly limited capital.   Having spent forethought, skill, time, and the bulk of his own money, in creating something, he valued it, and took care of it accordingly ; this, if his seniors noted it, was a portent.   Boys and girls of course pass through all sorts of phases, yet it ought to be possible for the scrutiny of discerning love to determine quite early whether a definite creative bent indicating special ability is present.

From his early years William further betrayed the budding scientist by making such chemical experiments as were within his limited power and means ; but in Quaker and evangelical circles, in those days, and indeed for long afterwards, science was looked upon with suspicion and the budding experimenter may not have been very warmly encouraged ; perhaps those who instinctively distrusted an omnipotent science may not have been entirely wrong.

[1] Appendix Nine.

WILLIAM ALLEN, 1770–1843

In time Job Allen reconciled himself to his eldest son's dislike of the silk business, and accepted his fixed determination to become a scientist ; Margaret Allen could never quite bring herself to doing so.

However fortunate in the love of his family and surroundings, the time comes when a youth must make his own decisions, face his own difficulties, and begin to live fully his own life.

That William was sensitive, introspective, and lonely, is proved by the fact that at an unusually early age he started a diary and with one break of two years, kept it with exemplary patience and regularity all his life ; after his death it was edited by his nieces with somewhat excessive rigour.[1] With his cardboard telescope William could humbly examine the work of the Creator in the universe ; pen in hand he could trace the leaven of godliness ebb and flow within his own soul. Extroverts may, like Benvenuto Cellini, write their autobiography or objectively record events ; unlike introverts, they do not, in any real sense, keep subjective diaries. It cannot be pretended that the diary of William compares with such great journals as those of George Fox or John Wesley ; the famous diary of John Evelyn is not a diary at all because frequently it was obviously written up long after the event. William's is, however, authentic inasmuch as the day's events were oftenest recorded by the day's end ; and, it is exact, factual and truthful. Therefore, as a first-hand document giving a vivid self-portrait of the man, a clear, if limited, outline of his background, and a correct account of his doings, it will be used whenever possible. Moreover, William, with his intuitions, shrewd eye for character, and a real gift for describing events, gives us sketches that often throw fresh light on historic personages and scenes. As a Quaker he, like Joseph Gurney Bevan, always referred to the days and months by numbers. On the ' 19th day of the 1st month, 1788 ', the first diary brief entry—a most revealing one was made :

Experienced some degree of comfort in striving against evil thoughts.

[1] Life of William Allen, with selections from his Correspondence (London, 1846, Charles Gilpin, Bishopsgate Street Without).

William was seventeen years and seven months old.

Pope was his favourite poet and a year later he transcribed the passage from the *Essay on Man* where, speaking of the up-surge and expansion of love, the poet wrote the quatrain set as an epigraph to Book Two of this story.

In it the poet who was born in Plough Court epitomises William Allen's creed and life-long practice ; but the youth did not then know that in the poet's birthplace he would fulfil his destiny and amply live out his boyhood's dreams. Because of William and his dedicated life some of the greatest figures in the contemporary scene were to pass in and out of the City of London archway that joined his home and business not only to the community but to the world. High affairs of State and great reforms were debated, and history made in number two Plough Court, and its modest walls frequently echoed to the voices of the illustrious in many walks of life ; better still, needy pilgrims of all classes and colours found there refreshment and a resting place ; best of all, it was a temple where the inhabitants regularly communed with their Maker and received inspiration, guidance and strength from the unseen and eternal.

The first years of the diary are mostly taken up with recording religious experiences and affairs and, in particular, an account of early efforts towards the abolition of the Slave Trade, a matter, as already noted, very dear to every Quaker heart, and which, young as he was, had long claimed William's zealous aid. It came to him that one of the most effective ways to oppose any illicit trade was ' disusing those commodities procured by the labour of slaves '. He therefore gave up the use of sugar and kept his resolution until the slave trade was abolished within the British dominions nearly half a century later ; then, liking sugar, and being attractively human, he resumed its use.

On April 18th, 1791, William occupied a front seat in the gallery of the old House of Commons and listened for nearly four hours to the great speech in which William Wilberforce, Member of Parliament for Hull, brought in the Bill for the abolition of the slave trade. He gives up many of his pages to a telling description of the great fight in the House, a momentous event with which the name of William Pitt and Thomas Clarkson [1] will always be honourably associated.

It is significant that, even then, William's philanthropic aspirations and efforts took precedence in time and importance to his business career. Nevertheless, from his teens onward he was not spared the salt flavour of criticism and, with a humility hard won from his inner sensitiveness, he recorded :

Remember that thou hast been accused of deceitfulness and underhandedness, therefore, though I hope and believe that the charge is false, it is necessary to keep a strict watch against it, and to adhere still closer to sincerity.

Another diary entry shows that, like George Fox himself, this youth was not only above many of his contemporaries in his relations with the animal world, but that, in its countless manifestations, love was essential to his lonely heart :

A day of bitterness and sorrow, occasioned by the death of my faithful, loving dog, who was killed by accident in the street. I assuredly bestow too great a share of affection on the animals I have care of. Resolved not to have any more than I have at present.

Soon after this he wrote :

There appears to me such a meanness and lowness of disposition, in those who are cruel to animals, that I think I could not put confidence in them, even in the common concerns of life.

In April, 1791, the name of Joseph Gurney Bevan occurs in the diary for the first time ; but it is evident that Bevan and Allen, both ardent Quakers and social reformers, had long been friends. Unfortunately for our immediate purpose the one gap in the diary covers the period now being dealt with but, from other sources, we know that Joseph Gurney Bevan offered to take William Allen into his nearby chemical establishment as it was then called and, his father Job reluctantly yielding, William abandoned the silk trade and settled in at Plough Court at the

[1] Appendix Ten.

end of 1792. It throws considerable light on the family heart-searching and anguish which must have been gone through before the great decision was made, that after a lapse of eighteen years, his mother could write : ' It was a bitter cup to me to part with thee.'

That William was in his right sphere is evidenced by the fact that he was soon elected a member of the Physical Society at Guy's Hospital, and became a physician's pupil at St. Thomas's Hospital, both of which were then, as now, amongst the great teaching hospitals of the world.

William learned shorthand which he needed for taking notes at lectures and making notes for the lectures he was himself to begin almost at once delivering. Of an early visit to Guy's he says : ' Received the thanks of a poor patient, which did me more good than a guinea fee.'

But scientific affairs were not occupying all William's thoughts. In July, 1796, he recorded :

> Disappointed in my expectations of a letter from my dear M. H. this morning . . . very low to-day and oppressed with a variety of concerns. . . .

So sensitive and reserved was Allen about his deepest feelings that he could not, even in his private diary, use the full name of the young woman with whom he had been for some time in love. She was Mary, daughter of J. and E. Hamilton of Redruth in Cornwall, who was born at Marazion. Eventually Mary's reluctance was overcome. On November 13th, continued William :

> Our marriage was celebrated this day at Tottenham meeting. I felt it a time of divine favour before a word was uttered . . . it was a time never to be forgotten. My mind was unusually humbled and tendered. My precious Mary seemed equally sensible, that it might emphatically be termed ' a good day '.

We do not know the source of Mary's initial reluctance. Did some premonition warn her that within ten months she would die, leaving to her bereft bridegroom an infant daughter ?

William wrote of 'his tortured heart'; the child was 'a sweet infant', but thinking of 'how we should have enjoyed her together' he 'could not bear to nurse her long'. Some six weeks after Mary's departure he exclaimed : 'O how I loved her—how we loved each other !'

His mother now, as always, was his greatest refuge ; and, as always, Joseph Gurney Bevan and his wife proved themselves true friends.

Short as had been their life together it was, as it always is, the recollection of the things they had shared that proved most poignant. Alluding to his frequent rides to the laboratory at Plaistow, where, with Samuel Mildred, he had started the making of chemicals, William wrote :

> This road brings the idea of my precious, my sweet endeared companion strongly before me. How often have we, in sweet harmony, travelled it together. How my soul was united to her. . . . O, it was my chief pleasure to make · her happy and comfortable. What delight did I take in doing little things to please her.

CHAPTER 2

ALLEN'S SCIENTIFIC ACTIVITIES

IF, as we must, we follow the clear implications of his diary, we have no option but to give William Allen's manifold scientific and philanthropic activities precedence of his purely commercial interests. As shown by the hundreds of letters he wrote, he was an excellent man of business, who never shirked his business responsibilities, whose talents and acumen were always at the disposal of others ; yet, to use his own words, ' my aim never was to accumulate riches ' ; what money he did make he mostly gave away, and, to his honour, died a comparatively poor man.

At the age of twenty-three he attended the classes of Bryan Higgins,[1] where Luke Howard, Q.V., and Richard Phillips [2] also acquired the rudiments of the science : it was not, however, until the age of thirty that he began the study of botany to which he applied himself to such purpose that two years later he was elected a Fellow of the Linnean Society.

He notes that he went to Walthamstow in March, 1801, to meet his friend, Lewis Dillwyn, the naturalist and author of *British Confervae*, ' . . . he got through classes and orders ' ! In July of the same year we find him botanizing in Essex with Dillwyn : ' We had a rich feast of Botany, looking over my specimens. They tell me I have found one very good thing— the Juncous Acutus ' ! He continued to study the subject during that summer. An account of one of his botanical excursions with several friends, the first of the season, bears some resemblance to that of the ' herbarizings ' indulged in by apothecaries at an earlier date :

We had a coach for the day and went to Harrow to break- fast. We then set off on foot over the cornfields, which by

[1] Appendix Eleven.   [2] Appendix Twelve.

the way were very unproductive, to Morpeth Field after the frittilaria, but our search was in vain : we however got the helleborus viridis, a scarce plant in those parts, and the ophioglossum, also the vinca minor, etc. We dined at the King's Head, Harrow, and set off home at six.

About the same time he went to the Royal Institution in Albemarle Street, London, to hear Davy's [1] first lecture on galvanism and described it as ' a most capital one ', sagely adding that the lecturer ' bids fair to rise high in the philosophical world '. The Royal Institution was then just two years old, having been granted its Royal Charter by George III in 1800. It owed its origin to Sir Joseph Banks, Lords Spencer and Morton, and several other noblemen and gentlemen interested in the science of the day, and, in particular, to the famous Benjamin Thompson who disguised his British-American nationality under his Holy Roman Empire title of Count Rumford.

Allen, already an accepted authority in his chosen vocation, was frequently called upon to perform chemical analyses which required skill and accuracy : indeed, Plough Court became noteworthy as a repository of chemical re-agents, a set of which was presented by Allen to Professor Pictet of Geneva and was exhibited at the National Institute of that city.

The Askesian Society was formed at Plough Court by some young men desirous of improving themselves by philosophical exercises. Its objects were to elucidate, by experiment, either facts generally understood, or to examine and repeat any novel discoveries. The meetings were held twice monthly during the winter. Each member was expected to produce a paper for reading and discussion upon some subject of scientific inquiry ; and many of these papers were afterwards published in *Tilloch's Philosphical Magazine*. Amongst the early members were William Allen, William Phillips, Luke Howard, Q.V., Joseph Fox, Henry Lawson, Arthur Arch, William Hasledine Pepys ; [2]

[1] Sir Humphry Davy, F.R.S., 1778–1829. English chemist. Inventor of the miner's safety lamp. June 2nd, 1801.
[2] William Hasledine Pepys, F.R.S., 1775–1856. Philosophic instrument maker.

Samuel Woods was President. Astley Cooper, Dr. Babington,[1] A. Tilloch, Joseph Woods, Jun., and several others afterwards joined the Society, which continued for twenty years.

From the files of *Tilloch's Philosphical Magazine* the following information about the papers read before the Members of the Society has been extracted :

> Vol. 7 (1800), p. 355—On a periodical variation of the barometer apparently due to the influence of the sun and moon on the atmosphere, by Luke Howard.
>
> Vol. 13 (1802), p. 321—On the Virgula Divinatoria or Divining Rod, by William Phillips.
>
> Vol. 14 (1802/3), p. 55—Considerations on Dr. Hutton's Theory of Rain, by Luke Howard, F.L.S.
>
> Vol. 16 (1803), p. 97—On the Modification of Clouds, etc., by Luke Howard. This is a classic scientific paper and must have been the most important of all the Askesian Society's publications. In it Howard announced his classification and nomenclature of the clouds, both of which still stand to-day. He introduces for the first time the very well-known names—Cirrus, Cumulus, Stratus and their combinations.
>
> P. 312—On the Purification of Nickel, by R. Phillips.
>
> Vol. 17 (1803/4), p. 193—On Gems, by W. H. Pepys, Jun.
>
> P. 313—Analysis of the Human Teeth, by W. H. Pepys, Jun. This was from a recent interesting publication, the Natural History of the Human Teeth, by Joseph Fox.
>
> P. 175—A New Process for Rendering Platina Malleable, by Alexander Tilloch.[2]
>
> Vol. 24 (1806), p. 342—Analysis of the Hot Springs at Bath, by Richard Phillips.

Not the least interesting gathering of the Askesians was that held in February 1800. Amongst those present were Astley Cooper, Dr. Bradley, Allen of Edinburgh, the two Lawsons and J. Fox. The entry in Allen's diary reads : 'Experiments on respiration.'

---

[1] Babington William, M.D., 1756–1833. Physician and mineralogist.
[2] Alexander Tilloch, 1759–1825. Inventor of stereotyping.

ANALYTICAL AND MANUFACTURING LABORATORIES OF
THE OLD PLOUGH COURT PHARMACY

We all breathed the gaseous oxide of azote. It took a surprising effect upon me, abolishing completely, at first, all sensation : then I had the idea of being carried violently upward in a dark cavern, with only a few glimmering lights. The company said my eyes were fixed, face purple, veins in the forehead very large, apoplectic stertor, etc. They were all much alarmed, but I suffered no pain and in a short time came to myself. (Note : Gaseous oxide of azote, nitrous oxide, or laughing gas, was first systematically studied by Humphry Davy, who inhaled it from a silk bag.)

William Allen also appears to have taken an active part in the formation of the Royal Jennerian Institution :

First Month, 9th, 1802. Joseph Fox invited me to meet Dr. Jenner, Astley Cooper &c., at his house, and go from thence to the Physical Society at Guys, a paper on cow-pox being before the Society.

Twelfth Month, 16th, 1803. Askesian Society, but left it to attend a meeting at the City coffee house, on the subject of an institution for the cow-pox. Dr. Lettsom, Dr. Bradley,[1] Dr. Pole, &c., were there. They put me on the Committee.

Many subsequent meetings were held on the subject, and towards the end of the month, William Allen wrote that he was ' much occupied in endeavouring to establish an institution for cow-pox inoculation ' :

Second Month, 17th 1803. I went to the London Tavern, between eleven and twelve, to the meeting on cow-pox. The report of the committee was read and approved. I am appointed a member of the board of directors.

Third Month, 24th, 1803. Askesian, Pepys paper on iron, satisfactory. Then with Woods and R. Phillips to the board of the Jennerian Society—carried the motion for the residence of a physician at the central house.

Jenner, the pioneer of vaccination, came up from Berkeley in Gloucestershire on February 3rd, and for the first time took his

---

[1] Thomas Bradley, M.D., 1751-1813. Physician.

seat as President of what was afterwards the Royal Jennerian Society. It established thirteen stations in London, and in eighteen months over twelve thousand inoculations were done and more than nineteen thousand charges of cow-pox virus sent to places at home and abroad. Statistically the Society was a great success, but internally all was not well ; the seeds of decay had been shown by quarrelling ; subscriptions dropped off, Jenner resigned from the Board, and the National Vaccine Establishment was formed in 1808 to take its place. Had this great prophetic missionary work prospered as it should have done, England might have been spared the smallpox scourge that ravished the country from 1813 to 1833.

Like his mother, some of William's Quaker friends feared that all this scientific work might turn his head, and he records :

> Dear Mary Stacey felt a draught in her mind yesterday to call in and hand me the word of exhortation . . . to be on my guard against the world's flattery and applause.

All his life earnest women were very apt to feel ' a draught in their minds ' concerning the spiritual, emotional and human needs of William, and wished to do their best to minister to them. This, of course, had little or nothing to do with the fact that he was a personable, attractive and comfortably-off widower with enviable future prospects !

At the end of 1803 Allen was elected one of the Presidents of the Physical Society at Guy's Hospital following the course of lectures that he had given to the students in the Hospital in 1802 on chemistry and other sections of natural philosophy.[1] These lectures led to Humphry Davy asking William to undertake a course of popular lectures on natural philosophy at the Royal Institution on the same lines as at Guy's. He consulted John Dalton and Dr. Babington and, after considerable deliberation, consented. The course was so successful that he was invited to deliver a second course the following year. Allen appears to have been a good lecturer and, although often apprehensive beforehand, never had any difficulty in holding an audience, his

[1] Appendix Thirteen.

assets being knowledge, careful preparation—he often sat up all night working on his notes—enthusiasm, and a warm and massive humanity ! Usually the last lecture of the course was a general survey.

During the winter of 1803–4 Allen delivered at Guy's and the Royal Institution no less than one hundred and eight lectures, of which twenty-one were given at the Institution. He continued the course during 1806 and 1807 but, although pressed by Davy to do so in 1808, he refused. He was beginning to feel the strain of preparing them, added to the demands made upon him by his business responsibilities and his ever-growing public work. In 1810, however, he yielded to Davy's urgent request and agreed to give one lecture a week.[1]

Allen was eventually elected a member of the Board of Managers of the Institution, and it is indeed remarkable how he found the time and energy for all his professional, scientific humanitarian and other activities. Emotionally he paid the price in frequent bouts of low spirits, midnight fits of weeping and, very occasionally, the hasty expression of petulance or impatience, mistaken later by Robert Owen, and perhaps by others, as signs of haughtiness, vanity or pride. One of his most consistent prayers was for humility.

Whatever his preoccupations, William never neglected his duties to the Society of Friends ; in 1799, at the age of twenty-nine, he was appointed a member for the Meeting for Sufferings ; was a diligent attender at meetings for worship and discipline, and those gatherings for waiting in quiet.

[1] Appendix Fourteen.

CHAPTER 3

ALLEN BECOMES A FELLOW OF
THE ROYAL SOCIETY

IN January, 1806, William Allen was married for the second time at the Devonshire House meeting. His own account of the event has been preserved :

> This week has been a most important one, having entered into a solemn covenant of marriage with my endeared friend Charlotte Hanbury, under, I trust, a precious degree of evidence of divine approbation. May I be enabled to fill up the measure of those duties which now devolve upon me.

The new responsibilities included his wife's spacious house in Paradise Row, Stoke Newington, with his wife's sister, Anna Hanbury, as an inmate ; William and Charlotte divided their time between Plough Court and Stoke Newington, which was in those days one of the most attractive parts of the north-eastern heights of London, and Allen liked to meditate while walking or riding from one home to the other. Charlotte and Anna Hanbury's two nephews resided with the family and soon became as his own sons to William.

In 1807, Allen, with Davy, Babington and a few other enterprising friends, ' instituted the Geological Society ' at a gathering at Babington's home, thus giving the nascent science a local habitation and a name.[1] On November 20th, 1807, he recorded :

> Dr. Babington called to inform me, that I was last night unanimously elected a Fellow of the Royal Society, and I afterwards received a regular notice from Davy, the Secretary.

Seven years earlier, Dr. George Fordyce, physician and F.R.S., had called on Allen at Plough Court, offering ' to have me

[1] Appendix Fifteen.

made a Fellow of the Royal Society ', but—probably because he felt it undeserved or premature—Allen refused.

At the comparatively early age of thirty-seven, Allen was thus joined to the oldest scientific body in Great Britain, the roll of which contains many of the most illustrious names in British history.

Previous to his election, Allen had been engaged with his friend, W. H. Pepys, on the experiments with carbon and the diamond : a paper read before the Society on June 18th, 1807, was entitled : *On the Quantity of Carbon in Carbonic Acid and on the Nature of the Diamond, by William Allen, Esq., F.L.S., and William Hasledine Pepys, Esq., Communicated by Humphry Davy, Esq., Sec. R.S., M.R.I.A.*

After full details of the experiments had been given, the conclusions arrived at by the two workers were as follows : they confirmed that Lavoisier's statement that one hundred parts of carbonic acid contain twenty-eight parts of carbon ' is very nearly correct, the mean of our experiments makes it 28·60 '. Up to that time Guyton's experiment, which allowed only 17·88 per cent carbon to carbonic acid, had been adopted in all the systems of chemistry. The diamond is pure carbon ; the different forms of carbon differing principally from each other in the state of aggregation of their particles. Charcoal, when properly prepared, requires the same amount of oxygen for its combustion as the diamond. The accuracy of the experiments had been made possible by the use of a new eudiometer, and a paper by W. H. Pepys, explaining this new instrument which he had invented, was read before the Society on June 4th, 1807, by Charles Hatchett, F.R.S.[1]

Davy told Allen that the Council of the Royal Society would have voted the gold medal for the paper on carbonic acid had only one person been the author, but they did not know how to manage it with two. Allen adds : ' It is, however, satisfactory to find that they thought it deserved one.'

Two further papers, this time on respiration, were read by Allen and Pepys during 1808 and 1809. Several important

[1] Proceeding of the Royal Society, 1807.

questions appear to have been cleared up, and the use of the eudiometer gave increased accuracy. John Dalton, in a letter to Allen, expresses himself as ' very well pleased with them ',[1] although he could not make up his mind on one or two points. Allen attended a meeting at the Royal Society on November 9th, 1815, when Davy, in his first lecture of the season, introduced his ' lamp for mines ', and read his paper on fire-damp. Allen noted : ' It appears to contain no olefiant gas, not exploded by red-hot charcoal or iron ; like mixture of olefiant gas, explodes, with one part fire damp and thirteen atmospheric air.'

By this time Davy had not only become Allen's close scientific collaborator, but his ardent admirer and close personal friend. The easy warmth of their relationships is perfectly illustrated by the following letter from Davy to Allen's intimate friend and unfailing help in all his scientific work, W. H. Pepys. Allen had been persuaded that fly-fishing as an occasional relaxation would prove delightful :

2nd April 1808.
I have proposed that we should leave town at about 5 or 6 Monday morning. Sleep at Foot's Gray and try fly-fishing there. Will you arrange with Allen, whom we must initiate in the vocation of the Apostles, as he wants nothing else to make him perfect as a primitive Christian and philosopher.

A letter from Davy written about a year later, after Allen had been ill, completes the picture of two men equally capable of the high office of friendship :

I hope you are now quite well—pray take care of yourself, for your own sake, for the sake of your friends, and for the sake of the world.

Allen was very friendly with the eminent Swedish chemist, Baron Jöns Jakob Berzelius, whose English manuscript on ' A View of the Progress and Recent State of Animal Chemistry ' he had revised. He had also visited him on one of his European tours.

[1] Appendix Sixteen.

In 1820, Berzelius sent to Plough Court a quantity of the metal selenium which he had isolated in 1817.[1]

In the late years of his life there are very few entries in Allen's diary concerning the Royal Society.[2] One for July, 1813, is worth mentioning.

It shows how much of his talents, time and energy he devoted to public affairs and, incidentally, what a good and loyal staff he had that he was able to record in January, 1813 :

John Barry, Q.V., took stock without me—this is the first time for nineteen years that I have not been actively engaged in it.

Nevertheless, with much heart-searching, he was wondering if he should resist calls to further and wider public service and a few weeks later he wrote :

This month has been a very busy one, but John T. Barry has taken almost the whole weight of the business off me.

For the public work Allen sacrificed his worldly advancement : indeed he sacrificed something greater—his inborn, intense love of things of the mind :

. . . the main object is the good of others ; for this I have, in great measure, given up my own gratification ; for if, instead of these things, my time were devoted to philosophical pursuits and experiments, to which I am so naturally prone, the path to honour and distinction stand fair before me.

Had Allen's Quaker business principles been followed with even moderate consistence he might have secured an earlier alleviation of the slave trade in many of the Colonies. Although he frequently expressed in public and private his belief in the ' benevolent views and good intentions ' of those who directed the affairs of the Sierra Leone Company, Allen did not consider them immune from criticism. On it being said that it was not

---

[1] Appendix Seventeen.   [2] Appendix Eighteen.

the business of the manufacturer or trader to inquire what the goods they supplied were required for, he observed :

> . . . When a man comes and says, I want a supply of articles for the purpose of buying slaves, or where we have every reason to believe that things are wanted for that purpose, they cannot be supplied without a degree of participation in the guilt. . . .

A merchant with whom Allen had done considerable business sent him a large sea-chest to refit : suspecting that it was wanted for the Slave Trade, he, after inquiry, refused the business and lost a customer. On a subsequent occasion when his friend, the Czar Alexander I, seven years his junior, urged him to undertake the supply of drugs for the Russian Military Services he gratefully but firmly refused.

CHAPTER 4

ALLEN'S HUMANITARIAN INTERESTS

QUAKERS were the first organized religious body in Great Britain or elsewhere to declare total war on slavery. This terrible problem was already awakening the public conscience during William Allen's childhood and youth, and the strenuous battle claimed and held the life-long allegiance of this doughty apostle of freedom ; and such illustrious crusaders for abolition as Thomas Clarkson, William Wilberforce,[1] Joseph Wood and Granville Sharp were Allen's life-long friends and collaborators.

Largely because he was in the House of Commons, the fame of Wilberforce has outshone in popular estimation that of Clarkson who really blazed the trail. On February 25th, 1807, Allen recorded :

> The young men from my house came home from the House of Commons this morning, at five o'clock, and brought the glorious news that the Bill for the Abolition of the Slave Trade passed the second reading. . . .

It may thus well be that the old Plough Court pharmacy was the first house of a private citizen in which the walls echoed to the great news of this milestone in British civilization.

An interesting and rather curious fact is that prominent members of the Society of Friends were from its foundation in close touch with Royalty. Their strong feeling for human equality never obscured their shrewd appreciation of the undeniable fact that where royal and highly-placed persons lead others will follow. Margaret Fell, ' the mother of Quakerism ', corresponded on terms of equality and simplicity with Charles II and, surprisingly

---

[1] William Wilberforce, 1759-1833. Philanthropist. Champion in the House of Commons of Abolition of Slavery.

recorded, that within a period of six weeks in London she had spoken to the King every week, sometimes twice or thrice. Margaret was a very beautiful and fascinating woman ; perhaps had she not married George Fox as her second husband, the wittiest of English sovereigns might have been converted to Quakerism !

' Farmer George ', the first English-born and English-speaking sovereign of the House of Hanover, was also the first member of it to attract some degree of affection from ordinary men and women. It was during his long reign that members of the Royal Family began to take an interest in various forms of philanthropic activity. British philanthropy never allowed its organizations to become soulless machines and, to avoid this calamity, invariably secured Royal, aristocratic or prominent personages as leaders, thus ensuring a warm humanity and lively sense of personal responsibility.

It is, of course, well known that all his life George III was subject to mental illness. On December 22nd, 1789, Allen wrote : ' The lamentable disorder of our dear Sovereign continues ' : the King, however, on that occasion rapidly recovered.

Young men in high circles always find it difficult to resist the fashionable vices of their time and it is unfortunate, if understandable, that some of the sons of George III fell into the depraved ways of the period. Nevertheless, paradoxical as it may seem, it was during the lives of the Prince Regent (who reigned for ten years as George IV) and his brothers, that the great tradition of undeviating public service by members of the Royal house first appeared.

William Frederick, Duke of Gloucester, who, admittedly, was not highly intellectual, was held up to contempt by the smart set of his day under the nickname of ' Silly Billy ' ; yet he had admirable qualities and warmly supported William Allen in many of his most useful philanthropic schemes.

George IV, when Prince Regent, only received William Allen once as leader of a deputation ; but his brothers, the Dukes of York, Cambridge, Sussex and Kent, all enthusiastically supported him, while his contacts with Queen Victoria's father, the Duke of Kent, developed into a warm and life-long friendship. During Allen's career the Royal example was widely followed by the leading members of the aristocracy, the Government and society, from the Duke of Bedford downward ; indeed the diary often looks like a page from Burke or Debrett !

Over one hundred and forty years ago William Allen and his realistic Quaker friends realized that the non-European races of the world, while retaining the best elements in their own civilizations could, if wisely led and advised, raise their own standard of living and, at the same time, benefit humanity as a whole by adding to the wealth of the world. Therefore, immediately ' the glorious news ' that the Bill for the Abolition of the Slave Trade was passed in the House of Commons, the Quakers took the next sensible step.

At Plough Court Clarkson and Allen were frequently joined in conference and counsel by Wilberforce, Babington, Lord Teignmouth and other sympathizers, including Henry Brougham and Vaux. It says much for Allen's tact and charm, and the binding nature of devotion to a common cause, that he got on well with a man as vain and dictatorial as Brougham, and with one from whom he differed so radically as Wilberforce.

On April 14th, 1807, Allen recorded :

Went to . . . the meeting of the Friends of the Civilization of Africa, at the Freemasons Tavern, Great Queen Street. The Duke of Gloucester [1] was in the Chair. Wilberforce made a speech after the Duke had opened the business. . . . Lord Spencer hailed with delight the recent Abolition of Slavery for the British Dominions : . . . William Smith . . . did himself great credit. . . . But for him, Clarkson, who had done more than any other individual, would have been left out of the vote of thanks. A Society was formed to be called the African Institution. The Duke of Gloucester accepted the office of President ; he is fine young man. . . .

' Steeple houses ', as they called churches, and all that belonged to them, were anathema to many Quakers. William Allen could claim to be a true Cockney because he was born and lived

[1] Later William IV ; then aged thirty-one.

within sound of Bow Bells ; the Church of St. Edmund the Martyr was almost opposite his front door, and every time he walked along to Poultry to hold a chemical séance in the laboratory of friend Pepys, he would have to pass the church ; nevertheless, even if he did not greatly appreciate prelates or prelacy, his tolerant mind and native honesty impelled him to complete his vivid account of that momentous meeting by adding, ' Several Bishops were there.'

On March 26th, 1808, he recorded :

Took Pepys with me to the African Institution . . . The Duke of Gloucester was there . . . we dined in the great hall on the anniversary of the Abolition of the Slave Trade. The Duke of Gloucester was president, and the Duke of Norfolk,[1] the Bishop of Bath and Wells, the Bishop of Durham, and a great number of the nobility, members of Parliament, etc., etc., were present. . . . I think there were between four and five hundred. . . .

Two years later Allen could rightfully claim progress :

African Institution at one. A large meeting. The Duke of Gloucester as usual, at his post, and manifesting a lively interest in the important subjects under discussion. The old veterans in the cause, Granville Sharpe, Wilberforce, William Smith and others were present,—indeed, the majority of the company were members of one or the other Houses of Parliament. . . . Brougham, also has lately been brought to Parliament.

[1] Charles Howard, 11th Duke, 1746–1815.

CHAPTER 5

BRITISH AND FOREIGN SCHOOL SOCIETY

ALLEN suffered from the sad but not ignoble delusion—as current now as it was then—that education can work miracles. He wrote :

The influence of knowledge upon the human mind is prodigious . . . where do we behold cruelty in its most terrific form, but in the uninstructed and neglected part of the community ? By whom are gaols principally inhabited but by the ignorant ? . . . Knowledge, properly understood and applied, sheds a benevolent influence over the minds of the possessors. . . . Men who have not been in the habit of thinking, and carefully investigating the ground of their opinions, are most of all liable to be carried away by the passions. . . .

No Quaker ever fell into the error of thinking that educational and scientific progress were something that man could achieve outside the integrating belief in an absolute moral order. Allen wisely spoke of knowledge ' properly understood and applied ' ; since his day knowledge has tragically outrun understanding !

Second only to his life-long, passionate fight against slavery was William's fight for education. His efforts took three principal forms : his noble and long-continued work on behalf of that wayward educational pioneer, Joseph Lancaster ; his prominent share in the educational side of the work of Robert Owen at New Lanark in Scotland ; and in later life, his own agricultural school which he established at Lindfield in Sussex.

Lancaster, the son of a Chelsea pensioner, and with an un-doubted streak of genius, was a difficult man to work with. Early in life he joined the Society of Friends and without their backing would have accomplished much less than he did ; and it is no exaggeration to say that in this, as in much else, William Allen and his educational fellow enthusiasts would have had a longer and stiffer fight for their reforms had they not been consistently backed by the Duke of Kent, fourth son of George III and father of Queen Victoria.

Lancaster, pioneer of the monotorial system in schools, began his notable work at the age of twenty by assembling a few poor children in a shed belonging to his father. Members of the Society of Friends helped him, and soon he had a building in Borough Road, London, capable of holding a thousand children. He is first mentioned in Allen's diary in the summer of 1808. The Borough Road experiment had already attracted attention in high places. Lancaster recorded :

> The second building I owe to the benevolence of the Duke of Bedford [1] and Lord Somerville, who appeared to be sent by Providence to open wide before me the portals of usefulness for the good of the poor.

Allen paid the first of many visits to Borough Road and was greatly moved :

> I can never forget the impression which the scene made upon me. Here I beheld a thousand children collected from the streets, where they were learning nothing but mischief, one bad boy corrupting another.

Allen was as favourably impressed by ' this meritorious young man ' as he was by his work, which he wished to see widely extended ; he of course did not then know that ' vain, reckless and improvident ' Lancaster was already deep in financial quagmires. Writing to Allen the Duke of Bedford spoke of himself and the Duke of Sussex as ' fighting in the great cause of education ' and said :

> You and I profess different creeds, yet we both wish for the education of the children of the poor, on the broad basis of religion, and a knowledge of the scriptures.

[1] 6th Duke, 1766–1839.

However, almost from the outset, his more mature and sober friends distrusted Lancaster's over-optimistic and financially muddle-headed temperament, and earnestly besought him to place the supervision of his affairs in the hands of trustees. He reluctantly consented. Joseph Fox, the rich Quaker surgeon and dentist living near Allen in Lombard Street, sold two thousand pounds' worth of his own investments to try and still the clamour of Lancaster's many creditors ; William Corston, a straw-hat manufacturer on Ludgate Hill, courageously accepted bills drawn on him by Fox for between three and four thousand pounds in favour of the creditors ; a baker in the neighbourhood of Borough Road gave Lancaster extended credit and, when surprise was expressed at the amount, said that the good that was done in the neighbourhood was such that as long as he had a loaf he would give Lancaster half. These incidents were indications of the fascination the man exercised over persons of all classes.

A Committee, including Allen, Fox and Corston, was set up ; Allen undertook the laborious task of preparing and keeping a proper set of books and minutes ; funds were raised and Lancaster's heavy debts discharged, David Barclay of Walthamstow ably assisting. At first Lancaster appeared to acquiesce in all this, but he did so with characteristic reservations. In one of Lancaster's many audiences with George III, the King, who gave him very great encouragement, expressed the wish that every poor child in his dominions should be taught to read the Bible. It has been said that Royal patronage, fame and public responsibility proved to be 'beyond Lancaster's own powers to sustain or control'.

With the King's approval, and with Allen as treasurer, Lancaster's friends next formed the Royal Lancastrian Institution which eventually became the British and Foreign School Society. Although Allen saw in Lancaster 'a peculiar talent for his work', he soon began to recognize the accompanying limitations. Lancaster signed an agreement not to incur any fresh expense without the sanction in writing of the Committee. Allen was indefatigable in stimulating old friends of education and enlisting new. On a late December afternoon in 1809 he took tea with Joseph Fox in Argyle Street and from there went on to Montague

Square to call on the famous and eccentric granddaughter of the great Earl of Chatham :

> . . . to Lady Hester Stanhope to talk about school concerns ; she possesses considerable abilities and extensive knowledge of persons in high life : she is a niece of the late William Pitt, and resided with him. She is going to Sicily for her health on second day next, to be absent about two years.

As it turned out, the valiant Lady Hester's remarkable energy, business ability, brilliant talents, satirical tongue, lively pen, and belief in inoculation against smallpox, were lost to the cause because she never returned to England ! The incident, however, again proves Allen's extraordinary flair for securing useful adherents without whose backing little of permanent value can be accomplished. Very soon Allen was, at her request, calling on the Duchess of Richmond—the lady who, six years later, gave the famous eve of Waterloo Ball in Brussels—who offered to become a patroness if branches of Lancaster's school could be started in Ireland !

In May, 1812, Allen wrote :

> Conference with Joseph Fox who has this day had an interesting interview with the Dukes of Kent and Sussex at their own request.

Three days later the first annual general meeting of the Institution was held at the Freemasons' Tavern, a message from the Prince Regent being read. Lancaster did not impress Allen favourably :

> J. L. gave some particulars of his Irish journey. There was too much bombast. . . . The Duke of Kent was in the Chair, and the Duke of Sussex was also present. They both did themselves great credit by their able conduct.

However, Lancaster soon quarrelled with his Committee, and, without their knowledge, set up a private school at Labrador House, Tooting. The Committee had eventually to decide that the time had come for ' drawing a close and strong line ' between

Lancaster's public and private activities, and Allen was constrained to write Joseph Foster :

> Of all the concerns that I have anything to do with, the Lancastrian lies the most heavily on my mind. . . .

Of the 1813 Annual General Meeting of the Institution Allen said :

> The Dukes of Kent and Sussex were there and behaved nobly. The Marquess of Lansdowne[1] made an excellent speech, and Whitehead also—a very animated meeting.

But Lancaster's career in England was nearing its end. It became known that his Tooting school adventure was on the verge of bankruptcy. A week after the general meeting Allen was :

> Sent for by the Duke of Kent. Fox could not go, so I went to Kensington alone ; told him the whole of the circumstances respecting J. L. He behaved very kindly, said we must not give up the cause, and promised his support to the new arrangements.
>
> He then entered upon private confidential business on his own concerns.

A week later :

> To the Dukes of Kent and Sussex with Fox, on the new Constitution for carrying on the School, (in Borough Road) a very satisfactory interview—they behaved nobly. An important day.

On July 17th, 1813, there is a long diary entry :

> Went to Kensington, with Fox and Corston, to meet the Dukes of Kent and Sussex, and the Duke of Bedford. We fully and frankly stated the nature of our difficulties with Joseph Lancaster ; but I observed that it would be proper for them to hear his account of the business. . . . They were all of this mind, and the Duke of Kent remarked, that

[1] 3rd Marquess, 1780–1863. Distinguished statesman. Championed Catholic emancipation, Abolition, and popular education.

as Lancaster was a man of violent temper it would be right to have some indifferent person present, and he knew of no one more likely to manage him than Whitbread. . . . The three Dukes showed themselves real men of business and feeling . . .

The story is continued in an entry dated August 13th :

To Argyle Street, then with Fox to Whitbreads, and thence all together to Kensington Palace, where Joseph Foster, W. Corston, and T. Sturge met us . . . and J. Lancaster. The Dukes of Kent and Sussex presided. The Duke of Kent opened the business in a masterly manner. . . . Lancaster behaved *very imprudently*, to say the least. . . . In conclusion, the Duke of Kent told him in substance that they had agreed upon certain points which they were determined to maintain,—that they would give him time to consider of them coolly, that he might still be the prominent feature in the business, but that if he persisted in the conduct he had lately pursued, they were determined to maintain the cause WITHOUT HIM. The patience and condescension of the Royal Dukes on this occasion, were very striking.

This important meeting had a sequel in the following letter to Allen who received it at Cromer where he was with his family ; the impetuously idealistic Lancaster could hardly have found at his back a fairer or more humane advocate :

Kensington Palace,
Aug. 15, 1813.

Friend Allen,
I duly received, this morning, your esteemed favour of yesterday, and was highly gratified in finding that the exertions of myself and brother, on Friday last, at the Committee, were noticed by you in so feeling and friendly a manner. . . . It can scarcely be necessary for me to observe, that your conduct, and that of the Trustees throughout, has impressed both of us with sentiments of admiration. With respect to the unfortunate J. L. I cannot help fearing, that vanity and distress united, have bereaved him of the power of judgment : but I trust, in a little time, we shall be able

to convince him of the folly of the former, and relieve his mind of the latter ; and that we shall yet be able to avail ourselves of his services, by remunerating them LIBERALLY, and marking out his line, so that he cannot possibly stray from it. . . .

With respect to my own affairs, the moment I can avail myself of your advice, with advantage, I will do myself the pleasure of addressing you again. In the meantime I remain, with regard and esteem, friend Allen,

Yours faithfully,
Edward.

But the wayward Joseph Lancaster proved incorrigible and the utmost efforts of his best friends failed to save him from himself. Let us here, with a grateful salute, take leave of the poor man's son, and poor lad's friend. Like all men, he suffered from the defects of his qualities. In 1818 he went to the United States and to Canada and had some success followed by failure. His friends in England, of which we may be sure William Allen was one, provided him with a small annuity. After many vicissitudes he was, twenty years later, run over by a carriage in the streets of New York—characteristically impetuous to the end.

CHAPTER 6

THE DUKE OF KENT'S AFFAIRS

THE Duke of Kent's financial embarrassments dated from
his youth and were by no means all his own fault.[1] Had
it been otherwise we may be quite sure that William Allen
would not have willingly bestowed time, energy and infinite
patience on the uncongenial task of releasing his royal friend
from a humiliating position. He was asked for help by one
whom he admired as a man and respected as a prince, and gave
it ungrudgingly. On June 10th, 1815, the Duke wrote :

> The Duke of Kent has just received his friend William
> Allen's letter, of this date from which he learned with very
> sincere concern, the indisposition of their mutual friend
> Fox, than whom, there does not exist a more deserving
> and valuable member of society. . . . The opinions given
> by William Allen, with respect to the establishment at the
> Borough Road, are altogether congenial with those enter-
> tained by the Duke of Kent on the same subject . . . If
> the Duke's services can be useful . . . he trusts that William
> Allen is well persuaded he may command them. . . .
> With respect to all William Allen says, in so friendly and
> affectionate a manner, with regard to his own affairs, the
> Duke will only allow himself to state that he hopes he
> appreciates it as he ought.

In 1815 the Duke's personal situation may well have given him
a fellow-feeling for rash Joseph Lancaster. At any rate, he
had invited, and gladly availed himself of, Allen's advice and
help and, as he himself phrased it, ' with advantage '. Allen
suggested the handing over of his affairs to two trustees and the
Duke consented provided Allen was one of them. Allen agreed,

[1] Appendix Nineteen.

and was fortified in his delicate task by the help and expert advice of Samuel Hoare, Samuel Gurney, Thomas Pitt and J. Kirkland.

It was said that Hoare and Gurney each lent two thousand pounds towards paying the Duke's most pressing debts and were not repaid until the following reign. The legend that these sums were borrowed for the specific purpose of enabling the Duke and Duchess of Kent to return to London from Anspach in order that their coming child should be born in England is chronologically impossible.

Allen says in his diary :

I feel peace in this affair, and if my feelings do not deceive me, this exertion to help him is right.

The Duke assigned the bulk of his income to the trustees in favour of his creditors and retired to Brussels where he lived in the simplest style possible.

In March of 1817 Allen wrote the Duke, whom he addressed as esteemed Friend, a long letter in the course of which he said :

The Duke of Kent knows that I have never courted his notice from any *interested* view ; indeed it is only in order to be more extensively useful to my country, and to mankind, that I wish to be known to those in the higher ranks of society . . . I have anxiously enquired into the state of those arrangements, which are admirably calculated to remove all these embarrassments, that must have pressed heavily upon thy mind, and which we all so deeply deplore . . . the absence of so powerful a patron from the country, is an injury to those works of benevolence, which distinguish England from the surrounding nations . . . and any interruption to the plan would put off that day, so honourable to the Duke and so gratifying to all his real friends, when he shall have discharged all his engagements, and be in full possession of all his revenues ; and *that* by a wise disposition of his own resources.

To this the Duke replied from Brussels on May 5th, 1817 :

. . . I am happy to find that you are perfectly convinced of my adherence to the spirit of my original agreement, and I will venture to say that nothing shall divert me from it. Indeed, when every three months I have the satisfaction of seeing between four and five thousand pounds wiped off, no other stimulus can be wanting . . . even if I were not bound by that most sacred of all ties, a promise to my friends. Upon the *other* point, to which you have so delicately alluded, I shall only say that I trust Providence will direct my proceedings for the best. . . .

On November 19th Allen recorded :

The remains of the amiable and deeply lamented Princess Charlotte are to be interred this evening . . . the shops are universally shut up, and every thing is like First-day. Friends have believed it right to close *their* shops also, in the manner that they do when death visits their own families.

It can hardly be doubted that Allen's grief and that of the Quakers was increased by the fact that Princess Charlotte firmly supported the Campaign against the Slave Trade.

The death in childbirth of the Heiress Presumptive to the Throne of course changed the position in the succession of all the younger brothers of the Prince Regent, and three of them hastened to make arrangements to get married and, it was hoped, produce an heir.

In May, 1818, the Duke of Kent married at Coburg the widowed Princess of Leiningen, thus gaining as a sagacious brother-in-law Queen Victoria's ' dear Uncle Leopold '. He brought his bride to England and on July 13th, to make assurance double sure, they were again married at Kew. On August 3rd, Allen wrote :

To Kensington Palace at the desire of the Duke of Kent, took R. H. with me, and the Duke promises to see if anything can be done in his case.

Next day he continued :

Went over to the Borough Road to meet the Duke and Duchess of Kent and Prince Leopold.

78

In his straitened circumstances the bridegroom could not long keep his bride in England and, having wasted no time in initiating her into the demands of English philanthropy, they set off for Amorbach, the Leiningen home in Franconia where, as Regent of the Principality, the Duchess had a palace.

However, it soon became apparent that the Duchess was to become a mother, and the bride and bridegroom hurriedly returned to London in order that their child should be born in England. This historic event took place at Kensington Palace on May 24th, 1819, and the little girl became Queen Victoria. She never knew her father who died eight months after she was born.

Allen's last diary entry concerning the Duke of Kent's affairs is characteristic ; it is dated March 19th, 1820 :

On seventh-day, the 18th, when, together with Thomas Pitt and J. Kirkland, I administered to the estate of a deceased, illustrious person, at Doctors' Commons, I entered my protest against the following title of the Archbishop of Canterbury, viz. : 'The Most Reverend Father in God', and left it on record, after my signature of the bond.

CHAPTER 7

FIRST EUROPEAN JOURNEY

WILLIAM ALLEN'S philanthropic work began in his
native parish of Spitalfields where, to relieve the
poverty and economic dislocation and unemployment
arising out of the Wars of Napoleon, he was instrumental in
having soup kitchens established. Allen never neglected unspec-
tacular duties near at hand, but, step by step, his work, example
and influence was to spread to Scotland, Ireland, North America,
West Africa, India, and throughout Europe. He might well
have echoed John Wesley's famous saying ' the world is my
parish '.

Allen's contact with Frederick Wilhelm III of Prussia [1] and,
more particularly, with Alexander I [2] of Russia, led to a series
of missionary visits to Europe, which cannot here be recorded
in detail. Countries visited included Russia, France, Spain,
Holland, Belgium, Switzerland, Germany, Norway, Sweden
and Finland. Russia has, however, been chosen as representative
because Allen spent more time there than in any other foreign
country ; what he has to say not only throws fresh light on that
enigmatic Empire, but is as pertinent now as when it was written
some one hundred and thirty-five years ago.

1814 was a notable year for the Western world. Peace was
made between the U.S.A. and Great Britain : the menacing
shadow of Napoleon over Europe appeared to be dwindling.
On March 20th, Allen thus recorded the turning-point, known
in history as the Battle of Orthez :

> The Tower guns fired to-day in consequence of a victory
> gained by Wellington over Marshal Soult between Bayonne
> and Bordeaux.

[1] 1770–1840.　　　[2] 1774–1825.

Within three weeks he was able to continue :

The public events of this week are truly astonishing. Paris taken by the Allies. The Senate denounce Bonaparte. Louis XVIII proclaimed in Paris. Bonaparte resigns the crown. Is not the hand of the Almighty conspicuous now ? . . .

At the end of May the Duchess of Oldenburg, sister of the idealistic Czar Alexander I, arrived in London. She must already have been acquainted with and liked the Society of Friends because one of the first things she did was with her suite to attend a Meeting for worship at Devonshire House. The consort of the Protestant ruler of a country largely Protestant, the Duchess, like her brother, was greatly attracted by the strongly mystical side of Quakerism, and by the simplicity, integrity, and practical Christianity of the Quaker way of life.

Ignoring subordinates and intermediates, as they ignore a priesthood, Quakers in all things believed in going direct to the fountain head. At this moment in history Alexander I of Russia enjoyed unique prestige shared, to some extent, by the King of Prussia.

On June 13th Allen wrote :

At a Meeting for Sufferings, held for the purpose at four o'clock this afternoon, the Addresses to the Emperor of Russia and King of Prussia, drawn up in pursuance of the direction of a special meeting for Sufferings, held on the tenth instant, were finally agreed to.

'Held on the tenth instant', that is on June 10th, one year and eight days before Waterloo !

Baron Jacobi, the Prussian Ambassador to the Court of St. James's, was approached and, on June 16th, a week after Frederick Wilhelm's arrival in London, Stephen Grellet, John Wilkinson, Luke Howard and William Allen attended at St. James's Palace. Allen vividly re-created this interesting scene :

. . . after waiting some time we were told that the King had been up all night, and was much hurried, and that the only chance we had of seeing him, was by standing in the passage through which he was to pass to his carriage. When he came up Baron Jacobi directed his attention to us, and the Address, together with some books, was presented; Stephen Grellet had only time to say a few words in French, and in adverting to some of our Society in his dominions, and to the Society's testimony against War, the King observed, they were excellent people, but without waiting for the conclusion of the sentence said 'war was necessary to procure peace'. . . .

Next day, not unduly disheartened by the Prussian King's characteristically brusque behaviour, William waited on the Czar.

. . . Went up to Count Lieven's . . . (he) informed me that the Emperor wished to attend one of our meetings, and that there was no other time for it but the present. . . . It was quite plain we must go to the nearest, which was Westminster. . . . I suggested that, to prevent annoyance from the mob, the Emperor had better go as privately as possible. . . . The Emperor and Duchess soon came down, the former in plain dress. I was introduced to them, and then gave the coachman directions . . . at Martin's Lane.[1] . . . A number of persons had collected. . . . I went at a respectful distance before the Emperor, and had just time to beckon out four Friends who sat near the door . . . A precious degree of solemnity covered the meeting. I showed the Emperor . . . to a seat fronting the meeting; the Duchess preferred the first cross form on the women's side . . . The Emperor and the whole party conducted themselves with great seriousness . . . my mind was sweetly calmed and refreshed, in the firm belief that the Great Master had the work in His own hands . . . nothing could have answered better, if it had been ever so well contrived.

June 21, 1814.

Dear Stephen Grellet went with us to the Pulteney Hotel . . . the Emperor stood to receive us; he was quite alone and dressed in a plain suit of clothes, and, with a look of

[1] The Friends' Meeting House was in St. Martin's Court, Leicester Square.

benignity, seemed to meet us as friends . . . We stood
around him . . . his questions were chiefly in reference to
the doctrines and practices of our Society . . . showed that
he was acquainted with the operations of the Holy Spirit
in the soul . . . he was himself in the habit of daily prayers
. . . the Emperor feelingly remarked upon the importance
of the trust committed to him—the many temptations with
which he was surrounded, and the few to whom he could
open his heart on such a subject . . . the Emperor, pressing
S. Grellet's hands with both of his, was much contrited, and
with tears in his eyes . . . several times . . . he took one
or other of the others of us by the hand, and to John Wilkinson he expressed how fully his spirit united with him in
prayer, at the meeting on first day . . . expressed a wish
to see a Friend's house ; but . . . from the shortness of
time . . . it seemed difficult. . . . S. G. having directed
his attention to suffering Africa, the Emperor went into
the subject with warmth and feeling, saying that the Africans
were men, and objects of redeeming love as well as ourselves ; and that when the articles of peace were framing, he
had done all he could for them . . . respectfully reminded
him that he possessed the power, in a greater degree than
any other person now in existence, for doing incalculable
good ; he said : ' if any of your friends visit Petersburg on
a religious account, let them not wait for any introduction,
but come direct to me, and I will do everything to promote
your views ' . . . He took each of us by the hand and
said, ' I part from you as friends and brethren.'

The idealism of Alexander I was sustained by extraordinary
pertinacity. John Glaisyer wrote to Allen as follows :

I think thou wilt be pleased to learn that the Emperor was
not willing readily to give up his wish to see a Friend's
family. My cousin Nathaniel Rickman, and his wife,
were standing at their own gate last first day afternoon, to
see the Emperor pass ; . . . he alighted, and asked N. R.
if they were not of the people called Quakers . . . he
requested permission to go into the house . . . The
Duchess then alighted . . . the Duchess asked if they might

go over the house . . . they were conducted into the principal apartments, the neatness of which they praised . . . were invited to take some refreshments, which they did and seemed much pleased with the attention . . . they seemed unwilling to take leave, but . . . had to go as far as Dover that night . . . On parting the Emperor kissed Mary Rickman's hand, and the Duchess kissed her . . . he behaved throughout in the most free and affable manner possible. . . .

If Count Lieven thought that the departure of the Czar would relieve him of helping to advance the cause of education in Russia—he did not yet know William Allen who, on July 9th, confided to his diary :

To Count Lieven's . . . and an important conversation with him . . . He desires me to suggest a plan, in writing, which he may read to the Emperor ; this is just what I wanted . . .

That autumn Allen made an excursion into Perthshire and, on his return to Edinburgh, visited the observatory where he and his party were kindly received by Professor Playfair, Lord Webb Seymour, and Sir George Mackenzie ; but wherever he went, he never lost sight of what was, after all, the centre of his life—the progress and well-being of the Society of Friends. In 1802 Francis Jeffrey, Scott, Horner, H. P. Brougham, Sydney Smith and others had with brilliant success started the *Edinburgh Review* :

R. Owen, J. Fox and I went to Hutton, about eight miles distant, to breakfast, with Francis Jeffrey, the editor of the ' *Edinburgh Review* '. We were kindly received, and I had some interesting conversation with him in the garden alone, when I gently expostulated with him on the treatment Friends had met with in his Review, and he frankly acknowledged that he knew but little about it. . . . I think the interview will be of great use.

It is characteristic of Allen's modesty that there is no diary record of the honour paid him when in this year he was elected a member of the Council of the Royal Society. The eventful 1814 was nearing its end. On October 17th he recorded :

> Favoured to reach Stoke Newington in health and safely after our long journey, and felt, I trust, reverently thankful. My feelings were excited on entering the late abode of our dear J. G. B., but I had a comfortable belief that he was safely landed . . . the office of an executor to the will of dear J. G. B. will increase my cares.

Some time after his second marriage Allen had an observatory built in the garden of his charming Stoke Newington home and there passed such happy hours of relaxation as could be snatched from his extraordinarily busy life : the stars, and the Creator of the stars, were ever his place of refuge. Here, at the end of a tiring day spent in the City or on his lectures, he would make his way and in peace and quiet of the country night he would seek that relaxation of body and spirit of which he was always so badly in need.[1]

It is always interesting to see great historic events through the eyes of a thoughtful, acute contemporary observer. On June 22nd, 1815, Allen wrote :

> Official news of a dreadful battle at Waterloo, near Brussels. Napoleon defeated by Wellington and Blücher. It is supposed on the whole that between forty and fifty thousand were slain.

This decisive battle—although he could hardly have realized it at the time—opened the way to Allen's many and prolonged visits to the Continent. By January, 1816, having firmly secured Lieven as a friendly and willing coadjutor, he was able to record : ' in Russia prospects open '. In July, accompanied by his wife Charlotte, Elizabeth Fry, Elizabeth Robson and Charlotte's eldest nephew, Cornelius Hanbury, Allen, as an office holder, set out at the behest of the Society of Friends to visit the Netherlands, Belgium, Germany and Switzerland, arriving at Berne in September. There, to his great satisfaction, he met the noble

[1] Appendix Twenty.

85

Johann Heinrich Pestalozzi,[1] greatest of educational pioneers, eminent philanthropist and advanced thinker, who saluted his welcome visitor ' with two kisses on each cheek '.

For some time Charlotte Allen had been suffering from the fatigues of the journey ; and at Geneva she felt that she was nearing her end and wrote in her private journal :

> I have felt very poorly and sinking for several days, and now, this 10th day of the Ninth month (1816), feel as if I must take leave of all here . . . what will become of my precious husband, dear Cornelius, and the two females ?— may the Shepherd of Israel keep and preserve them.

Allen describes himself as ' plunged into inexpressible anguish '. Three weeks later Charlotte passed quietly away and was buried in the Protestant cemetery of Sacconet, her husband and nephew being comforted somewhat by the presence of ' several kind and sympathizing friends '.

Soon William and Cornelius set out for Dover, where they were tenderly welcomed by brothers Samuel and Joseph and by Joseph's wife. Reaching home Allen wrote :

> I found my dear mother, daughter and sister, with whom I had a truly affecting meeting . . . my beloved mother addressed me with words of consolation . . . somewhat confirming and strengthening to my tempest-tossed soul.

Verbally and in writing, innumerable friends, such as Joseph Foster, Joseph Gurney, Rachel Fowler, E. J. Fry and William Wilberforce, expressed their sympathy with Allen in his loss.

---

[1] 1746–1827 : *Lienhardt und Gertrud* was published in 1781 ; his School at Burgdorf founded in 1799 and the one at Yverdun in 1805.

CHAPTER 8

LIFE AT STOKE NEWINGTON

WHEN, in July, 1817, William Allen arrived at Congenies, near Lyons, he was accompanied by his daughter Mary, his nephew Daniel Bell Hanbury and young George Majolier, who, having been for two years William's guest in England, was returning home to his parents. William wrote :

> I was very low in spirits, having, as we rode along, dwelt much on my great loss of my precious Charlotte. Louis Majolier and his wife had met us on the road to welcome their son.

A busy ten days was spent at Congenies 'labouring diligently for the spiritual and temporal welfare of Friends in that part of the world'; when the visitors took leave :

> Many tears were shed . . . L. and M. Majolier have agreed to let their little daughter, Christine, go with us to England.

Christine, born in 1805, was then twelve years old. From Charlotte's death a year earlier, her sister Anna had of course been in full charge of the Stoke Newington home and warmly welcomed William, Mary, Daniel and the young Christine when they arrived there after an absence of nine weeks, during which the missionary party had covered nearly two thousand miles.

The advent of Christine doubtless did something to compensate the Stoke Newington household for the loss of Charlotte. The little French girl was affectionate and intelligent, and soon adapted herself to the busy social and business life of Stoke Newington and Plough Court. She afterwards wrote her *Memorials* and in them we get vivid glimpses of William himself,

Mary, and Daniel and Cornelius Hanbury, and acute descriptions of some of their famous friends. She spent one half of the week at Plough Court, and the other at Stoke Newington, Daniel and Cornelius journeying daily to the City.

William informally 'adopted' Christine, and she thus described his life at Plough Court :

The first, second, third and part of fourth days were taken up by meetings, many of which were held there. His life was one of continuous engagements : he rose early and lighted his own fire. The early hours were generally devoted to correspondence, and during the time he was shaving, his daughter used to read to him in Latin from Livy, and immediately after breakfast he would hear his sister, Anna Hanbury, read French. He seemed literally to have time for everything.

Christine, or Chris, as William called her, recorded her delight in some of the experiments conducted by her 'father', and particularly in being allowed to count the seconds of his astronomical clock while he observed the passage of the stars through his circular instrument by which he took the time.

William Allen's business books were often brought to Stoke Newington from Plough Court for posting and were, in fine weather, carried out to the summer-house by 'black Tom', a negro whom he had rescued from slavery, and who was for years his devoted factotum.

Christine acted as William's French correspondent and translated his letters to correspondents using that language into French, but he always copied them afterwards himself and he would enclose the English draft also. He used oiled and black paper so as to produce two copies at a time.

Christine was taken back to her home at Congenies in 1820 and she did not return to Plough Court until November, 1822.

In the meantime, in February, 1822, Mary Allen had married Cornelius Hanbury ; they were living at Plough Court and upon her return Christine remarked that ' the house looked different from what it did when I was there before '. The two parlours which had been more like committee rooms had been re-furnished and as a result looked very comfortable ; Mary Hanbury was now the mistress at Plough Court. Christine lived entirely at the Stoke Newington house and tells us that William Allen went regularly to town directly after breakfast and returned to a three-o'clock dinner, often bringing company with him.

William Wilberforce, who had first met Allen in 1805, and his wife frequently dined at Stoke Newington, and Christine records one such occasion : after dinner they all walked to some cottages in Lordship Road where Allen was conducting agricultural experiments. At these cottages Wilberforce was weighed in the scales :

> . . . and though many have had the opportunity of recording his talents, few have been able to tell his weight, and this, insignificant as it is, may give some idea of his person and confirm the saying, ' The mind's the standard of man.' He weighed, including the five pounds for the iron stays he wore, seventy-six pounds !

Apart from his eminence, Wilberforce played such a major part in the life and work of William Allen that he demands a paragraph to himself. His appearance was not prepossessing. A diminutive edition of a man, he disliked himself ; Boswell, that acute observer, went to hear him speak and said : ' I saw what seemed a mere shrimp mounted upon a table ; but, as I listened, he grew and grew until the shrimp became a whale.' Wilberforce never enjoyed good health and for some twenty years on doctor's orders took opium to keep soul and body together yet, such was his self-control, that he never exceeded the prescribed dose. John Wesley, nine days before his death, wrote his last letter to Wilberforce urging him to carry on his crusade against the Slave Trade : ' His suffering, and his sensitiveness about his mean personal appearance acting on his inherent nobility, enabled him to do more than almost any other single man to stop the slave trade.' His monument in Westminster Abbey describes him truly as ' the Attorney-General of the unprotected and friendless '.

Lord John Russell first called at Plough Court in 1825, when he evidently made a favourable impression on Allen. Soon after he joined the Society for the Improvement of the Labouring Classes, and also began to take a prominent part in the affairs of the British and Foreign School Society. The respect Russell and Allen had for each other was mutual ; increasing acquaintance deepened it.

Henry Brougham used often to visit William, and sometimes dined at Stoke Newington. He is described by Christine as being ' plain in person and until I had heard him as a public speaker, there was little about him that I admired '. The friendship with Allen, begun in 1810, remained unimpaired for a long period, in spite of Brougham's occasional ' torrents of invective ' !

Christine says of Thomas Clarkson that ' he was an absorbed old man ' who was too much taken up with grave matters to take much notice of her. He always stayed at Plough Court when he was in London, there being one room only in which he liked to sleep ; this was called the study, it was over the kitchen and was approached by a very dark staircase, but it was the room of his choice.

There is overwhelming evidence of Allen's genius for friendships with men of all ranks and with all shades of political and religious opinion. The catholicity of William's circle is emphasized by Christine :

> As memory glances over the scenes of that period I feel bewildered by the motley assemblage which presents itself. I see men of all countries and of all shades of colour : Russians, Germans, Frenchmen, Swedes, Greeks, Italians, Spaniards, North American Indians, West Indians and many of the suffering sons of Africa partaking of that hospitality which he knew so well how to bestow without the least ostentation ; very little difference being made between their entertainment and the dinners given to Lord Brougham, Dr. Lushington, Wilberforce, John Smith of Dale Park, or to Gautier, or Alexander Vinet of Geneva, and other distinguished foreigners.

Christine Majolier's ' motley assemblage ' affords an opportunity for stepping aside to ask why, comparatively speaking, its range seemed to be so circumscribed? Apart from the Renaissance, and its immense repercussions in Tudor England, William Allen lived through many years of the richest cultural epoch of our long history, and would appear to have been strangely unaffected by its fertilizing impact. However, no human existence is lived in a vacuum, or subjugated by its vocational necessities. Allen, almost pathologically sensitive, so emotional that, like Shelley, he was easily moved to tears, cannot have spent his seventy-three years of life oblivious of the spirit of his times, the climate of opinion in which he lived and had his being, or totally ignorant of the influences of the great names in music, poetry and literature that made his age illustrious. With the current advances of the physical sciences and medicine of his day he was in close touch. Apart from his philanthropic and humanitarian interests his diary, being principally a spiritual exercise, leaves outside affairs (even business) largely unmentioned ; nor must it be forgotten that, unfortunately, it was severely edited.

No one who knew the Bible as well as Allen did could be considered uncultured. If not a classical scholar, he read Greek, and, more particularly, like so many pharmacists of his day, Latin with ease. A man who had Livy regularly read aloud to him while dressing must have seen in the great historian not only the eclectic lover of letters and art and the centre of a brilliant literary circle, but the author who ever upheld the rightful supremacy of moral values in history. Pope (because he was born in Plough Court) he could hardly have escaped, and his *Universal Prayer* was one of his favourite poems ; he had also a great admiration for Cowper's poems in general, and for particular poems like Prior's *Charity* and Addison's *How are Thy Servants Blest, O Lord* ; but obviously it was the didactic element in poetry, as in his prose reading, that most appealed to him.

While some Quakers were of course rigid, those of a liberal outlook could, like Silvanus Bevan, live in comfort, not to say luxury, surrounded by beauty and beautiful things. Yet, judging from his diary alone, it would seem that William Allen never even heard of Purcell and Handel and in it there is no mention of such vast creative giants as Mozart, Bach, Beethoven or Schubert, nor even of Haydn who throughout William's life was capturing London from the King, George III, and the Royal family down- ward. True, he once quoted Dr. Johnson, but there is no mention of Goldsmith, Sheridan, Scott, Jane Austen, Lamb or Hazlitt, all of whom were during his life publishing masterpieces ; his understanding of Clarkson's enforced dependence on opium might have been supposed to awaken some sympathy for de Quincey ; it is obvious that Smollett, Pepys, Byron and Burns would have been uncongenial ; yet Shelley, Tennyson and Browning should surely have appealed.

Although he never seems to have met any of the Lake poets, Allen must have known much about them from Clarkson who built himself a long white house on Engemere at the foot of Ullswater. Coleridge, who was one of Clarkson's great friends, called him ' slave of the slaves ' : although not a Friend, Coleridge was closely associated with Quakers and copied their ways and turns of speech ; no West Indian rum or sugar were ever seen on his table. He admired Clarkson so much that when his *History of the Abolition of the Slave Trade* [1]—much of which was written at Plough Court—appeared in 1808, Coleridge departed from his rule never to review books and wrote a glowing account of it for the *Edinburgh Review* : the dinner on April 8th of that year may well have been in celebration of the publication of Clarkson's *History*. William, noting the event in his diary, said : ' Coleridge is one of the most eloquent men in conversa- tion that I have ever met with.' This was prescient, because it was not until December, 1811, that Byron wrote : ' I dine with Rogers, and am to *hear* Coleridge who is a kind of rage at present.' That the acquaintanceship between Allen and Cole- ridge developed is proved by an unpublished letter dated from Bristol in May, 1814, which is given in the Appendix because it throws light on Coleridge, on Allen, and on the period.[2] What- ever his failings, Coleridge, in his prime, richly deserved Hazlitt's

[1] Allen read the manuscript in January, 1807, and said : ' I think it excellent.'
[2] Appendix Twenty-one.

encomium : ' He had angelic wings, and fed on manna. He talked on for ever ; and you wished him to talk on for ever.'

It was perhaps one of life's minor tragedies that his Quakerism prevented William Allen from going more into general society. Lady Davy, wife of one of his greatest admirers and most intimate friends, was a noted fashionable hostess and entertained all the famous men and women of the period, and there he would have met Byron who was as stalwart an opponent of Slavery as any of the Abolitionists. His *Journal* says :

> But there is *no* freedom, even for *Masters* in the midst of slaves ; it makes my blood boil even to see the thing. I sometimes wish I was the Owner of Africa . . . to do at once what Wilberforce will do in time.

It is rather strange that Allen showed so little interest in art and artists, as his friend and colleague on the Council of the Pharmaceutical Society, Jacob Bell, nominally a Quaker, counted as his intimate friends such artists as the Landseers, especially Sir Edwin, H. P. Briggs, R.A., W. P. Frith, E. M. Ward, T. S. Cooper, Frank Stone, Holman Hunt and others ; he bequeathed several well-known pictures to the nation.

Allen certainly knew H. P. Briggs who painted his portrait, which was not finished, however, until just after his death. This hangs in the Council Chamber of the Pharmaceutical Society of Great Britain and was paid for by subscription.

He must have known also T. F. Dicksee, who painted the excellent portrait of him that was exhibited at the 1843 Royal Academy Exhibition and is now in the possession of Allen & Hanburys : this was presented to the British and Foreign School Society, of which Allen was Treasurer, a few months before his death, by the artist, who had been an old pupil of the Institution ; engravings made from it were common in the houses of Quakers of the period. There is another painting of Allen, designed or intended for Mademoiselle Munier Romilly and engraved at Geneva in 1823.

Allen must have known that ill-starred artist Benjamin Robert Haydon, as at least two groups were painted by him in which

Allen appears. One is the National Portrait Gallery Group entitled *Meeting of the Anti-Slavery Society*, where Allen is depicted just below Thomas Clarkson ; the other portrays a meeting of the British Scientists at the Royal Institution, where Allen is shown somewhat in the background.

Many Quakers were familiar with Haydon's *Quiet Hour*, now hanging in the Library of the Society of Friends, depicting Allen's friend, Frederick Smith, Quaker druggist of the Haymarket, London, and his wife reading the Bible after the day's work had ended. Haydon painted this as some set-off for a loan he had contracted from Smith's son.

It is a tribute to Allen's modesty that no reference by him has yet been traced to any of the above portraits and any information concerning them has been obtained from outside sources, or it may be that no mention was made of them because the Quakers did not in general favour the painting of portraits of their members. Nevertheless, it was not the fanaticism of the more frigid Quakers, but probably sheer lack of time and energy, that prevented William entering sympathetically into the ennobling, liberating and consoling worlds of music, poetry, literature and art. Nor had he a narrow religious outlook. To him ' steeple-houses ', as strict Quakers called Anglican churches, were not gateways to spiritual death ; he was a believer in Catholic Emancipation ; when in Russia he sought the acquaintance of the highest dignitaries of the Orthodox Greek Church ; at home he welcomed (and praised) the Bishops for the early support they gave to the Anti-Slavery movement ; and when starting his own experiment in educational reform at Lindfield he journeyed to Chichester personally to secure the support of the Bishop and the Dean— in his own words willing always everywhere to : ' Take every creature in, of every kind.'

CHAPTER 9

JOURNEY TO RUSSIA

FOR a man of such extreme sensitiveness, William Allen had extraordinary pertinacity. From their first meeting a feeling of deep affection and admiration bound him to Alexander I and, behind all his activities at home and abroad, burned a strong desire to visit Russia, mainly because of his belief that the Czar ' possessed the power for doing incalculable good '. By the middle of 1818 the way at last seemed open.

A Special Meeting for Sufferings having approved of their projected pilgrimage, Allen at once set about perfecting plans for a prolonged visit to the Continent by Stephen Grellet and himself. As they were to travel overland via Scandinavia he saw the Swedish Ambassador and, of course, Lieven, with whom he ' had a very satisfactory interview ', and who gave him an introduction to Prince Alexander Galitzin. On August 8th, 1818, he wrote :

My natural feelings have been deeply tried in taking leave of my dear aged mother . . . many near connections and friends . . . my beloved child . . . my dear sister Anna Hanbury. . . . Priscilla Gurney came all the way from Norwich on purpose to see us. . . .

In Norway Allen followed his customary plan of seeing leading personages whose interest and support might forward his plans, presented introductions, met philanthropists and educationists prominent or humble, held meetings, and, as always, carried away with him, and left behind him, inspiring and lasting memories. As with all travellers in moments of reverie, his thoughts hurried home. He envisaged :

. . . our dear relations and friends assembled in our meeting at Gracechurch Street, and fancy that I see my precious child sitting in her usual place with Christine by her.

95

At Stockholm, Sidmouth's friend, Lord Strangford,[1] the British Ambassador, smoothed their path and advanced their business in every possible way. At their first meeting he promised to send his visitor a copy of the *Quarterly Review*, containing 'an excellent article on the education of the poor'; Allen discovered that Lady Strangford was 'a most benevolent, tender-spirited and sensible person', and, when the time came to part, both Allen and the Ambassador did so 'with affectionate feelings'. The new King,[2] Bernadotte, twice received Allen and Grellet; they discussed prisons, education and the poor, and, at the second audience, the King accepted 'a memorial of a comprehensive character on the education of the poor'.

In November the travellers reached St. Petersburg, where they put up at an inn opposite the huge Winter Palace. The Czar was absent, but they were welcomed by Lieven's brother, by Prince Alexander Galitzin, and by Lord Cathcart,[3] the British Ambassador. Allen confided to his diary:

> . . . I have a uniform and increasing evidence that this is a period in my life in which I am called upon to labour, and in a manner a little out of the common track.

While waiting for the return of the Czar Allen met everyone of importance and went everywhere, especially prisons, hospitals and poor-houses. He found the lunatic asylum 'a superb establishment, and exceedingly well managed'; of a large hospital he said 'the general neatness and cleanliness of the whole I have rarely seen equalled—never surpassed'. A large hospital under the patronage of the Dowager Empress was visited:

> . . . a magnificent building, with a portico supported by lofty columns in the centre. It is open day and night to all applicants. . . . The Dowager Empress places large sums at the disposal of the Senator for the relief of cases of peculiar distress. . . . Every thing in the power of art to

---

[1] 6th Viscount, 1780–1855.

[2] Bernadotte, Jean Baptiste, 1763–1844, one of Napoleon's generals, was elected Crown Prince of Sweden in 1810 and ascended the throne in 1818 as Charles XIV.

[3] 1st Earl, 1755–1843.

relieve human nature appears to be done here. There is an excellent system of ventilation ; the most perfect neatness and order prevail, and, in short, it may be considered as a complete model,—I have not seen its equal anywhere. It seems the work of a most benevolent mind, guided by superior intellect and working with unbounded means.

Allen was even more impressed by the institution for ' Les Enfants Trouvés ' which the Dowager Empress visited constantly without notice ; he was told of an institution for five hundred lying-in women where she did likewise. About this time Allen heard of the death of his old acquaintance, the Queen of Württemberg, the Czar's devoted sister, ' a reliable, clever woman '. On February 6th, 1819, he recorded :

. . . to see a large school in the British and Foreign plan. . . . Little did I think when I endeavoured to impress the importance of the subject on the mind of the Emperor, when in London, that the day would come when I should see the plan in its perfection at Petersburg . . . We went from hence to see the hospitals for the guards, cavalry, etc., which . . . are conducted upon the same excellent and enlightened plan as the others . . . the men are exceedingly well cared for—indeed the Emperor is like a father to them.

The death of the Queen of Württemberg prevented an audience with the Dowager Empress and delayed the audience with the Emperor. At last, on the evening of February 10th, 1819, the interview between Stephen, William and the Czar took place :

We were shown in at the Emperor's private door, and conducted to the private staircase. There was not the least pomp ; not a single soldier on the stairs, and the servants had no sword nor any livery or uniform. The Emperor was in a small apartment, with a sofa in it, a table and chairs —the whole very neat and plain. He was dressed in a blue uniform, with gold epaulettes, he received us very kindly, and we were soon sensible of a renewal of those feelings which we had experienced when with him before . . . he invited us to sit down . . . no one was present but ourselves . . . He loves vital religion . . . We were . . . about two hours with him. We heard afterwards that he drove off immediately to the Princess Mestchasky, we having told him that she had a copy of the Scripture Lessons used in our schools in England.

Allen and Grellet were duly received by the Empress Mother, by the Czar's consort, the Empress Elizabeth, and a second time by the Czar himself, who wanted to have a Bible Society on the English model founded in Russia ; he knew all about Robert Owen, and he personally, and the Lanark experiment, were discussed ; education in the Russian Army, world peace, and philanthropic and educational projects for Russia were closely examined. Then, as at their previous audience, the Czar and his two English Quaker friends knelt down side by side and prayed. As, after an audience of two hours, Allen took his leave, the autocrat of all the Russias ' raised my hand to his lips and kissed it '.

High Government officials, the aristocracy and intellectuals all welcomed the two Quaker missionaries, smoothed their path, and sped them on their way. The heads of the Orthodox Eastern Church received them and said that, if outward ceremonial differed, their truths were the same. The Emperor would fain have kept them in Russia for their lives, and sponsored and supported their work for religion, education, prisoners and prison reform, and philanthropy. Most appreciated compliment of all, Allen was elected an honorary member of the Imperial Academy of Sciences.

Armed with a special passport and introductions from the British Ambassador, with letters to all the Governors of provinces through which they were to pass, recommending them ' as persons well-known to the Emperor ', and with imperative instructions from the Minister of the Interior that they were to have horses at need, the pilgrims set out via Novgorod and Tver for Moscow. There they found the prisons and hospitals clean and in excellent order. Institutions for the aged, lunatic asylums, schools for children of both the peasants and the nobles, relief organizations—all were visited, reported upon, and the suggestions for improvement sent, at his request, to the Emperor. A long, special report was sent at her wish to the Empress Mother. Their inn was opposite the Kremlin and, dining with Prince Serge Galitzin, Allen says, ' his appearance strongly reminded me of Sir Humphry Davy '. In Moscow, as in Petersburg, Allen came continuously into contact with the beneficent activities of the Empress Mother, to whom her upright, lonely son undoubtedly owed much of his humane and enlightened character. Allen, who knew and worked closely with such noble, disinterested women as Elizabeth Fry, wrote :

> I have not heard of any woman in the whole world, who is so heartily, so incessantly, and so extensively engaged in works of benevolence, as the worthy mother of the good Alexander.

Visits to a number of Russian centres, ending at Odessa, were followed by visits to Constantinople, Smyrna, Greece, Italy ; then, via Geneva and Paris, home to Dover.

At Chambéry a servant reported a rumour of the death of the Duke of Kent and Allen wrote :

> If true, it will be a great public loss, and particularly to the British and Foreign School Society.

Geneva awoke tender memories :

> I had a boy from the inn to show me the way to Sacconet . . . I went by myself and had a solemn time at the grave of my dearly beloved and precious Charlotte. I was very much broken and contrited . . .

February 26th, 1820 :

> . . . arrived at the Crown Inn, Rochester, where I had the inexpressible pleasure of meeting my beloved child, and dear brother, who came from London the evening before . . . We dined at Dartford and, passing through London, proceeded direct to Dalston ; I found my dear aged mother in a feeble state, but quite as well as I had any reason to expect ; she was contrited in humble gratitude . . . After tea with her, my brother, Joseph, drove us to Stoke Newington, where I was joyfully received by dear sister, Anna Hanbury, and the rest of the family.

CHAPTER 10

THE CONFERENCE OF VERONA

IT is a measure of the great success of the work of the Abolitionist in England that when the Congress of Vienna met in the autumn of 1814, in spite of the stupendous European interests involved, the British representatives, to their honour, worked wholeheartedly for the total abolition of the Slave Trade ; but, owing to differences amongst the Allies as to how this should be done, all Castlereagh's immense efforts could achieve was a general declaration in its favour. As Allen's boyhood devotion to the cause of negro emancipation never diminished, he shared fully the bitter disappointment of his fellow workers at the negative results obtained at Vienna.

Nevertheless, his faith in Alexander I never wavered and when, six years later, it was made known that a final congress was to meet in the autumn of 1822 at which the Czar would be present, he began to feel it laid upon him that he should make a further personal effort in the matter. After prolonged and prayerful consideration, he wrote on August 21st :

My mind is, within this day or two, pretty powerfully impressed with the feeling that it may possibly be right for me to go to meet the Emperor of Russia at Vienna.

Allen saw Lieven, who thought such a visit desirable ' seeing how well the Emperor was acquainted with me, and the very great influence which he possessed '. More imperative still, his mother encouraged him to go.

Without an appointment he went to Downing Street and, such was the man's personal prestige, that Bathurst [1] not only saw him immediately but also approved of his intention to go to

---

[1] 3rd Earl, 1762–1834, Secretary for War and the Colonies 1812–27. He favoured abolition.

Verona and gave him an introduction to the Duke of Wellington, the British representative to the Congress. Wellington also received Allen at once; they conferred upon the whole question of the Slave Trade, Allen urging that, still cankering the world, it could only be swept out of existence by the Great Powers outlawing it as piracy. From their first meeting the Czar had repeatedly told Allen to approach him direct whenever he wanted to, so he now wrote 'à sa propre main' to 'his dear Emperor', as he always called Alexander, 'to prepare the way' for another meeting.

In September, accompanied by his nephew, Daniel Bell Hanbury, armed with a special passport from Bathurst visaed by Numain the Austrian Ambassador, they set forth, arriving at Vienna at the end of the month. There Allen found his old acquaintance Strangford lodging in the same house 'and quite glad to see him'.

Two days later Alexander received his friend alone and they spent a long evening together. A condensed account of the subjects they discussed takes up five closely printed pages of Allen's diary, the Slave Trade being given first place and Allen urging the Czar to take the lead in getting the Congress to declare it piracy. In support of his plea he handed over letters from Wilberforce, and from Clarkson, whose handwriting on the direction the Czar immediately recognized.

Allen's innate diffidence always inclined him to dread the appearance of being a busybody and, as he was still doubtful of the wisdom of going on to Verona (where the concluding sessions of the Congress were to be held), he asked the Czar for his advice, and Alexander said he would think it over and let him know in a few days.

At the end of their long conference, taking Allen's hand, Alexander said : 'Have you anything for me ?'

The diary gives the answer :

We were both contrited with the sweet feeling of Divine Goodness, and on my remarking that this made me forget for the moment the difference in our relative situations he put his arm affectionately round me. On parting, he repeated his wish to see me again after three days . . . I returned to my nephew at the inn, with reverent thankful-ness . . .

At a second audience Alexander said he would be ' gratified ' if his Quaker friend went on to Verona, but advised him to take the precaution of consulting Wellington. After much further talk the Czar invited Allen to take tea with him. When it was brought it contained sugar, and the host, remembering his friend's early vow, immediately ordered it to be changed : ' This led me to speak further of the poor Africans.' But, once again, they inevitably turned to religion and the humble lonely Autocrat of all the Russias declared : ' When I am with you, and such as you, *I can breathe.*' They knelt on the floor side by side : ' he then embraced and kissed me '.

Everywhere he went in the Austrian capital the humble Quaker owner of the Plough Court Pharmacy in London was treated by the numerous great personages who received him as if he were an Ambassador Extraordinary and Minister Pleni-potentiary—as indeed he was, not from his Britannic Majesty but, as he rightly felt, from the King of kings. Wellington—who detested fools, busybodies and bores—frequently received him and advised him to go on to Verona.

At Munich he saw from the outside Count Rumford's institu-tion for the poor ; to facilitate his movements Brook Taylor, the British Minister in Bavaria, gave him a special passport as ' Courier to the Duke of Wellington ', which the Austrian Minister in Munich visaed. He was received by the Crown Prince,[1] ' who talked so much, and so quickly, that I had some difficulty in edging in what I had to say '. But edge in he did. Perhaps Allen was for a second nonplussed when Ludwig asked him why he ' didn't put an end to the *white* Slave Trade ' !

Wellington, Allen wrote, ' encourages me to go to him when-ever I wish '. Regarding the Conference objects in general, and the Slave Trade in particular, the Duke confessed that he ' had

[1] Afterwards Ludwig I, 1786–1868, a munificent patron of science and all the arts, he fell under the influence of the Irish adventuress, Lola Montez, in 1846, and eventually abdicated.

not merely to consider what was desirable, but what was practicable ; that if the other Powers made it piracy, how were they to act against France without going to war'. Wellington even went so far as to ask Allen to brief him, and supply him with data : upon being tactfully reminded by Allen that the people of England would be disappointed at his failure to impose their wishes in the Congress, Wellington said : ' he was aware that he stood in no enviable situation'.

Satisfied that he could do no more at Verona, Allen turned homeward. He had a third and final long audience with Alexander :

> The dear Emperor received me most cordially, and again asked me to take tea with him ; his little handbell has a watch attached to it ; when tea was brought in he remembered that I did not take sugar.

As usual when parting, they prayed together. Allen wrote :

> When I rose he embraced and kissed me three times, saying ' Remember me to your family,—I should like to know them. Ah,' said he, ' when and where shall we meet again ! '

They never met again.

Three years later (in 1825) the man whom Napoleon's downfall made the most powerful sovereign in Europe, passed away. Idealist, visionary, mystic, he said that he died ' crushed beneath the terrible burden of a crown '. Known as the Peacemaker of Europe, his personal friendship, once bestowed, was never lightly withdrawn. It is impossible to say how much Alexander's innate good qualities were influenced by his knowledge of and admiration for Quakerism. Perhaps no Friend got nearer to his inmost feelings than William Allen did. At their last meeting he said in benediction :

> I not only respect you, but I love you from the bottom of my heart.

After the Czar's death Allen's intimate part in European affairs may be said to have come to an end.

CHAPTER 11

WILLIAM ALLEN AND ROBERT OWEN

FOR a decade or more wide interest had been aroused by the pioneer work of Robert Owen and his business associates in introducing what is now known as welfare principles and practices into their cotton mills at New Lanark on the River Clyde near Glasgow. Towards the end of 1813 Owen, desiring more freedom to experiment, decided to break with his partners and start a new firm, paying strictly limited dividends. Owen, in the correct sense, a communist, disapproved of capital and capitalists, but—like many others since—had to learn that he could not do without it or them. He visited London to raise funds and approached Allen, who had long been enamoured of his work. They had several interviews and, on December 27th, 1813, Allen wrote :

> A most important meeting on second day with Robert Owen, Joseph Fox, and John Walker ; we settled the whole business about Lanark ; but I had much conflict of mind on account of the responsibility involved . . .

His initial ' conflict of mind ' about Robert Owen's projects was premonitory. With the possible exception of the Lancaster affair, none of his manifold philanthropic activities caused him so much anxiety—and disappointment. The fundamental difficulty was that Owen was by every instinct a materialist, Allen a Christian who wholeheartedly believed that men's inner beliefs governed their way of life and, consequently, determined the pattern of their society. It is this age-old fundamental conflict that is working up to a climax in the world of to-day.

The partnership agreement specifically provided that in the schools controlled by the Lanark management definite religious instruction would be given. To Robert Owen will always belong the credit of being the founder of infant schools in Great Britain ; but, his beliefs being what they were, he must have signed the agreement with mental reservations.

Within less than two years, in a long, revealing, very sad letter, Allen said to Owen :

> What humble pleasure did I not anticipate in giving my humble co-operation to such work . . . with what zeal did I endeavour to bring others to assist, who may now consider me as having been made a dupe to designs which my heart could never approve. It is now the general opinion that my friend is the determined enemy of all revealed religion . . .

Then, in a poignant sentence, he summarized the problem :

> If a man will believe nothing which cannot be mathematically demonstrated to him—nothing which is beyond the reach of his limited capacities and powers, he must remain in darkness . . .

By the middle of 1822 Allen wrote to Owen saying ' our *principles* are diametrically opposite . . . it is quite plain to me *that we must part* '.

The break was delayed by Allen's natural reluctance, by his mission to the Conference of Verona, and by the death of his daughter Mary. Nevertheless it was inevitable. In November he recorded :

> The Lanark proprietors met at Plough Court. We showed Robert Owen that we were firm, and at one time there seemed nothing to be done but dissolve the partnership. We told him that our object was solely to have the schools on a Christian plan . . . He at length gave way . . .

Owen, like many reformers, was a difficult man to work with. C. E. M. Joad says :

> Amid much that is ridiculous, both in the man himself and in his followers, something cast in the heroic mould remains.

No one of Owen's contemporaries realized this more clearly than Allen ; hence the long-suffering manner in which he put up with Owen's vagaries. On the other hand, this five-per-cent philanthropist, who has been called 'the father of English Socialism', knew well the supporting value of names such as those of Jeremy Bentham and William Allen. Owen's plans for an England consisting solely of little Lanarks seemed to many people impracticable ; but his plans for primary education and for the cure of pauperism were widely accepted, and one of his most consistent and zealous friends and supporters was the Duke of Kent.

CHAPTER 12

DEATH OF ALLEN'S DAUGHTER AND THIRD MARRIAGE

IN May, 1823, after a brief illness, William's daughter Mary died in childbirth : 'I hardly knew how to constrain my grief. . . . Cornelius is divinely supported under the agonizing trial.'

Allen found himself a very lonely man.

In September he wrote his dear friend, Stephen Grellet :

I now live entirely at Stoke Newington, and have taken a little estate in Red Lion Lane, leading to the New River, where I have built stables, a cottage for the coachman and his family, and another for a school.

Even second marriages were not generally approved by Quakers, and the third marriage of William Allen caused to many of his friends and contemporaries so much pain and misunderstanding, and gave ground for so much criticism amongst those who disliked him and wished to discredit the Society of Friends, that something must be said about it.

In the beginning of 1827 Allen said in a letter to a friend that a new epoch was opening in his eventful life. He was fifty-seven years of age, and, as it turned out, had sixteen active years before him. Even now he would be considered past the prime of life ; to his contemporaries he was an old man. It is quite plain that Allen liked feminine society—and that friendships with members of the complementary sex always meant much to him. For years he and Grizell Birkbeck had been upon terms of friendship. 'The peculiar circumstances of his family', say the editors of his *Life and Correspondence*, 'led him often to seek her help and counsel ; and in his close and deep bereavements, she was his kind, sympathizing adviser.'

Allen's view is both legitimate and convincing :

It was not, however, till after I lost my beloved child, who was, as it were, my last earthly prop, that a more intimate union than that of friendship opened to my view ; and now the time nearly comes for its completion. We propose, if nothing unforeseen prevents, that the marriage shall take place on the 9th instant. Should this step appear singular, let it be remembered, that the dispensations through which I have had to pass, have been singularly afflictive.

The marriage took place on the appointed date and soon afterwards Allen left the Islington home which had belonged to Charlotte Hanbury—and which they had shared for ten years —and went to reside with his new wife at her house in nearby Paradise Row.

That, officially, the Society of Friends never entirely exonerated Allen from blame for contracting late in life a third marriage with a rich woman, is evidenced by the fact that, in the formal 'Testimony concerning William Allen of the Gracechurch Monthly Meeting' issued soon after his death, the marriage was curtly dismissed in a brief sentence.

CHAPTER 13

THE LINDFIELD EXPERIMENT

ALLEN refused to allow his natural disappointment over New Lanark to damp in any way his enthusiasm for the cause of education—in its widest sense. As early as July, 1824, while staying at Brighton, he had paid a first visit to Lindfield in Sussex to procure land for the establishment of a school of industry. As always, he began by making useful friends. He rode to Stanmer and 'had a satisfactory interview with the Earl of Chichester, the Lord of the Manor', and explained to him 'my plans about Lindfield'; he called on the Dean of Salisbury, and made friends with the Bishop of Chichester. During 1825 a commodious school with separate departments for boys, girls and infants was erected at considerable expense at Lindfield. Teachers were engaged, a lending library formed, and a good general education planned on the liberal principles of the British and Foreign School Society. Because he held that children should be made to contribute to the expenses of their education, some boys, under a skilled husbandman, worked on the farm, others were taught printing ; the girls learnt knitting, needlework and other necessary crafts ; even the infants learnt patchwork and how to plait straw. Like the Greeks, Allen knew that to obtain poise and balance mental and manual activities should be complementary ; now, some one hundred and twenty-five years after he began his experiment, the same wise principles have been embodied in an Education Act and are, in general, accepted and practised. John Smith, M.P., of Dale Park, Sussex, became interested in the experiment, purchased one hundred acres of adjoining land at Gravely and built eighteen cottages for labourers with an acre and a quarter of land to each, and Sydney Smith wrote a typical letter to Allen on the scheme.[1]

[1] Appendix Twenty-two.

Each cottage had a convenient out-house and a pig-sty ; half an acre of the land was planted alternately in potatoes or a green crop, an acre in fruit and vegetables, and the rest as a garden. Later seven cottages with from five to six acres were added, and a small house—afterwards greatly enlarged—known as Gravely Cottage, built as an occasional residence for Allen himself.

A brilliant propagandist, Allen started the *Lindfield Reporter* ; he also wrote and circulated a useful pamphlet on the rotation of crops entitled *Colonies at Home* ; it passed into several editions and he sent a copy to the Grand Duke of Württemberg, whose acquaintanceship he had made on his way home from the Verona Conference ; he also sent him a copy of an *Address to Students at Guy's Hospital* and ' a model of a cottage made at our works at Lanark, in Scotland '. A copy of *Colonies at Home* went to Maria Edgeworth in Ireland, where he had recently been, and to Nicholas I, brother and successor of his ' beloved Emperor ', whose death he sincerely lamented, and who had wished to see the pamphlet. Wilhelm I of Württemberg replied with a charming letter ; Nicholas and the Dowager Empress also did so through Prince Alexander Galitzin. Maria Edgeworth's letter is so sensible and revealing that it is given in the Appendix.[1]

Allen continued to take a warm and ever-increasing personal interest in the Lindfield experiment, frequently occupying his cottage. Eventually he set up a small boarding-school for boys, to whom he gave lectures in chemistry or natural philosophy ; or he would have them to tea, talk to each one separately, and then give the group a lesson in astronomy. They were, in fact, his family.[2]

Christine Majolier had remained at Stoke Newington until William's third marriage. Not feeling too comfortable when the old establishment was broken up, she went to the Christys for a time until a home was found for her by Allen at Gravely Cottage, where she superintended the working of the colony, George Bentley and his wife acting as her servants. Every morning she walked to the schools, about a mile away, and attended at the printing office correcting proofs, which was

[1] Appendix Twenty-three. [2] Appendix Twenty-four.

a work of patience ' as there were as many mistakes as words ! '
The schools were not then on too good a footing when she took
over, the master and mistress being inefficient, so that Christine
had plenty of work to do. Her health suffered and eventually
she left Lindfield and went to live with Cornelius and Elizabeth
Hanbury at the old home in Newington.

In January, 1847, Christine married Robert Alsop in the Friends'
Meeting House at Stoke Newington. He died in January, 1876,
and she followed him in the June of the same year. Her body
was buried in the same grave as that of her husband in the Friends'
Burial Ground at Stoke Newington.

CHAPTER 14

PHARMACEUTICAL POLITICS

IN the year 1813 occurs the first allusion in William Allen's diary to pharmaceutical politics ; he appears to have taken no part in the opposition put up by the apothecaries and chemists and druggists, united for once, against the Medicine Act, which became law in June, 1802, and which seriously affected the selling of certain simple remedies because, under the Act, such were adjudged to be liable to a stamp duty.

On March 6th, 1813, he wrote :

Called on Wilberforce, Whitbread etc., on the Apothecaries Bill. This is a new cause of anxiety and much of the labour of opposing it will devolve on me.

It is necessary to explain briefly what this Bill meant. It was for regulating the practice of apothecaries, surgeon apothecaries, practitioners in midwifery, and compounders and dispensers of medicine, throughout England and Wales. Introduced by the Associated Apothecaries, but not officially sponsored by the Society of Apothecaries, many of the suggested provisions seriously threatened the interest of chemists and drüggists and, or so it was stated, would place a monopoly of compounding and dispensing medicines in the hands of the apothecaries.

A general meeting of chemists and druggists was therefore held at the Freemasons' Tavern, Queen Street, Lincoln's Inn Fields, on March 4th, 1813, and at this ' Allen of Plough Court and Bell of Oxford Street ', amongst others, were elected to serve on a committee. Several meetings of the Committee were held at different places ; one was at Plough Court and another at the Globe, Fleet Street. On the 29th March Allen was able to report : ' The Apothecaries Bill withdrawn on account of the opposition to it.'

The next entry dealing with pharmaceutical politics was made on 6th March, 1815 :

Went with J. Barry to Freemason's Tavern to attend a general meeting of chemists and druggists, on the Apothecaries Bill, agreed to petition against it.

Although this Bill was presented by the Society of Apothecaries in conjunction with the College of Physicians, the Committee of the chemists and druggists found it to be as objectionable as ' the former Bill presented by the Associated Apothecaries, and as injurious to the chemists, druggists and to the public at large '.

The result of a meeting of a Sub-Committee with the Society of Apothecaries was that a clause to protect chemists and druggists was inserted in the Bill and this was subsequently accepted by the Committee of the House of Commons on the Bill.

Nineteen years elapsed before any further reference was made by Allen to pharmaceutical matters, when the following appeared in one of the letter-books of the Firm :

> Paradise Row,
> Stoke Newington.
> 22nd of 3mo: 1834.

My dear Friend,
   Thy note of the 19th is perfectly satisfactory ; if I had not frankly asked for an explanation—I might have considered myself unhandsomely treated, and the friendly regard we once had for each other, as at an end—but the way is now open to notice a rumour—that the Medical Education Committee have it in contemplation to propose an interference on the part of Government with the Trade and business of chymist and druggist under the specious pretence of increasing the respectability of the Profession—now experience has shown that all interference and muddling of Government in matters of Trade and business does positive mischief—and depend upon it if the attempt is made it will be met on the part of the country in the language of Let us alone.
   The Corporation of the Apothecaries Company ought not to be permitted to exist in a Country like England—and I

hope never to see the day when monopolies shall be encouraged and Trade fettered in England as it is in some foreign countries.

I hope fair time will be given to all parties interested to consider any measure that may be proposed tending to interfere with free Trade.

I remain
thy sincere friend,
Wm. Allen.

To H. Warburton M.P.

This letter evidently refers to the work of the Medical Education Committee set up by the House of Commons in 1834, of which Henry Warburton, the mathematician, one-time timber merchant, politician, and F.R.S., was the chairman. However, nothing came of those efforts, and it was not until 1839 that a Parliamentary inquiry was instituted by a Committee of the House of Commons, of which Warburton was again chairman. Its terms of reference were to revise all laws relating to the medical profession, to obtain all information possible in all departments of the subject, and to suggest reforms for any abuses found to exist. Although much of the evidence collected was destroyed by the fire which took place in the House of Commons,[1] including that relating to pharmacy, sufficient remained to enable Warburton, assisted by Mr. Wakley and Mr. Hawes, to prepare a bill entitled : 'A Bill for the Registration of Medical Practitioners, and for establishing a College of Medicine, and for enabling the Fellows of that College to practise medicine in all or any of its branches, and hold any medical appointments whatsoever, in any part whatsoever of the United Kingdom.' The machinery outlined for registering not only the medical but the pharmaceutical profession was so complicated that the Bill was withdrawn at an early stage. The following entries in Allen's diary tell their own story :

Fourth month 15th, 1841. Trade Meeting at the Crown and Anchor, Strand. The Pharmaceutical Society of Chemists and Druggists was unanimously formed.

---

[1] October 16th, 1834.

Sixth month 1st, 1841. The Pharmaceutical Society organized. I am appointed president of the Council.

Seventh month 15th. Favoured in my retirement ; constantly looking forward to the end of all things here. Attended the Council of the Pharmaceutical Society ; passed the bye-laws unanimously ; a very satisfactory meeting. Our vice-president, C. J. Payne, is a very clear-headed, sensible man.

Jacob Bell is indefatigable, and one of our most useful members.

Eleventh month 17th, 1841, (at Lindfield). Received a letter requesting me to come to town, to join a deputation of the Pharmaceutical Society to the College of Physicians, to-morrow—an unpleasant interruption, but I must go.

First month 1st, 1842. Interview with Sir James Graham on the subject of the Pharmaceutical Society, together with C. J. Payne and Jacob Bell. He received us very cordially. I informed him of the origin, nature and extent of the Society, and my friends also gave satisfactory explanations. He promised that nothing should be done, bearing upon our trade, without communicating with me which we acknowledge as very kind.

CHAPTER 15

PARTNERSHIP WITH LUKE HOWARD

IN August, 1797, Mildred and Allen dissolved partnership, Mildred retiring in consideration of the sum of five hundred and twenty-five pounds. That same year Allen took into partnership his friend, Luke Howard, the title of the business being changed to Allen and Howard. Howard, who was two years younger than Allen, was born in Red Cross Street, London, in November, 1772. His father, Robert Howard, a sturdy Quaker, was one of the founders of the Bible Society and it was he who introduced into this country from Switzerland the Argand burner, which could be used with oil or with gas, giving a light then far superior to any other form of illuminant.[1]

When Luke was eight years of age he was sent to Thomas Huntly's school at Burford in Oxfordshire. He left at the age of fifteen and was duly apprenticed to Ollive Sims, a pharmaceutical chemist at Stockport in Cheshire. At the end of his apprenticeship he joined a London firm of wholesale druggists in Bishopsgate, Moore and Sharp, but his stay there was short owing to an injury to his hand which laid him up for some months. On his recovery in 1795 his father set him up in Temple Bar as a retail chemist, and it was to this shop that a year later he brought his bride, Mariabella Eliot.

The Allen and Howard partnership, although not financially too satisfactory, must have been a happy one. Both partners were Quakers from birth, both had attended Higgins' lectures, both had sound experience of the pharmacy of the day, both had recently married, and both had been blessed with the gift of a daughter, each of whom was named Mary.

Luke Howard had a flair for devising apparatus for the making

[1] The first factory to be lighted by gas was that of Boulton & Watts in Soho, London, in 1792.

LUKE HOWARD, 1772–1864

of heavy chemicals, probably inherited from his father, Robert Howard, who was in business in Old Street in the City, as a tinsmith, and it was arranged, therefore, that he should take charge of the Plaistow factory—then rapidly developing under the control of Joseph Jewell—Howard living nearby with his young wife, but occasionally visiting Plough Court.

William Allen remained at Plough Court, taking charge of the establishment there, including the laboratory as well as the retail business, finding time, somehow, to attend the meetings of the Askesian Society and to prepare and deliver his lectures to the students at Guy's Hospital, to members of the Royal Institution, and to carry on his other work.

The Allen and Howard partnership lasted for nine years; in 1806 it was dissolved with mutual goodwill. The decision to make the change was no doubt a wise one; both sides of the business, chemical and galenical, were developing at such a rate that the undivided attention of each partner was very necessary in his own particular branch. Howard undertook to make certain heavy chemicals, and process other articles of which the subliming of camphor was one. Allen, on his part, was to concentrate his activities on the making of galenicals as well as of certain chemicals not usually required in large quantities, but in the manufacture of which more skill and knowledge were essential by the laboratory workers than was required in the making of large quantities of chemicals on a commercial scale. Some of these were what to-day are known as chemical reagents, that is, chemicals used for the detection of other bodies; they had to be free from impurities. In the Firm's price lists of the period they occupied a separate section from that of drugs, and the sales of such were separately shown in the cash books. There were two hundred of these reagents listed, but not all were necessarily made at Plough Court.

There would be more room for this work at Plough Court when the laboratory was not required for many of the operations which would, under the new conditions, be carried out at Plaistow, and where the plant was such that new methods of making the many chemicals then coming into use could be tried.

More space was certainly required for the making of such volatile preparations as ether ; the following account of a fire at Plough Court during the Allen and Howard period illustrates the risks. It is from a letter of Robert Howard, the father of Luke, to his daughter, Elizabeth :

> The fire at Plough Court was on this wise—W. Allen was in the wholesale cellar abt 7 on 7 Day Evg—soon after this fumes of Vitriol alarmed them, from whence none could discover, W. A. went into the Cellar with a candle, the fumes extinguished the flame and would soon have extinguished his, if he had not quickly retired, he could see a Red glow among the Straw, no flames then, soon however the house was filled insufferably with Vitriolic fumes and flames rose in the Cellar, a few Bottles of Aether burst and came up the openings in Vivid white flames bursting like gunpowder, the Sun Fire Office was applied to but no water could at first be procured from the Plugs, a Supply by Pails and Buckets was procured from their own Worm Tub and from the Neighbours Cisterns, some holes were cut in the floor by the dauntless Firemen, and about 9 the fire to the astonishment of every one was suppressed without proceeding further than the Cellar, even some Bottles of Aether had boiled over without catching flame, there was about £1,000 worth of Camphor in Boxes, perhaps a fourth of it damaged or lost—Wm. Allen was sadly fatigued, G. Eliot junr happened to be at W. Phillips and ready to assist.

An examination of the Allen and Howard cost books throws light upon the price of materials and labour at the end of the eighteenth century. In 1799, at the Plaistow factory, a quantity of one hundred and seventy-four pounds of oil of peppermint was distilled from about sixty tons of the herb.[1]

An entry in the Cost Book for January, 1805, shows that a small quantity of malleable platinum, or ' platina ' as it was then called, was made in the laboratory at Plough Court. Details in Allen's writing are given showing the quantities of the materials used and the weight of ' platina ' produced, the name T. Cock

[1] Appendix Twenty-five.

Platina   1ˢᵗ mo 1805

Stock

Platin. crud   4/5 356 A   12.12.
Acid mur   10   25 "   1. -10
    Nit. ao   2/- 10 "   1.
Coals   1ℬ   1. 6
Charcoal   4ℬ   6
mur ammon   2/- #1½   3
Filtering Paper   " 1 "
Cloth   1.
        Carr d for ⌐   15 : 5 · A

bro't for ᵈ ── 15 - 5 · A
Earthen Pan ──────────────   3 -
attendᵗ ── 2 Wks ──   2 . 8 ──
wear & Tear ──────────────   10

335¼   dedut scraps   18 6 . ℬ
    11/7 £ 18.1.10   4 . 6
                            18 " 1 · 10

COST SHEET OF A BATCH OF MALLEABLE PLATINUM MADE AT THE
OLD PLOUGH COURT PHARMACY, 1805

Dear William Allen Playford
January 18. 1833

You know, when I was in London
last, that two Cataracts had been formed in my Eyes.
they have continually increasing and obscuring
my sight since that Time. About fourteen Days
ago I lost all Power of Reading, which has greatly
abridged my former Comforts; and since then
the Power of saing to write, that is, I can scarcely
see thereof how to direct my Pen, and this has
become so alarmingly the Case in the last two
Days, that I doubt whether this very Letter which
I am now trying to write to You, will not be the
last that I shall ever write unless my Eyes
should be relieved an Operation and belision

Playford. July. 22.1835

my dear Friend
William Allen

A Letter arrived here from Cornelius Han-
bury this morning conveying to me the painful Intelligence—that your
dear Wife had quitted her mortal Existence. I was then suffering under
the mournful Thoughts, that more of my beloved Friends had left their Earthly
ly Habitations in the last three Months then in as many Years before; among
whom were Friends whom you esteemed also. I alluded, among others, to W.
Smith, the late Member for Norwich, and dear Joseph Hooter of Bromley, whose
Loss I shall never cease to deplore, at least as often as his Name is brought to
my Recollection. You may imagine then what my feelings were, when the Intelligence of this Morning was communicated to me; for it brought up the
Recollection of early and interesting Circumstances in my Life, which
it will always be dear to me to remember. The very first House in the
Country about London in which I was received and encouraged on my
early Pursuits in the Cause of the Abolition of the Slave—Trade, was that on

LETTERS TO WILLIAM ALLEN FROM THOMAS CLARKSON

being attached as assistant. In February a somewhat smaller quantity of 'platina' was made and this was converted into four crucibles, one for Luke Howard, one for William Henry, one for R. Phillips and one for Davy, no doubt Humphry Davy (he was not knighted until 1812).

It is pretty certain that Cock, who was a brother-in-law of Sir Astley Cooper, the surgeon, was a pupil or worker in the Plough Court chemical laboratory, as his name is attached to costings of other chemicals, including phosphoric acid and yellow prussiate of potash. So far as can be traced, this is the first recorded instance of the manufacture of malleable platinum in Great Britain. Cock afterwards became acquainted with Percival Norton Johnson, the founder of the London firm of Johnson, Matthey and Company.

With the ending of his partnership, Luke Howard passes out of this story, but he cherished his friendship with Allen for the rest of his life, and in Allen's diary there are many references to their association in philanthropic and humanitarian activities : they went for holidays together and made meteorological records whenever they had the opportunity.

Howard's essay, read in 1803 to the Askesian Society, entitled *On the Modification of the Clouds, etc.*, has been mentioned ; in it he propounded his Latin classification and nomenclature of the clouds. He introduced the well-known primary names of cirrus, cumulus, stratus and their derivatives ; these have survived over a century of criticism and attempted amendment, and remain the scientific terminology to this day. The essay attracted the notice of Goethe, who wrote a poem on the subject and entered into correspondence with Howard.

In 1818 Howard published a work in two volumes on *The Climate of London*, a very useful publication ; he also wrote a little volume called *Seven Lectures on Meteorology* ; to assist him in preparing his data he made a clock fitted with a recording barometer, the first of its kind.

Howard was made a Fellow of the Royal Society in 1821. He retired from active work in his business at Stratford—it had been removed from Plaistow—at a comparatively early age and the actual management passed into the hands of his partners, Joseph Jewell and John Gibson, and of his sons, Robert and John Eliot Howard. The well-known chemical firm of Howards and Sons Ltd., of Ilford, is to-day still a family business, having been handed down in unbroken succession from Luke Howard.

Like other Friends, Howard concerned himself with the state of Europe after the Napoleonic Wars, and personally superintended in Germany the distribution of funds raised by himself and others ; he received generous acknowledgments and presents from the Kings of Prussia and Saxony for his exertions.

About 1840, owing to theological differences between himself and members of the Society of Friends, he and his wife resigned from that body. As he had always been a generous supporter of many religious and philanthropic movements, some of his Quaker friends feared, apparently, that this support was in danger of being withdrawn from certain causes in which they were particularly interested. This feeling was reflected in the following rhyme from *Quakerites for 1839* quoted by Edward Pease in his Diaries :

> Luke Howard, Luke Howard,
> Why fretful and froward ?
> Why leave us ? We miss thee and thine now
> And then, what is more
> We miss thy long purse
> For Friends have an eye to the rhino !

Luke Howard survived his wife by twelve years, passing away in 1864 at the age of ninety-two.

CHAPTER 16

JOHN THOMAS BARRY

FROM 1806, the year in which the partnership with Luke Howard ended, until 1816, William Allen carried on the Plough Court business in his own name ; with his many activities he must often have had, to use his own words, 'a tight time'.

Like his predecessors the Bevans, William Allen never lacked loyal and devoted helpers in his business. During the earlier years he had the valuable assistance in the laboratory and the shop of Richard Phillips ; William West,[1] eighteen years younger than Phillips, also did good work there ; Thomas Cock has already been mentioned.

The laboratory records of the Old Plough Court Pharmacy exist ; from an examination of these a good idea can be obtained of the nature of the work carried on. Many chemicals and galenicals, not apparently made there before, were being made in quantity. One preparation, the cost which should be of interest to pharmaceutical historians of the future, was Confectio Damocratis, which was similar to Venice Treacle, but with fewer ingredients than the usual seventy-four : a batch of seventy-one pounds of the confection was made in the laboratory as late as August, 1809, with forty-seven ingredients only. Ninepennyworth of charcoal was used for heating, and twelve shillings was paid for three days' attendance.

The sales of test chemicals, or ' tests ', the making of which began in the Allen and Howard period, developed considerably in the years following. There were no standard chemicals, analytical or indeed any other, in those days, and orders soon came along from laboratories attached to heavy industrial concerns, such as coal mines and iron foundries, where chemical

---

[1] Appendix Twenty-six.

analysis and research were beginning to develop. The making of what are to-day known as fine chemicals was also a feature of the work of the laboratory.

There was in the counting-house a lad who came to Plough Court in 1804, at the age of fifteen, as a clerk who was destined to exercise no small influence on the fortunes of the Old Plough Court Pharmacy and who during many of the years of his association was—as Allen testified in his diary—to make it possible for him to leave this country for long periods with an easy mind so far as the business was concerned. John Thomas Barry, born in 1789, the son of Alexander Barry of Fratton, near Portsmouth, was the eldest of a numerous family, several of whom were of conspicuous talents. His brother, Alexander, a hospital lecturer at the age of twenty-one, was one of the youngest men ever elected to the Royal Society ; in 1832 his life of early promise was cut short by an accidental explosion occurring in the course of a scientific investigation. Another brother, Dr. Martin Barry, the biologist, highly distinguished himself during a brief career ; in 1834 he ascended Mont Blanc and published an account of what was then a rare feat. He received the gold medal of the Royal Society—of which he was also a Fellow—for his biological researches.

John Thomas Barry himself had unusual ability, but in his early years, being deprived of both his parents by death, the responsibility for the care and education of the family fell on him, and he was therefore unable to concentrate on his own education until a later period in his life.

During part of the time Allen was lecturing at Guy's Hospital on chemistry and natural philosophy, Barry also attended the Hospital for the purpose of pursuing certain branches of medical science, as apparently at that time his intention was to adopt the medical profession. He distinguished himself particularly in anatomy, his talents being noticed by Sir Astley Cooper, who, in after years, often spoke of the brilliant success Barry might have attained had he devoted himself to the practice of surgery. In practical chemistry he was a very neat and exact worker, his method, for instance of adjusting the strength of hydrocyanic acid, greatly in advance of the practice of the age, elicited the approbation of his friend, Dr. William Hyde Wollaston.

Barry's help in taking stock at Plough Court without his principal has been mentioned ; the letter-books from 1807 onwards contain many letters from him to customers, some of them regarding unsettled accounts. Before long Barry was in charge of the manufacturing laboratory and, in 1818, became a partner, the firm thereupon being styled William Allen and Company.

Previous to this Barry had begun the reorganization of the retail side of the business, devoting particular attention to the dispensing department; one of his innovations was that the few poisons allowed on the shelves were to be kept in angular bottles.

He must have been a martinet in disciplinary matters and from a study of the many rules which are still preserved and for which he was mainly responsible, it is clear that the twelve-hour day was not too long for the assistants to do all that was expected of them.

There were rules for dusting the shop and its contents, for filling the shop bottles from the stores in the warehouse (records were kept of these transactions), for determining the times when certain work was to be done, and rules to be observed when dealing with customers. Hours of relaxation, if business permitted, were also noted and a book has been discovered, the contents of which seem to indicate that on First Day (Sunday) the place of worship attended by the assistants had to be recorded. Fines for breaking these rules were imposed on partners as well as assistants. The money so collected went into a pool and bonuses were paid from it to assistants whose records were good and conduct exemplary. Although discipline was strict, work hard, and hours long, Plough Court was regarded by the young men as a home from home and greatly superior to many similar establishments where work was even harder and the amenities of life fewer and less refined.

For those who lived in—and even the boy in the warehouse had his bed under the counter—the food was plentiful and good. There were four wholesome meals a day to which both partners and assistants sat down at convenient times. For the assistants there was a sitting-room in number three Plough Court over the warehouse, and a housekeeper looked after their well-being. She it was, who, before the early breakfast, was expected to read a portion of Scripture to them. She looked after their clothing, and attended the Borough Market to buy fresh fruit and vegetables for the household needs.

Barry possessed considerable mechanical knowledge and he patented in 1819 a vacuum apparatus, which, if not the first, was certainly one of the earliest to be used in this country. The patent describes it as an apparatus for distilling and preparing colours ; its application to pharmaceutical purposes, such as the making of vegetable extracts, was not mentioned. A considerable number of medicinal extracts were made by this process and these attracted some attention amongst medical men. An account of the method of their preparation of these extracts appeared in *Medico Chirurgical Society Transactions*, Vol. X. Amongst other extracts mentioned as having been prepared by the process were aconite, belladonna, hemlock, henbane and rhubarb, often noted in quotations to correspondents at home and abroad.

Although the vacuum apparatus did the work claimed for it, it was never a commercial success, because of the length of time taken in operating it and its use was gradually discontinued in favour of an apparatus in which a pump was used to exhaust the air, in place of Barry's method of creating a vacuum by condensation.

Barry was not a committee man like William Allen ; self-reliant and individualistic, he never sought to operate through organizations. He worked so quietly and unostentatiously that it was not until 1826, when the *Morning Star* gave some details of his labours for the abolition of the death penalty for certain crimes, that the extent of his philanthropic labours was realized by any but his closest friends—if even by them.

In 1830 he was actively engaged in bringing pressure to bear on Members of Parliament in order to secure the success of the amendment which, arising out of legislation to consolidate the

Forgery Acts, sought to abolish capital punishment except for the crime of forging of bills and powers of attorney. For this purpose a large correspondence with interested persons in the provinces had to be maintained, statistics prepared and arranged, Members of Parliament to be addressed through their constituents, and every possible influence brought to bear on the legislature in order to secure the success of the amendment. Almost single-handed Barry engaged in this work. He kept a list of friendly legislators who could be relied upon for franking his voluminous correspondence and he estimated that his anti-forgery law agitation alone required franks in lieu of postage to the value of one thousand pounds. Just before his death he stated that he had spent at least five hundred pounds in cab fares to the Home Secretary in endeavours to get the death sentence lifted from poor wretches whose crimes to-day would probably be punished with a short term of imprisonment or a fine. It is not generally known that Barry's intimate knowledge of Parliamentary customs and procedure was of the greatest service to William Allen, John and Jacob Bell, and others whose labours on behalf of the chemists and druggists of those days resulted in the formation of the Pharmaceutical Society in 1841.

We get a good idea of the attitude of the assistants to William Allen from a book published in 1897, entitled *Family Fragments*, by Richard Low Beck. Beck was sent to the same school at Rochester as William Allen, although many years later. He was apprenticed to a well-known chemist at Croydon in Surrey, Frederick Smith, and afterwards became an assistant at his branch shop in the Haymarket in London. Beck's uncle, Joseph Jackson Lister, F.R.S., father of the first Lord Lister, was a close friend of Allen ; both were interested in scientific pursuits and eventually Beck entered the Plough Court Pharmacy as an assistant. He admits that the hours were long :

We begin business every morning at nine, and leave off at nine at night, the other twelve hours we have entirely to ourselves. An afternoon is allowed off every week. . . . William Allen pays the postage on letters for all his servants.

In due course Beck left Plough Court and entered the service of his uncle, a wine merchant with a business at Tokenhouse Yard in the City. He speaks of his kind and generous master at Plough Court who, before he left, gave him some good fatherly advice.

Of Allen's attitude towards his assistants there is a touching expression in the first volume of the diary. In September, 1803, Jonathan Middleton and Thomas Smith, two of the young men then employed at Plough Court, were present at the marriage of Quaker friends at Brentford. They were returning by Kew and, at Richmond, Jonathan was drowned while bathing. After describing the arrangements for the funeral, in which Luke Howard was of considerable help to him, Allen recorded of Jonathan :

> During all the years he has been with us I never remember to have heard an unguarded expression fall from his lips, he was a pattern of strict integrity and a bright example to the family. My loss is great : he loved me with the affection of a child, and mine to him was reciprocal : he had the care of all my little matters and was worthy of the unbounded confidence I placed in him, my companion, my friend, more than a servant, a brother beloved.

CHAPTER 17

THE APPROACHING END

THE last decade and a half of William Allen's life can be briefly summarized. It was consistent throughout. As an eminent Quaker he led the deputation from the Society that waited upon William IV on his accession. He visited the Continent : saw the Crown Prince and Crown Princess of Prussia and, oddly enough, found Berlin ' the most beautiful city in Europe that we have seen ' ! At Weimar he was received by the Grand Duchess, sister of his ' dear Emperor ', who invited him to dinner, but—as was his custom—he refused all purely social invitations from Royalty ; he saw many local institutions, but never even mentions Goethe ! Vienna and Munich once again then Stuttgart where he and Stephen Grellet were received by the King and Queen. Later, Allen and Grellet went, via France, to Spain ; ' with facilities granted by the King ', they visited all sorts of institutions and ' heard some anecdotes of the present Queen of Spain which are highly creditable to her '. They were received by the Spanish Sovereigns, and subsequently sent Fernando VII a long report of their visit filled with good advice.

At home, Lindfield, his religious exercises, and proper activities as a leading Quaker, anti-slavery work—all his usual duties and responsibilities continued with no perceptible abatement.

By June 1835, Grizell Allen's health was causing her husband and friends grave anxiety. She died on July 15th, and her heartbroken widower wrote :

How she was made a *blessing* to me in every way ! Her judgment was sound, her integrity great ; much as she loved me, she always gave me up cheerfully for the service of the Church. . . . O, how I shall miss her society—and love !

Writing to Allen, Thomas Clarkson said :

The very first house in the country, about London, in which I was received and encouraged, in my early pursuits in the cause of the Abolition of the Slave Trade, was that in which you now live and in which she, my deceased friend, died. She and her brother, Samuel Hoare, and I, dined there together forty-nine years ago ; it was then her father's and I think he was present.

CHAPTER 18

ALLEN'S CLOSING YEARS AND DEATH

IN July, 1837, Allen led a Quaker deputation to Buckingham Palace to present an address to the young Queen Victoria who received them ' sitting on the throne, at the further end of the presence chamber . . . she read her answer in a very clear and audible manner '. At the time there appeared in a popular periodical a picture of the members of the deputation having their hats removed in the anteroom by Royal footmen before entering the throne room. Later, through Lord John Russell, Allen sent the Queen a bound copy of the British and Foreign School Society's Report. In a subsequent letter he thanked her for continuing the patronage of her three predecessors, sent his ' dutiful and kindest respects ' to the Duchess of Kent, and bluntly suggested that the young Sovereign should follow the good example of her three predecessors, all of whom had subscribed a hundred pounds per annum to the Society's funds. He got his one hundred pounds.

In February, 1840, he again went to Buckingham Palace on a Quaker deputation to congratulate the Queen on her marriage. They were received first by Prince Albert, of whom Allen said : ' I was struck with the amiable countenance of the Prince, and saluted him in my heart.'

After the Duke of Kent's death, the Duchess continued her friendship to William Allen, and there can be little doubt but that Queen Victoria knew him not only as a leading Quaker and notable philanthropist but as her father's close, loyal and valued friend.

By 1839 William Allen's health had begun definitely to fail. He wrote :

I have certainly been much over-done, and am too anxious ; I must make a change ; my memory is failing,—I have noticed it for some time past. . . . I am now in my seventieth year, and feel the infirmity of age creeping on. Lord, prepare me to come to Thee.

Nevertheless, he still did not noticeably curtail his activities at home or abroad. During 1840 he spent five months on the Continent, travelling about five thousand miles by sea and land.

1841 was a trying year. He lost his sister-in-law, Sarah Hoare ; also his niece, Eliza Bradshaw, whom he loved ' deeply and tenderly '. His last letter to a foreign monarch, dated from Paradise Row, Stoke Newington, Middlesex, on the 8th of the 5th month, was to the King of Sweden and Norway (Bernadotte), reminding him of their first meetings at Stockholm in 1818, of his interview with the Crown Prince at the Verona Congress in 1822, and beseeching protection for members of the Society of Friends in Norway who were then suffering persecution. Reluctantly he took the chair at the Annual Meeting of the Anti-Slavery Society, the exertion being almost too much for him.

Of his inner life at the time he said : ' Favoured in my retirement ; constantly looking forward to the end of all things here.' On July 12th the Brighton Railway was opened and William travelled by it to Haywards Heath Station, riding from there to Gravely which was ' looking very beautiful '.

In August he accompanied a deputation to Lord Palmerston about the continued persecution in Norway of members of the Society of Friends. In November he joined a deputation of the Pharmaceutical Society to the College of Physicians. On December 31st he could write :

I am much oftener than the returning day, looking towards the end of all things here . . .

Frederick Wilhelm IV of Prussia was in London in January, 1842. He met Elizabeth Fry, Joseph Fry, and other eminent Quakers who presented an address. Accompanied by Samuel Gurney and Peter Bedford, Allen went to the Prussian Embassy to pay his respects . . . The manner of the Prussian monarch 'was kind, even affectionate', and Allen was gratified to meet the great Humboldt once more.

In the early summer of 1843 Allen wrote from Lindfield to a friend :

> I endeavour to divide my time between this place and Stoke Newington, being affectionately cared for by my niece, Lucy Bradshaw, who has long smoothed the path of my declining years, and done all in her power to supply the place of my only child.

During this last phase of his life Allen's thoughts were much with such beloved friends as Joseph, John and Samuel Gurney, also with Elizabeth Fry and Stephen Grellet, both of whom were, like himself, nearing the end of their days.

First Day, October 15th, was the last time he attended Meeting ; he remarked that it was a good time ' though nothing had been said '. Almost his last earthly thoughts were of Borough Road School and Africa.

On December 30th William Allen died at Lindfield. A week later he was buried at Stoke Newington close to many fellow wayfarers whom in life he had greatly loved.

In an obituary in the *Notices of the Astronomical Society* he was described as :

> . . . an original member of the Astronomical Society and a distinguished Professor of Experimental Philosophy at Guy's Hospital and the Royal Institution of Great Britain. His taste for astronomy, as evinced by his elegant private observations and his extensive astronomical library . . . he united in a remarkable degree, sound knowledge, suavity of manners and sterling principles, and he deservedly possessed the esteem of all who knew him. Such was William Allen, whose life was devoted to the best interests of mankind.

BOOK THREE: CONSOLIDATION

THE HANBURY PERIOD

1794–1893

Candied apples, Quince and plum and gourd
And jellies smoother than the creamy curd,
And lucent syrups tinct with cinnamon,
Manna and date in Argosy transferred
From Fez; and spiced dainties, every one
From silken Samarcand and cedared Lebanon.

KEATS : *Eve of St. Agnes.*

CHAPTER 1

THE HANBURY FAMILY

FROM its foundation Allen and Hanburys has always been
fortunate in attracting to its service those who were in
every way worthy in that they displayed character as
well as ability : it is noteworthy that a high proportion of
those who served the Plough Court Pharmacy attained distinction. As business organizations increase in size there is often
a danger that *esprit de corps* may disappear. This has never
happened to Allen and Hanburys largely because the men who
made the business have always had a strong sense of vocation,
looked upon their chosen way of life not merely as a liveli-
hood but as a calling, and have always lived as members of
a community with ideals, purposes, and responsibilities in
common.

As was done in describing the Bevan Period, it is now fitting
to pay tribute to the men who as partners, or colleagues high
or humble, whose devotion, loyalty, and professional attainments
not only made William Allen's invaluable public career possible,
but who contributed directly to everything that he attained.
From Samuel Mildred in 1794 until Cornelius Hanbury I became
his son-in-law in 1822 and qualified worthily with Daniel Bell
Hanbury as one of his successors, William Allen never lacked
devoted colleagues.

Some such as Cookworthy and Luke Howard left Plough
Court to found valuable business concerns that are enriching the
communal life of Great Britain to this day ; others, like Barry
(who might have become a great surgeon), were content and
proud to serve the old Pharmacy faithfully and fruitfully throughout their professional lives.

The Hanburys of Hanbury in Worcestershire were the senior
branch of a family ancient, widespread and influential. In the

135

twelfth century Roger de Hanbury held land in the neighbourhood, and his descendants continued to do so for many generations.
As was then common they derived their surname from their
native place.

During the seven hundred years that have passed since Roger
flourished, the parent tree has thrown out innumerable branches ;
Hanburys have achieved success and honour in the Church, the
services, diplomacy, parliament, the professions and commerce.
Here we are only concerned with those Hanburys who, becoming
merchant venturers, or merchant adventurers, gave generation
after generation until this day, lasting service to the community.
As early as 1330 a Henry de Hanbury was M.P. for Worcester
City.

A branch of the family also took root at Elmley Lovett in
Worcestershire between Droitwich and Kidderminster. Richard
Hanbury, who was the ancestor of this branch, was according to
some pedigrees the son of the John Hanbury who is recorded as
having lived in the reign of Henry IV. Four generations later
another Richard Hanbury, who married Margery Bradley, had
two sons : John Hanbury of Purshall Green, and later of Elmley
Lovett and later still of Feckenham (Worcestershire) and of
Gloucester ; and Philip Hanbury, of Trevethin and Panteg.

John Hanbury was a staunch parliamentarian, and in 1642
during the civil wars he had to flee from his Worcestershire
house which some of the King's army plundered. They carried
away all the movable goods that were in it including ' bedding,
linnen, woollen, brasse, and burnt the bookes and accounts which
had been left in the house '.[1] The inscription on his tombstone
in St. Nicholas Church, Gloucester, states that he was a citizen
of London and of Gloucester, and that in 1625 he was ' Burgesse
of the Parliament for the city of Gloucester '. Sometime before
1617 he married Anne, daughter of Christopher Capel, whose
surname has been repeatedly used by her descendents as a
Christian name. As a result of his being nominated by his uncle,
Richard Hanbury, Goldsmith of London and Datchet (Bucking-
hamshire), executor of the latter's will, in 1608 (or 1609) he

[1] *The Hanbury Family*, Vol. I, page 122, by A. Audrey Locke.

acquired his first interest in the ironworks at Pontymoil and Pontypool in Monmouthshire. It is believed that he bought the ironworks himself in order to pay for some of his late uncle's debts, for Richard Hanbury had died with debts outstanding to the extent of £2,000 in excess of his personal estate. In 1635 John Hanbury was described as a ' dealer in merchandise of iron ', but the business was managed for him by a William Glazebrook of Bewdley.

John's third son, Capel Hanbury, married his first cousin Elizabeth, granddaughter of Christopher Capel mentioned above ; and their eldest son, also called John, was born in 1664. To distinguish him from his grandfather he has always been known by posterity as Major John Hanbury of Pontypool. In 1681 he matriculated from Pembroke College, Oxford ; and in spite of having taken up law as a student of the Middle Temple he soon abandoned this professional career in order to devote his attention to his family's mines and forges in Monmouthshire. These he inherited indirectly from his grandfather, but he would never have been able to develop them to the extent that he did were it not for his marrying (in 1701) Albinia, daughter and heiress of John Selwyn of Matson, Gloucestershire. In that same year, through the Selwyn's influence, he was chosen as member of Parliament for the City of Gloucester which he represented continuously till 1708.

Major John Hanbury took an active part in the development and improvement of the ironworks at Pontypool ; and in order to supervise these activities personally he moved his residence there, having built himself the house which is known to this day as Pontypool Park. Among the improvements in the processing of iron for which he was responsible were the use of furnaces and refineries resulting in increased output, and a new method of manufacturing tin-plate.

Before tin-plate could be made in Great Britain two separate techniques had to be mastered. Thin, uniform, and easily worked iron sheets had to be supplied economically and a method had to be devised whereby their surfaces could be prepared to take a coating of tin. John Hanbury, probably between 1695 and

1697, was the first man in the world to roll iron plates for tinning where previously they had been hammered down under water-driven tilt hammers ; this had been the technique in Saxony from where Britain had drawn her imports since about 1620. Thus by 1704 the iron-works at Pontypool were rolling sixty tons of plate a year, which sold for about thirty pounds a ton, roughly one-third of its previous price.

After Albinia's death in 1702, in the following year Major John Hanbury married his second wife Bridget, daughter of Sir Edward Ayscough, of South Kelsey in Lincolnshire. Bridget was a personal friend of Sarah, Duchess of Marlborough, and in 1721 John Hanbury was made one of the trustees for the administration of the Duke's household goods, and also an executor of his will. In gratitude for discharging these duties the Duchess later presented him with a service of plate and Bridget with a set of jewels. It was at this period that Pontypool Park was being built, and the Duchess gave the fine ironwork central gates which still stand at the Pontymoil entrance at the present time.

John Hanbury had no children by his first wife Albinia ; but he and Bridget are the ancestors of several branches of the Hanbury family that exist to-day. Among these are the Hanbury-Williams and the Hanbury-Tracys.

Philip Hanbury of Panteg and Trevethin, the younger brother of John Hanbury of Gloucester, had a son Richard (1610 to 1695) who was the first of this branch of the family to become a member of the Society of Friends. In fact, in 1683 and again two years later he and his wife Elizabeth were fined £220 each for eleven months' absence from 'the national worship'. But in 1689, in the reign of William and Mary, the Toleration Act was passed by Parliament, inaugurating an era of greater toleration between the various Christian denominations in the country.

It was Capel Hanbury I (1678 to 1740), one of Richard's grandsons, who moved away from Monmouthshire and achieved prominence as a soap merchant of Bristol. In 1714 he married Elizabeth, daughter and heiress of Harry Newton of Stapleton, near Bristol. They had two children ; Elizabeth, who married

Mark Beaufoy senior, brewer of London ; and Capel II, who by entering into partnership with his cousin John Hanbury of Tower Street and Holfield Grange, as Virginia tobacco merchants, consolidated the connection of the Hanbury family with the City of London, where generation after generation they have since held an honoured place. In 1750 Capel II married Mary, daughter and heiress of William Lunn, a citizen and vintner, of St. Botolph's in the City ; and by her he had four children, each of whom is important to this narrative :

John married Elizabeth Bell ; Capel III married her sister Charlotte Susannah Bell ; Anna remained unmarried ; Charlotte married William Allen, thus linking the names of Allen and Hanbury and establishing the commercial régime that was destined to spread from the old Plough Court Pharmacy to the four corners of the world.

CHAPTER 2

CAPEL HANBURY OF WARE

CAPEL HANBURY III became established at Ware as a corn merchant and later as a dealer in malt ; and, amongst much else, malt products are manufactured there by Allen and Hanburys to this day.

That great anthropologist, Francis Galton, coined the term eugenics and taught the importance of hereditary laws and the recurrence of family traits and tendencies. The Hanburys have always been noted for common sense, moderation, circumspect adventurousness, prudence, industry and public spirit.

However, Capel III was to some extent an exception. Optimistic and mercurial, he did not dislike rashness in business and, attracted by likeminded people, he entered into partnership with a very speculative man in the corn trade, and became insolvent. A descendant recorded that he once characteristically said to an old servant : ' I have sixty thousand pounds for one son and must make a like amount for the other ' !

At Ware the family had lived in some style in a large house at the top of the lane leading to the River Lea upon the banks of which Capel III had a wharf. Eventually the family moved to eight Grove Terrace, a small house near the Seven Sisters in the present north London suburb of Tottenham. As sometimes happens, what looked like misfortune turned out to be the opposite. This migration set the rising generation on the road to success and, over one hundred years later, Allen and Hanburys secured the old flour mills at Ware and several acres of land where the foundations of their present commodious factory were well and truly laid in healthy and attractive surroundings.

In marrying Charlotte Susannah Bell, Capel Hanbury III had secured a splendid wife. She inevitably suffered from the speculative tendencies of her husband and used to say to her sons :

'Live within your income and avoid speculation, and then you have a fair prospect of comfort in life.' When their second son was baptized she said : 'He shall be called Cornelius because Cornelius was a just man' : these two sentences reveal the woman.

The Quakers have always scrutinized the affairs of any member of the Society who ever became insolvent and, if found culpable, he was temporarily suspended from full membership. That no blame was attached to Capel III for his failure is proved by two facts : he remained a Quaker all his life, and, such was the esteem in which he was held locally, that the creditors refused to accept his share of the assets of the unlucky partnership.

CHAPTER 3

DANIEL BELL HANBURY

CAPEL III and Charlotte Susannah Bell had two sons : Daniel Bell (named after his mother) and Cornelius, both of whom played worthy parts in the development of the business. Daniel Bell Hanbury was born at Stamford Hill to the North of London in 1794 when the Terror in France was at its height, England was forming the first European coalition against Revolutionary France, and reform—but not revolution—was sweeping across the English Channel from Paris to London.

Daniel Bell received a somewhat meagre education partly at the Quaker school at Tottenham Green and partly by private tuition. Of remarkable natural ability, he became a man of unusual attainments, being, in the best sense of the phrase, self-educated.

In the spring of 1808, two years after his father's younger sister, Charlotte Hanbury, had married William Allen, Daniel Bell entered the Old Plough Court Pharmacy ; but, as far as is known, was never formally apprenticed.

Daniel Bell's first business letter, dated 26th of First month, 1809—ten days after Sir John Moore's glorious victory and death at Corunna—was addressed to Thomas Thompson, a chemist of Liverpool, and stated that the consignment of goods about which an inquiry had been made was duly forwarded by Pickford's Canal Waggon from the Castle and Falcon of Wood Street, London. He added : 'My uncle desired me to say that he has forwarded a copy of the letter respecting the Slave Ship to William Wilberforce and the original to T. Clarkson.'

He was fifteen years old at the time and his writing was then clear and well formed and showed little sign of change or weakness until he was in his eighty-eighth year. It was obvious that

DANIEL BELL HANBURY, 1794–1882

such a gift should be used to its best advantage in the business
and quite early, as his other work permitted, he spent some time
in the dispensary where clear direction labels for affixing to
bottles of medicine was an essential ; he was soon a dispenser
at Station Number Three on the dispensing counter. Indeed,
throughout his long business life the dispensing of medicines
had for him peculiar interest. He was a founder-member of
the Pharmaceutical Society (of which William Allen was first
President) and held the office of Treasurer to the Society from
1852 to 1857.

Close association with William Allen brought Daniel Bell
while still young and malleable into intimate touch with many of
the scientific and philanthropic movements of the day. He had,
as we know, enjoyed the enlarging experience of accompanying
his uncle-by-marriage on more than one continental journey.
In 1817, at the age of twenty-three, he was a member of the
party when William and Mary Allen, and the young Frenchman
George Majolier, set out via Paris and Lyons for Congenies,
where he would have had his first experience of the practice of
Quakerism on the Continent. However, the journey that left
the most lasting impression was when, five years later, he went
with William Allen to the Congress of Verona. As William's
nephew and assistant he was in the centre of great events.

During Daniel Bell's twenty-eight years of life Napoleon had
arisen, liquidated the worst evils of the French Revolution,
conquered Europe, suffered the retreat from Moscow, been
defeated at Waterloo, and died at St. Helena. At Verona
Daniel's acute, young and observing mind had intimate opportunities of observing the Czar Alexander I, Metternich, and the
great Wellington, who displayed such flattering trust and reliance
on uncle William Allen.

In 1824, at the age of thirty, at the Friends' Meeting House
at Wandsworth, London, Daniel Bell married Rachel, eldest
daughter of Thomas and Rebecca Christy of Broomfield, Essex,
and Clapham, London, by whom he had six sons and one
daughter.

In 1868 Daniel Bell retired from the Plough Court business

to which he had wholeheartedly devoted himself for forty years, and in which he had been a partner since 1824. He welcomed the leisure that enabled him to help in the scientific studies of his eldest son Daniel who succeeded him in the Plough Court business. Before sketching Daniel, however, something must be said about Cornelius Hanbury, the brother of Daniel Bell.

Daniel Bell Hanbury died in 1882, and was buried at the Friends' Burial Ground, Wandsworth, London.

CHAPTER 4

CORNELIUS HANBURY I

CORNELIUS, younger son of Capel III and Charlotte Bell Hanbury, was born at Ware in 1796 ; he was unquestionably quite as remarkable a man as his elder brother Daniel Bell. To differentiate him from his son Cornelius II, he will be known here as Cornelius I. His mother named him happily. As a child he was noted for his very amiable, docile disposition and, like his father, he was endowed with great buoyancy of spirits. We are told by his son, Cornelius II, that his uniform good humour and sprightliness made him a general favourite with youth, while his deference and suavity of manner to older people gained their affectionate regard. This, probably, indicated a too-yielding disposition, of which he became aware at an early age, and sought to strengthen. When his school-days ended he tells us that he was very sorry to leave his pleasant country home at Ware and migrate to London.

In 1814, at the age of eighteen, he joined his brother Daniel Bell at the Plough Court Pharmacy. He was regularly apprenticed for a period of seven years to William Allen, described in the indenture as a Citizen and Woolman, ' to learn the Art of a chemist and druggist'. In due course he was granted the Freedom of the City of London ; both his indenture and the certificate of his Freedom have been preserved.

The handwriting of Cornelius, like that of his brother Daniel Bell, was very clear and distinct ; he was at first placed in the counting-house, although his work as an apprentice would naturally take him to all parts of the shop, warehouse and laboratory. During the next few years the brothers acquired a sound knowledge of the business of a chemist and druggist.

Few technical books were available for study in their spare time, as there were then no examinations to pass. There is no doubt, however, that William Allen, and in a lesser degree, John Thomas Barry, would act as tutors and there may have been opportunities of attending the lectures at the Askesian Society.

Daniel Bell and Cornelius I lived with William and Charlotte Allen in the Stoke Newington home. It was a happy and harmonious family group, including William's daughter Mary, aunt Anna Hanbury and Christine Majolier.

Possibly fired by William's example, Cornelius I started keeping a diary in 1815, while not yet twenty years old. Like William's, it dealt largely with his continuous care to cherish and develop the beauty and leading of the Inward Light.

A man of intense religious feeling, inevitably Cornelius I became devoted in early life to the many humanitarian interests centred at Plough Court. When, as a senior office holder of the Society of Friends, William Allen was commissioned, in 1816, to visit scattered Quaker congregations in Great Britain and on the Continent, Cornelius I accompanied him ; he made no other visits abroad, but was always very active in paying visits in the British Isles. In 1817 he was asked to accompany two women Friends from America who wished to visit Meetings in Norfolk and Suffolk : ' I was rather discouraged at the prospect at first,' he said, ' but after some time I found my peace concerned in it.' It was on this journey that he spoke in Meeting for the first time with such success that he was frequently heard in his own and other Meetings, and, in December, 1819, he was discharged from the office of Elder and acknowledged a Minister in Unity by the Gracechurch Street (London) Monthly Meeting.

In 1822, aged twenty-six, Cornelius I married Mary, the only daughter of William Allen and the apple of her father's eye. Seeing each other daily under such favourable and congenial circumstances, it is small wonder that they came to wish for a closer union. The ceremony took place at the Devonshire House Meeting and in the Appendix will be found William Allen's full account of the marriage, which gave him great pleasure.[1] Their happiness was short-lived for, in the following

[1] Appendix Twenty-seven.

146

CORNELIUS HANBURY, 1796–1869

year, Mary Hanbury died a few days after giving birth to a son, William Allen Hanbury.

When, a year after Mary's death, Daniel Bell and Cornelius I were admitted into partnership in 1824, the style of the Firm was changed from William Allen and Company to Allen, Hanburys and Barry. At the time Allen was aged fifty-four, Barry thirty-five, Daniel Bell thirty, and Cornelius I twenty-eight.

Barry, in the increasingly frequent absences from Plough Court of William Allen, took charge of the business ; Daniel Bell spent most of his time in the shop and interested himself particularly in the growing dispensing department ; Cornelius I worked in the counting-house and was the partner to whom Allen wrote when away from Plough Court.

In 1826 Cornelius I married a second time, his wife being Elizabeth, youngest daughter of John Sanderson, a China tea merchant and Quaker of Old Jewry in the City of London. This event altered the domestic arrangements of the Plough Court and Stoke Newington establishments. Cornelius I, who had con-tinued living with his father-in-law after the death of his first wife, took his second wife to Plough Court, where they remained till some time after the birth of Cornelius II in 1827. He then bought a house of his own and about two acres of land at Stoke Newington, travelling to the City every day on horseback or driving in a four-wheeled chaise, which was stabled in Finsbury Square.

Because a section of Quakers objected to music, singing and dancing it is often forgotten that Quakers were to be found amongst the most cultured people of their day. Elizabeth (Sanderson) Hanbury was well-read in literature and poetry. She had learned by heart and would repeat to her children long passages from the poets, especially Milton and Cowper. All her life she herself wrote agreeable verse. She liked and culti-vated flowers and the two acres surrounding the new Stoke Newington home were divided, one-half being a vegetable, and the other half a flower garden. A second child, Charlotte, who turned out to be a remarkable woman, was born at Stoke Newing-ton in 1829.

Just as Barry in the early years of the nineteenth century had made it possible for Allen to carry on his public work by relieving him of the greater part of his routine business responsibilities at Plough Court, Daniel Bell and Cornelius I in later years took over much of Barry's work so that for periods of several months at a time he could devote himself wholeheartedly to a cause he had made particularly his own—the abolition of the death penalty for crimes other than murder. William Allen, as early as 1808, with six others, had dined together at Plough Court and formed the ' Society for diffusing information of the subject of punishment by Death '.

Cornelius I also concerned himself with the welfare of working people suffering from distress caused by accidents, with the cause of Temperance, Juvenile Delinquency, and many other pioneer philanthropic movements. It is sometimes forgotten that such men and women were the real originators of what are now known as the Social Services.

In his home, his business, and his philanthropic activities Cornelius I displayed a large and tolerant personality. His cheerfulness of deportment towards the young, intense sympathy, a liberality of sentiment that disregarded minor differences, and a high appreciation of mental excellence, marked him as in every way a man of quite unusual distinction. His forty-four years of work well and faithfully done at Plough Court provide a notable example of the truth—nowadays so often questioned—that there is nothing incompatible between a high state of spirituality and business aptitude and success.

When Cornelius I retired from active work at Plough Court in 1858 he settled down at Ford House, near Wellington in Somerset, where he made many friends and enjoyed the companionship of his relation Sylvanus Fox. Seven years later the family removed to a commodious and dignified creeper-clad house called The Firs ; it occupied a ridge of the Blackdown hills between Somerset and Devon near by the Wellington monument and some three miles from the town from which the victor of Waterloo took his ducal title. Surrounded by about twenty acres of land, the spacious gardens gave Cornelius I ample opportunities of indulging that inherent love of botany and horticulture which were amongst the main earthly sources of his life-long happiness. He died in March, 1869, beloved and mourned by all who knew him—especially the neighbouring poor.

CHAPTER 5

ELIZABETH SANDERSON HANBURY

ELIZABETH, widow of Cornelius I, and their daughter Charlotte continued to live at The Firs until 1886. It was then decided that they should both join Cornelius II. He had a house, Downe Lodge, Richmond, Surrey, on the terrace commanding the famous view of the Thames Valley and river. However, a larger house was now essential and he moved to Dynevor House. There his mother joined him, the old lady of ninety-three declaring : ' Nothing I should like better than to end my days in thy house.' As she lived another fifteen years and her long life covered the transition from the eighteenth to the twentieth century, Elizabeth (Sanderson) Hanbury merits a few paragraphs to herself.

She never lost her zest for life or her interest in, and love for, her fellow human beings. The longer she lived the more she came to love and understand mankind, always seeing in the worst some reflection of the best. In her autobiography [1] her daughter Charlotte wrote :

> My dear Mother, in her hundred and fifth year, had all the mental powers of her young days, with their vivid pleasure and sympathies ; composing verses, and exercising the wide influence of her life with new joy and vigour.

Cornelius II tells us that Elizabeth continued very cheerful and happy, liking to hear of all that was passing both public and private. Her sight and hearing lasted remarkably ; the sight did not quite fail until she was about one hundred and five and, with the aid of a trumpet, she could hear to the end. To her great sorrow, her devoted daughter Charlotte predeceased her by about a year ; however, she continued cheerful, feeling that

---

[1] London, 1901, Marshall Brothers.

ELIZABETH SANDERSON HANBURY, 1793–1901

their separation would be short. Near the end she used to say : 'Do not ask for my longer continuance.'

In October, 1901, Elizabeth died in her son's home at Richmond aged one hundred and eight years and some five months, that is to say one hundred and six years after her mother who died in 1795. Their joint lives thus covered the stretch of English history from the end of the reign of George II to the first year of that of Edward VII, who lived through the French Revolution, saw the rise and fall of Napoleon I, the restoration of the French Kingdom, the beginnings of the Republic, the rise and fall of Napoleon III, and the beginning of the German Empire ; she lived long enough to see Edward VII (as Prince of Wales) use motor-cars in preference to horses.

It brings the past very close to recall that in addition, Elizabeth, who died only fifty years ago, could clearly remember a London that still contained green fields. The Leadenhall Street house in which she was born had a garden in which was a summer-house ; cows were milked in Moor Fields just north of the City of London boundary where Finsbury Circus now is. Elizabeth often spoke to Cornelius II of 'a pretty walk through the corn from Moor Fields to the village of Islington'. She watched the building of East India House in Leadenhall Street, and never forgot the opening because she was taken to see the illuminations.

Through her Quaker father, John Sanderson, Elizabeth was early brought into touch with most of the notable philanthropists of her day. Plough Court, where so much advanced social history was being quietly made, was but a stone's throw away and William Allen, twenty-three years her senior, was already known as a stalwart opponent of the Slave Trade. Elizabeth in her youth worked with her relation Elizabeth Fry, known to Charlotte and Cornelius as 'Cousin Betsy', Charlotte accompanied her on visits to Newgate, and took special care for women who were sentenced to transportation and sent overseas in convict ships under the most demoralizing conditions. She fought against slavery with Allen, Wilberforce, Thomas Clarkson and Lord Brougham, and was associated with Allen and John Thomas Barry in their pioneer efforts to bring about the abandonment of sentences of capital punishment for minor offences against the law. Gentleness, tranquillity and simplicity were her principal characteristics, and she never abandoned her simple Quaker dress.

Of Elizabeth Sanderson Hanbury it could truly be said that, when old, she continued to be fresh like a child.

CHAPTER 6

WILLIAM ALLEN HANBURY

LTHOUGH he played little part in the affairs of the Firm, William Allen Hanbury, born in 1823, as the only child of Cornelius I by his first wife Mary Allen, cannot be left out of this chronicle. Much pains, says his half-brother Cornelius II, were taken with his education, first at Stoke Newington under a Quaker called Bedford Gilkes and afterwards at Grove House, Tottenham, which he entered in 1837. On leaving school William entered the Plough Court Pharmacy : however, it soon became clear that he had little liking for the business of a chemist and druggist, although he became interested in pyrotechny and was the first to take an interest in the family history.

In 1861 he married Countess Maria, eldest daughter of Adelbert, Count van der Recke Volmerstein of Schloss Craschnitz, near Breslau in Silesia. He brought his bride on a visit to his parents at Stoke Newington where she was warmly welcomed. However, they soon settled down in Germany where their only child Adelbert William Allen de Hanbury was born and brought up. Maria died in Germany in 1885 and her husband in Paris in 1898.

CHAPTER 7

CORNELIUS HANBURY II

PERHAPS no member of the Hanbury family had a larger share in consolidating the foundations of Allen and Hanburys than Cornelius II.

As his mother disliked Grove House, the school at Tottenham which her stepson William Allen Hanbury was attending, Cornelius II was tutored at home by Josiah Richardson, whom he some sixty years later described as ' an ardent student with a real love of learning ' ; he remained continuously under Richardson until he became a medical student. He records that during part of his time under Richardson he used a room on the top floor of Plough Court as a study, journeying there daily in the chaise with his father, and, before long, coaxing the coachman to allow him to drive.

William Allen Hanbury's disinclination to settle down to the Plough Court business was the principal reason for the decision that Cornelius II should qualify as a surgeon and apothecary. In 1845, at the age of eighteen, Cornelius II was apprenticed to Henry Callaway, a young surgeon-apothecary, for the required period of five years and lived most happily with him in his home in Bishopsgate opposite St. Botolph's Church, spending his Sundays at Stoke Newington with the family. Callaway abandoned medicine and surgery and became a missionary in South Africa, ending up as Bishop of St. John's, Kaffraria. He and Cornelius II remained close and life-long friends.

Early in his apprenticeship Cornelius II became a student at St. Bartholomew's Hospital, and increasingly devoted his time to work there. To be able to do so more conveniently he went to live at a lodging in Charterhouse Street near the Hospital. His advance was rapid, he became clinical clerk under Doctor (afterwards Sir) George Burrows, Bt., with whom he formed

CORNELIUS HANBURY, 1827–1916

another life-long friendship. . Cornelius II passed the examination for membership of the College of Surgeons at the end of 1849, and that of Licentiate of the Society of Apothecaries' at the end of his apprenticeship in May, 1850. A month later he married Sarah Jane Janson, daughter of Frederick Janson, underwriter at Lloyd's, by his wife Sarah Tindall. They were neighbours at Stoke Newington and Sarah Jane was a friend and fellow pupil of the bridegroom's sister Charlotte. The engagement had been a long one ; now all the circumstances were propitious, not least the wedding breakfast at the Star and Garter, Richmond, which followed the simple Quaker ceremony at the Friends' Meeting House at Stoke Newington. Among the many relatives present was Samuel Gurney, the well-known and highly esteemed financier of Lombard Street, he and his brother Joseph John Gurney of Earlham being first cousins of the bridegroom's father. It was Joseph John who influenced Cornelius II to adopt the Friend's coat which he wore all through his years at Bart's and for some time after his marriage without, however, as he says, attaching much importance to it. In after-life he left the Society of Friends and with his wife and young family became members of the Church of England.

Immediately after his marriage he attended classes at the Birkbeck Laboratory, University of London, and became a Fellow of the (now Royal) Institute of Chemistry. Of his early business experiences he left a record in his diary :

I now [1849] began to attend daily to the business at Plough Court. . . . I was soon instructed in doing the ' Schedule ' and posting the expense book, etc. and from that time I have kept on pretty steadily, but at first it was far from congenial and agreeable to my tastes. I almost longed for my studies again especially when I found myself much at fault and more ignorant of business than a warehouseman or even a porter. . . . I became intimately associated with my cousin Daniel. We eventually each took part in the daily routine of the business, including some amount of Counting-house work, and as had been the custom for a generation previously gave personal attention to the

Dispensing and other details of the business. The Firm had in this way and with careful attention to all other details acquired a great reputation to which the scientific attainments of William Allen and my cousin Daniel, both Fellows of the Royal Society—had largely contributed.

It is not only fitting but necessary that we should now devote some time to the consideration of ' my cousin Daniel ', hitherto a stranger to these pages.

CHAPTER 8

DANIEL HANBURY

'COUSIN DANIEL', the eldest son of Daniel Bell Hanbury and Rachel (Christy) Hanbury, was born in September, 1825, at Bedford Lane, now Bedford Road, Clapham, Surrey.

He received his early education at Pritchard's, afterwards Clapham Grammar School, Clapham, which he entered at the age of eight years.

He acquired at this school a knowledge of languages and some skill in water-colour drawing ; he supplemented the former by private study after his day's work at the Plough Court Pharmacy, which he entered in 1841 at the age of sixteen, was finished.

Like William Allen, Daniel kept a diary, of which unfortunately there is no trace ; he also at the age of seventeen began a series of note-books, principally on scientific subjects, from which emerge a clear idea of the man himself and his methods. His work was always characterized by meticulous order and sound method.

In 1842 he attended the first course of lectures given at the Pharmaceutical Society's House in Bloomsbury Square, and made a précis of each lecture. Latter-day students of the School of Pharmacy at number Seventeen may like to know that Daniel began work at 8.30 a.m. Chemistry, materia medica and pharmacy were the subjects ; George Fownes, F.R.S., was in charge of chemistry, Jonathan Pereira [1] taught materia medica, on which at the time he was probably the leading authority in the country, and Theophilus Redwood taught pharmacy.

Daniel recorded his absences from 17 Bloomsbury Square as well as his attendances. One day in January, 1844, he was away because he was at the funeral of William Allen ; another day it

[1] M.D., F.R.C.P., 1804-1853.

157

was intensely cold with snow on the ground. Umbrellas and outer garments were left in the entrance passage and he complained that three umbrellas were stolen, one of them being his. Daniel was also doing practical work in the evenings at Plough Court ; chemistry appears to have been his favourite subject. For example, he made pure silver from a silver coin, he made oxide of silver for shop use, prepared ' photogenic paper ', made some of the ' tests ', and under the direction of John Thomas Barry examined a sample of aconitine.

Daniel did not qualify as a pharmaceutical chemist until 1857 ; he had joined his cousin in partnership in 1856. Three years later he was appointed one of the examiners of the Pharmaceutical Society, giving the whole of his attention to the subjects of botany and materia medica. In 1868 he was elected President of the British Pharmaceutical Conference held that year at Norwich ; and was re-elected President for the following year when it was held at Exeter.

He contributed valuable papers to the pharmaceutical press, and, in 1864, read a paper at the British Pharmaceutical Conference at Bath entitled *A Chemist's Holiday*, an account of a vacation he and a friend spent in rambling in different parts of France, and of the botanical specimens they collected. This holiday, the first of many spent in the south of France, was to have far-reaching consequences.

There are indications in the early note-books that even before his student days Daniel developed the marked interest in botany which he shared with many members of the Hanbury family. The main work of his life, however, was to be the study of pharmacognosy, or the knowledge of drugs, especially in their natural or imperfect state. He called himself a pharmacologist, a word which to-day connotes a much wider meaning than it did then. Except in the case of extracts from his note-books, the words pharmacognosist and pharmacognosy are used in this account as signifying the man and his work.

In 1845, on the recommendation of Pereira, who became one of Daniel's closest friends, the Council of the Pharmaceutical Society of Great Britain decided to appoint :

DANIEL HANBURY, 1825–1875

. . . a Scientific Committee for the promotion of pharmacological knowledge, the immediate object to be the elucida-
tion of the natural history and origin of substances used in
medicine.

The Committee published in the *Pharmaceutical Journal* from
time to time what were described as pharmacological desiderata,
that is, lists of substances, mostly vegetable, from stated districts
concerning which specimens and information were desired. The
Committee consisted of several well-known pharmacists, but
Daniel Hanbury—he was only twenty years of age at the time
—did not join it till later. However, he threw himself with
enthusiasm into the general work of the Committee, his first
inquiry being sent to the Cape of Good Hope in December,
1850. It asked for information concerning the plants from
which buchu leaves were collected and sent to this country ;
other inquiries were about Cape aloes and galbanum.

Another letter was sent to Dr. Hobson, of ' Shangae '. This
has some historical interest as it would appear to be the beginning
of Daniel's association with correspondents in China, which in
due course resulted in his important contribution to the history
of Chinese materia medica.

Always interested in Indian drugs, Daniel devoted much
laborious work to the compilation of the *Pharmacopoeia of India*,
and his delight was great when he found that a schoolfellow of
his named Charles Horne had become an Indian Civil Servant,
and that his father was living on Clapham Common. Further-
more, Horne had sent home a collection of sketches of colonial
plants, which, in Hanbury's judgement, showed botanical accuracy ; a correspondence was begun and kept up over a period of
years, Horne sending to Clapham details and sketches of many
Indian drugs. Much of his correspondence was dealt with at
home before breakfast, some at Plough Court : Frederick
Janson Hanbury spoke of Daniel coming to the City with a
green-baize bag, tied with tapes, which contained not only
specimens and letters but an apple or orange, or a Bath Oliver
biscuit for his midday meal.

Many of the specimens Daniel received were kept for his own

herbarium, some, usually seeds, he planted in his garden or greenhouse ; others were sent to such institutions as Kew Gardens, London, or to the Jardin des Plantes in Paris. Payment, or some recompense, for the services of his many collectors was often a problem. Occasionally he was able to send a present such as a book or literature, or reciprocate by purchasing in London some special article not obtainable overseas, or he would entertain some member or members of his correspondent's family when they visited this country.

A typical letter was sent to Senator S. A. Benson of Grand Bassa, Liberia, who had promised specimens of cardamoms ; an addendum said :

> A copy of the new illustrated edition of Mrs. Stowe's book [1] and a glass paper weight of which I hope my friend thou wilt accept as a small acknowledgement of thy kind attention. A few pairs of scissors and some common spoons for any of thy servants who have kindly procured me specimens.

On occasion he appears to have sent out suitable tools to aid his collectors. In a letter to Dr. W. J. White of Colon, when alluding to the death of one of his correspondents, he asked if a contrivance in the shape of a hook for cutting a small branch fifteen or twenty feet from the ground was among deceased's effects ? If so :

> . . . he would like this back, as it belonged to his grandfather, if it is disposed of—no matter.

Daniel wanted living plants of *Hanburia* and in asking Hugo Finck, Prussian Vice-Consul in Cordova, Mexico, to obtain these for him he wrote :

> I shall be glad to pay you all expenses, say, not exceeding £10 (Ten pounds sterling) if you will inform me how I can do so.

In repaying his correspondents he often sent sovereigns or half-

---

[1] Probably *Uncle Tom's Cabin* published in 1852 and translated into a score of languages.

sovereigns. He sent to his friend, Dr. Charles Dorat, of Guatemala, a supply of chemicals and bottles for photography :

> The last named bottle contains two sovereigns which I send
> to defray freight you must have paid on the last box. I
> forward also some camphor to keep insects from the dried
> plants, two glass funnels, some straps to tie up bundles of
> plants, and some new coppers to give away to children.

He himself would occasionally sell on the market drugs sent to him by correspondents. In sending to one such a statement of the disposal of three tins of kousso, just then coming into fashion as a vermifuge, for which he had obtained 1s. 2½d. per ounce, he added :

> I have taken no profit on this lot of kousso as I prefer the
> recompense of thy communications on scientific subjects.

As early as 1850 Daniel began a series of contributions to the *Pharmaceutical Journal* and to other scientific papers on the pharmacognosy of a number of drugs. These, to the number of eighty, were collected after his untimely death, by his friend Joseph Ince, F.L.S., and published in one volume entitled *Science Papers* ; [1] not all were of interest to the pharmacist, but all were characterized by careful original research, sometimes extending over many years. It should be borne in mind that in 1850 there were few, if any, official standards for vegetable drugs, and there were very few text-books which a student could consult for accurate descriptions.

As a purchaser of drugs and constant attendant at the London drug and spice markets Daniel knew that sometimes drugs offered were not of the quality required for use in medicine ; occasionally they were even incorrectly named. He recorded one instance where on visiting a certain drug market he discovered that ' dragons' blood ' was being offered as kino !

In some of the articles in *Science Papers* Daniel devoted attention to certain products about which doubts had arisen in his mind. His investigations covered the history of the article, its correct

[1] London, 1876, Macmillan & Co.

botanical name and characteristic appearance, its source or sources, and its use in medicine or pharmacy. Many of these investigations implied some knowledge of languages little used by scientific men of the day, such as Turkish and Arabic, in addition to modern Greek and Spanish. In 1860, accompanied by his friend Dr. (afterwards Sir) Joseph D. Hooker, Director of Kew Gardens, Daniel visited the Holy Land to collect scientific material.

It is not possible here to go into details regarding any of those investigations. Storax, otto of rose, balsam of Peru, frankincense, scammony, cardamoms, gamboge, Winter's bark, manna and jalap, the latter, which he grew in his garden at Clapham, were a few of the vegetable articles dealt with in *Science Papers*.

Daniel Hanbury's notable contributions to the history of Chinese materia medica were spread over the years 1860, 1861 and 1862. A considerable knowledge of the Chinese language as well as the literature of East Asia were essential for his work. His brother Thomas Hanbury, who became a silk merchant in Shanghai in 1853, gave him considerable help in collecting specimens of Chinese medicinal articles and drugs ; these Thomas presented to the Museum of the Pharmaceutical Society of Great Britain in 1892, seventeen years after Daniel's death.

The crown of Daniel Hanbury's scientific work, however, was the compiling of the *Pharmacographia* in conjunction with Professor F. A. Flückiger, who was academical teacher of pharmacognosy in Berne, as well as the manager of the State pharmacy of that city. Daniel became acquainted with Flückiger through reading his *Lehrbuch des Pharmacognosie des Pflanzenruches*. He wrote to the author introducing himself, making a few minor criticisms, and offering his help in the shape of any specimens Flückiger might desire.

The outcome was that Flückiger agreed to collaborate with Hanbury in the writing of a book which should be ' a history of the principal drugs of British origin, met with in Great Britain and British India '. The title of the book was, after much discussion, agreed upon as *Pharmacographia* (a writing about drugs).

Thus began in 1867 a literary collaboration, and indeed partnership, which at the time, considering all the implications of the arrangement, was unique. In 1872 Flückiger was appointed Professor of Pharmacognosy at Strasbourg University. There were many difficulties to encounter. Hanbury was not too good at translating Flückiger's German and Flückiger was not fluent in speaking or writing English. Therefore, a translator with scientific knowledge was employed.

Daniel's release from business was on the way, for in a letter to Flückiger dated 17th October, 1870, he enclosed a cutting from one of the London daily papers, showing that the partnership dating from 1856 of Daniel Hanbury and Cornelius Hanbury was dissolved.

After Daniel Hanbury's retirement, progress with *Pharmacographia* became more rapid.

There were, however, still difficulties to overcome. A sharp difference of opinion arose about whether the lowest natural order should be described first, followed by the highest orders. Flückiger suggested this procedure and appears to have insisted on it : Hanbury, after taking the advice of Professor Oliver of Kew, who stated that in English works on botany the higher orders always came first, persuaded Flückiger to concur.

On the 11th September, 1874, Daniel Hanbury made the last correction in *Pharmacographia* and returned to the printer the proofs and index. The reviews of the work were most favourable. Henry Bowman Brady wrote in *Nature* :

It will be received with no grudging hand and will be recognized at once and without misgiving as the standard authority on the subjects of which it treats.

To-day, seventy-five years after the above was written, that verdict still stands.

No account of the work of Daniel Hanbury would be complete without some brief reference to the several gardens in which he was deeply interested, and three of which were often referred to in his note-books.

His first love was the garden attached to his ' dear Bedford

Lane house', next door to which he was born and which his father left in 1863. This adjoined Broomfield, the home at Clapham, Surrey, of his maternal grandparents, Thomas and Rebecca Christy ; there were large rambling gardens with greenhouses attached. Both houses with their gardens have now disappeared ; the Hanbury house was badly shaken by bombs during the Second World War and was demolished in 1950 ; the demolition of the Christy house soon followed.

The second garden in which Daniel was particularly interested and to which many allusions are to be found in his note-books is now partly built over, although the house attached, badly shaken, is still standing and is known to-day as number three Nightingale Lane, Clapham Common.[1] When Daniel Bell Hanbury took over the premises in 1863 there was no greenhouse and he had one built.

The third garden was the notable one at La Mortola, between Mentone and Ventimiglia, owned by his brother, Sir Thomas Hanbury.

The first allusion to these gardens occurs in a letter to H. Bolus, of the Cape of Good Hope :

> My friend Professor Oliver of Kew recommends my writing you on the subject of seeds of Cape Plants, a sort of begging letter in fact. I am interested in a garden belonging to a brother of mine, on the Mediterranean Coast between Nice and Cannes and I am ambitious to see it stocked with all the rare and precious shrubs that can be grown in that spot without much attention and gardening skill. Our grounds are close to the shore but slope backwards by terrace to 500 feet above the sea level. There is tenacious loamy soil and vegetable mould and sand are not procurable in plenty. The summer drought is considerable and paucity of water is a frequent source of anxiety. The olive, aleppo pine, and cypress thrive well and the lemon and orange in places where they can be watered every ten days during the dry season.

To make, and leave behind you as a memorial, a garden is

[1] Appendix Twenty-eight.

perhaps the loveliest thing a human being can do. La Mortola has been visited by hundreds of thousands of people and cherished in the memory of many of them as something incomparable. Scores of artists, including the Empress Frederick and her sister Princess Louise of Great Britain, spent serene hours painting there. Happily it still exists and this is how a well-known writer in France saw and recently described it :

> Sir Thomas Hanbury was a wealthy and generous English-man whose memory is venerated on either side of the frontier. He founded schools in the villages, gave to Garavan the fountain which bears his name, and took a prominent part in the researches of the Barma Grande, the largest of the caves. Purchasing the large domain of the Mortola, on the road to Ventimile (Ventimiglia) . . . he created the finest botanical gardens on the coast. They contain plants from China, Egypt, Mexico—from every part of the globe. In these wonderful gardens is the fourteenth-century palace of the Lanteris (Palazzo Orengo), one of the principal families of the Riviera.[1]

Thomas Hanbury would like it recorded that La Mortola gardens owe their origin to the early visits Daniel paid to the Riviera and his searchings there for rare botanical specimens. It was he who discovered the promontory of La Mortola, interested Thomas in its possibilities and, after its purchase, helped in every way in making the gardens a permanent source of usefulness and joy.

Daniel Hanbury was accustomed to stay every year for a short time with his parents at La Mortola ; the majority of his holidays were spent on the Continent, generally his absences from home were short, but they had always some definite end in view. He particularly favoured the southern provinces of France, where he cultivated the society of every botanist of note ; it was a constant remark in his home circle how assiduously he sought the society of French-speaking people, losing no opportunity of conversing with them in their own language, which he spoke with fluency and charm.

[1] Huddleston, Sisley, *Mediterranean Blue* (London, 1948, Evans Brothers).

In all his journeys, as far as possible, he made personal observations on everything connected with his special studies. Thus, at Smyrna, he gained information about the collection of scammony; at Grasse and Cannes he described the process of enfleurage. He went to Sicily in 1872 on purpose to learn something about the production of manna, and, it is recorded, narrowly escaped capture by brigands. At the same time he gained authentic information on the cultivation of liquorice and the preparation of the juice. As a rule, scanty records of these journeys have been preserved, with the exception of his visit, in the autumn of 1860, to the Holy Land, the events of which were recorded by Sir Joseph D. Hooker.

The trip extended over several months; Malta was reached on the homeward journey on November 10th; the attractions of the trip were such as to draw from even the reticent Daniel a contrast between them and the sober realities of a shop in Lombard Street. On these journeys he usually made sketches, and in September, 1865, wrote Dr. Charles Dorat:

I am myself addicted to water-colours and have a small number of sketches made chiefly during rapid visits to some of the more picturesque districts of France, Switzerland and Germany, a few also taken during a short tour in Syria.

Daniel was fortunate in his friends and associates, numbering amongst them the savants of all countries. Such were Nicholas Jean Baptiste Guibourt, an authority on materia medica; Señor Joaquim Correa de Mello, of Campinas, Brazil; G. Thuret, of Antibes; Gustave Planchon of Paris; Leon Soubeiran, of Montpelier. His intimates also included the chief scientific writers in America and, at home, the distinguished members of the Linnaean Society of which he was a Fellow, notably, George Bentham, Professor Thiselton Dyer, Frederick Currey and Professor Oliver. In addition to Pereira, his friends in pharmacy comprised many well-known men such as Henry Bowman Brady, destined, like himself, to attain the highest distinction science can offer her devotees, a Fellowship of the Royal Society.

Flückiger said of Daniel Hanbury that he was 'truth, every inch of him'; this characteristic, which found expression in his whole being, was, as has been shown, revealed with great distinctness in his early work as well as in that of his maturer years. Frederick Janson Hanbury said of him that he believed no verbal statement regarding his favourite science until he had verified it; nor did he necessarily believe a statement because it appeared in print.

In countless instances secondhand knowledge could not stand its ground before his critical acumen and had to give way before his superior observation. The best book-knowledge offered for sale in the market did not content him; he insistently referred to the sources of information, testing them minutely.

He disliked and shunned anything approaching ostentation and luxury, and self-indulgence was utterly alien to his life. He disliked meetings of all kinds, particularly those attached to dinners and luncheons, even in company with his scientific friends. He disliked both tobacco and alcohol; his food was of the simplest and when on the Continent he was practically a vegetarian. Although he never enjoyed robust health, he never complained of any disabilities, and it was suggested that his lack of resistance to the illness which caused his death was probably partly due to his frugal method of living. He never married.

Daniel never alluded to his honours, which were many. He only lived fifty years and, into some twenty, he crowded memorable achievement. A mere chronological list of the honours bestowed upon him by his peers is eloquent of the rapidity and sureness of his advances in professional and public status and esteem. In 1855, at the age of thirty, he was elected a Fellow of the Linnaean Society, on the Council of which he frequently served, and to the *Journal* of which he contributed. In 1858 he became a Fellow of the Chemical Society, and was on its Council in 1869; from 1860 until 1872 he was on the Board of Examiners of the Pharmaceutical Society, and was appointed adjudicator of prizes both at the London Exhibition of 1862 and the Paris Exhibition of 1867; indeed, 1867 was a memorable year for

Daniel, because not only was he elected a Fellow of the Royal Microscopical Society but, at the age of forty-two, he achieved his greatest honour by being elected a Fellow of the Royal Society, and was placed on its Council two years later ; his high reputation on the Continent was signalized in 1872 when he was made an Honorary M.D. of the University of Munich.

Of his crowning honour he spoke with characteristic modesty :

> For some time I strenuously refused to allow myself to be placed among the candidates for admission to the Royal Society, feeling that it would be invidious were the honour of membership conferred on a pharmaceutist [1] who had really accomplished so little for science, and who had, in many ways, smaller merits than several others who could be selected. But it was urged, ' You must leave that to the judgment of your friends.' So this I did and I do not know who drew up my certificate and, with one exception, by whom it was signed.

Daniel Hanbury died at Hollywood,[2] Clapham Common, on March 24th, 1875. His body was placed in the burial-ground of the Society of Friends, of which he was a member, at Wandsworth.

His name is perpetuated in pharmacy by the Hanbury Memorial Medal [3] to be awarded biennially for original research in chemistry and pharmacy ; appropriately, the first recipient was Professor Flückiger. In 1903 Sir Thomas Hanbury handed over to the Pharmaceutical Society securities to provide an award of fifty pounds to be coupled with the presentation of the medal.

To Daniel Hanbury science was unconfined, breaking down all national barriers. Flückiger recognized this when he paid tribute to his collaborator in these words :

His warm patriotism, which he never renounced, did not

[1] In 1874 he wrote : ' I dislike the word pharmacist and have never used it hitherto. But I am assured it is well chosen and much better than pharmaceutist and that it must be allowed a place in the English language.'
[2] Now number seven Nightingale Lane, purchased by Daniel Hanbury in 1874.
[3] Appendix Twenty-nine.

for one moment prevent him from being perfectly just to German culture, and to German pharmacy.

But his true and fitting epitaph lies in the words of Professor Dragendorff :

An Englishman by birth, he lived and worked for all civilized peoples.

CHAPTER 9

THE OLD PLOUGH COURT PHARMACY

IT is time that we returned to the Old Plough Court Pharmacy and noted the progress made under Cornelius II and ' Cousin Daniel '.

The dispensing side of the business, which flourished under the direction of Allen and Barry, had assumed still greater proportions. Although the majority of London merchants and business men no longer lived in the City, they continued to attend there daily ; for convenience they often left their prescriptions in the Pharmacy in the morning, as well as lists of other needs, calling for them in the afternoon or evening. Finsbury Square then, like the Harley Street area later, was the fashionable abode of medical and surgical specialists, and a study of the prescription books of the period reveals the number of prescriptions from residents in the neighbourhood dispensed at Plough Court.

The type of prescription was changing. The six or twelve draughts which were once ordered, each in a separate bottle, were being superseded by one bottle containing six or twelve doses—a great saving of bottles and labour. Twelve or twenty-four pills were, in the majority of cases, ordered with the mixtures ; these were made up freshly on each occasion ; many were silver-coated, the pearl-coating process was not patented by another firm until 1854, and in any case it was not practicable with such small batches. Five dispensers were employed ; there were also two shopmen who dealt with the miscellaneous orders.

In 1856, the year in which Barry retired and Cornelius II became a partner with Daniel Hanbury, extensive alterations were made at number two Plough Court ; four hundred pounds, a considerable sum in those days, was spent on structural altera-tions ; the shop was enlarged by the addition, on the ground floor, of the assistants' dining-room, and a bigger shop window

INSIDE THE OLD PLOUGH COURT PHARMACY

ARMS OF THE APOTHECARIES SOCIETY AND THE
PHARMACEUTICAL SOCIETY
From the window of the old Plough Court Pharmacy

with enclosure was fitted.[1] This took the place of the three windows described in the lease of the premises as ' sashes with Crown Glass to slide, both parts with boxes, lines, weights and pulleys '. The object of the new window was not so much for display purposes as to give more light in the shop in daytime. A feature of this window was the two oval panels in the centre displaying the arms of the Society of Apothecaries and the Pharmaceutical Society in colours proper. When the premises were pulled down in 1873, these much-prized relics of the old pharmacy were suitably mounted and hung in the new pharmacy. Most unfortunately they were destroyed in 1941 when the premises were badly shaken by a bomb which fell a few yards away.

Another improvement was a new counter of which many details are preserved. It was divided into stations numbered one to five, each allotted to a dispenser ; these were not separated, the limit of each man's territory being marked with a slip of white wood let into the top of the counter. The lighting was important : Argand burners were used and they were arranged to throw the maximum amount of light on to the actual work of compounding. There is a suggestion on record, although there is no evidence that it was put into practice, that customers who did not wait for their prescriptions and wished to call again should be given a numbered disc, which, when returned to the head dispenser, would indicate the station where the ' script ' was being dispensed. A coloured disc was to be used when the filling of the prescription was likely to occupy more time than usual.

Other alterations and improvements made were a speaking-tube from the shop to the dining-room on the first floor, improved ventilation, the interior repainted and bottles relabelled. Special attention was given to the display of ships' medicine chests and travelling medicine cases, all dispensing being done in full view of the customer.

These alterations coincided with a reorganization of the

[1] The architect was William Beck, 1823–1907, the eldest son of Richard Low Beck, once an assistant in the Old Plough Court Pharmacy.

different departments of the business : fresh connections with many classes of the community were anticipated because many people were becoming interested in the practical application of the new chemistry to scientific and commercial purposes. This necessitated the preparation of circulars for apothecaries, merchants, firework-makers, fluoric acid for glass stainers, ships' chests for shipowners, mineral waters for physicians, essential oils for confectioners, chemicals for laboratories and professors, photographic chemicals for professional and amateur photography. There is evidence that firework-making was carried on at Plough Court during his short stay there by William Allen Hanbury, but no details have been discovered. The supply of chemicals for use in photography probably refers to those used in the ' wet plate ' process, which dates from 1851.

The issue of these circulars, with an appeal wider than that made to customers who frequented the shop, marked the beginning of the wholesale side of the business in so far as the home trade was concerned. The Firm was gaining a reputation for preparations made at Plough Court outside the circumscribed limits of the retail dispensing and sale of medicines. Orders began to come in from chemists for drugs and galenicals. Some of those ordering them had been assistants at Plough Court and appreciated the quality of the articles supplied ; others acquired the habit of sending for small emergency supplies ; in a few years this side of the business assumed considerable proportions, orders coming in regularly from all parts of London, from the south coast as far as Cornwall, and from as far north as Edinburgh and Belfast.

In the year 1865 changes were made in the manufacturing laboratory at Plough Court. Hitherto much of the work of making galenicals had been done in the basement of numbers two and three, which then had no sub-basement, as it was only added when the new premises were built in 1872. During 1867, premises at the back of number one were taken and into these was fitted some of the old plant dating back to William Allen's time, as well as a new still and other apparatus.

The preparations made were galenicals such as tinctures,

extracts, confections, ointments, and so on. There was no room for such an operation as drug-grinding, nor at the time was there a great demand for this type of work except for the Firm's own manufacturing requirements. When drugs had to be ground they were taken to one of the drug-grinders in the neighbourhood by an assistant whose duty it was to see the actual grinding done and bring back the product.

CHAPTER 10

THE NEW PLOUGH COURT PHARMACY

THE year 1872 saw the final structural alteration of the Plough Court premises, made necessary by important building changes in Lombard Street. Cornelius Hanbury secured a building lease for a term of eighty years. The old premises were very reluctantly pulled down, and the existing (although badly shaken) building erected on the same site, but with a different aspect. As the original premises stood, the archway of the title led from Lombard Street to Plough Court, a small paved, open courtyard ; it was immediately east of the modern entrance, which still retains the name of Plough Court, though the site of the original court is now covered by the premises of the English, Scottish and Australian Bank. The two houses leased by Allen & Hanburys (two and three Plough Court) looked out over the open court direct to Lombard Street ; the retail pharmacy was number two. Stretching away at the back of number one, with an entrance into Three King's Court, now Lombard Court, were the laboratories of the Firm. The lease of the ground covered by these laboratories, held from the Merchant Taylors' Company, was surrendered at the time of the alteration of the premises in 1872, and in the new premises the laboratories were transferred to the third floor.

The greater part of the ground floor was occupied by the Pharmacy, which was arranged somewhat in the shape of a horseshoe—an ample counter of old mahogany extended practically round the interior, and behind the counter the drugs were arranged on screens. The public floor space was occupied by a double settee in mahogany, and there were six fine old Georgian oak chairs of about 1790, relics of the old Pharmacy. On the right of the ground floor was the Surgical Department where orders for dressings and surgical sundries were dealt with.

INTERIOR OF PLOUGH COURT PHARMACY 1897

Behind this department was situated the registered office of the Company.

The pulling down of the old building prompted an unidentified customer of the Firm to write the following lines :

The poet's birth-place is demolished now,
The house where Pope was born is seen no more,
But Fame has wreathed her laurels round his brow,
Why then should we his infant home deplore ?
And since his day that house has well been known
As the resort of men of high renown.

Foremost of these may Bevan notice claim
For wisdom, learning and true piety
To all who knew his excellence a name
Esteemed an honour to society.
And Allen next, whose rich expansive mind,
The admiration won of all mankind.

A brilliant circle he around him drew
Of men of science and philanthropy.
And many a noble institution grew
Beneath his fostering kind paternity.
When leagued with others of congenial mind
'Twas his delight to succour human kind.

There Clarkson, Wilberforce and Buxton reared
The banner of deliverance to the slave.
And 'gainst harsh law firm Barry interfered
The culprit from untimely death to save.
And there beside a noble phalanx stood,
Promoting objects of the public good.

There Brougham gave his influence and his name
For better education of the poor.
And foreign sufferers with various claims
Soliciting relief besieged the door.
There too the younger Clarkson, friend of peace,
Announced that Christian men from war should cease.

Such then the annals of that house have been
Thus has it gained a just and wide renown.
And now the desolation there is seen
Its glory like the setting sun gone down.
Let us remember how there oft remain
Long after sunset tints of golden hue
From his last rays, and thence may hope ensue
That that once favoured site may yet retain
Traits of the past that still shall commendation gain.

12th mo, 1872   John—brother of Thomas Clarkson.

Before leaving the Plough Court Pharmacy, *Old* Plough Court no longer, as a manufacturing centre where on the third floor the head of the laboratory, John Fordred, was always busy turning out small experimental batches of new products, it is worth glancing at the sort of conditions in which so much good work was carried on. One of the retired veterans of the Firm who entered Plough Court over seventy years ago supplies the following description :

. . . The laboratory on the third floor was rather on the crowded side—with three stills, an extraction tank . . ., 5 steam pans (one solid tin tilting), mash tun, vacuum pump and vacuum pan, furnace and fume cover for distilling prussic acid, hydrobromic acid, sweet spirits of nitre, etc., copper and earthenware percolators, marble mortars, and in an adjoining room, edge runners, stampers, and a huge bell metal mortar the steel pestle suspended on a long springy branch, which helped the operator considerably, and he wanted it—when he was told to ' bruise 64 lbs. of Jamaica ginger thro' a No. 11 sieve *and make no dust* ' that was always the strict order ! Then of course there was an hydraulic press with press box—and a supply of horse hair bags for pressing fresh dandelion roots, green (fresh) henbane, belladonna, etc., etc.

There can be little doubt that long before he became sole head of the Old Plough Court Pharmacy, Cornelius II was fully aware of the great commercial expansion that was taking place everywhere, and the steady growth in the demands made upon the manufacturer of drugs had early determined that the accommodation and manufacturing resources of the old Pharmacy were too limited to enable him to achieve his purpose. He also visualized the Firm formulating and preparing its own medicinal specialities.

In the successful carrying out of this ambition he was to enjoy the valuable help of his elder and only surviving son, Frederick Janson Hanbury, who, at the age of twenty-two, joined his father at Plough Court, bringing with him not inconsiderable knowledge and experience.

Educated at the Friends' School, Grove House, Tottenham, he entered as an apprentice the notable pharmacy of Henry Deane at Clapham Common, from the door of which he could almost see the residence of his cousin Daniel Hanbury at number three Nightingale Lane, where, retired from business, he was busy with his garden and the writing of the *Pharmacographia*. In Deane's pharmacy he gained a thorough insight into every phase of his calling.

Apprenticeship in those days was a strenuous experience. The hours were long and the intervals for recreation few. Henry Deane was a botanist of some distinction and he encouraged young Hanbury, in whom the love of botany was, like other members of the family, inherent, to spend some of his precious spare time botanizing on Clapham Common in company with fellow apprentices. Several good botanical specimens were discovered and found their way into the Herbarium which gained the Silver Medal offered by the Pharmaceutical Society for the best herbarium made in a single year.

Another recreation was walking, and he records that he often walked to St. Alban's, Holborn, in time for Holy Communion, returning for breakfast at Deane's at eight o'clock. After apprenticeship he passed the Minor and Major Examinations of the Pharmaceutical Society, qualifying as a pharmaceutical chemist in 1872.

CHAPTER 11

BETHNAL GREEN FACTORY,
THE BEGINNING

IN April, 1874, part of an old match factory called Letchford's Buildings at Bethnal Green, to the east of London, was secured on lease by Cornelius Hanbury for providing for the growing manufacturing and wholesale work carried on at Plough Court.

Bethnal Green was, in 1874, a district semi-rural in character and very different from what it is to-day. The buildings were flanked with poplars, and a picturesque caretaker's lodge adorned the south-eastern and south-western entrances. The premises are actually situated in Three Colts Lane and entered by a short road from this lane, then called Primrose Street. Not a great distance away is the Bethnal Green Library erected on the site of Bethnal or Bednal House, where, in the garden, Pepys, on June the twenty-sixth 1663, ' saw the greatest quantities of strawberries and good '. Three years later he fled from the Great Fire of London to Bednal House, taking with him his precious Journal.

Letchford's Buildings comprised a number of small factories where the bottling of mineral waters, cane-splitting, the manufacture of disinfectant and the making of matches had been carried on. It was not possible to take over all the buildings required at once ; the leases of some had many years to run. It was not until 1907 that the last one fell in, and Cornelius II was able to secure an overriding lease of the whole of the premises, and gradually the manufacturing and wholesale work was transferred from Plough Court.

Cornelius II appears to have continued to make Plough Court his headquarters so that, almost from the outset, Frederick Janson nursed the new and continuously growing factory at Bethnal

BETHNAL GREEN FACTORY, 1873

BETHNAL GREEN FACTORY, 1900

Green; in 1878 (four years after he was given his partnership) the Firm, its good luck continuing, recruited the services of William Ralph Dodd, a pharmaceutical chemist, who began nearly forty years' service with Allen & Hanburys as a dispensing assistant at Plough Court; he was soon removed to Bethnal Green where his work became invaluable. Born in Montgomeryshire in 1856, he was educated at Nantwich Grammar School and later at University College, Bristol (as it then was), under Sylvanus Thompson. After a somewhat exiguous apprenticeship at Market Drayton he became an assistant in the historic house of Giles and Son of Clifton, Bristol, where he thoroughly learned his job as a pharmacist. After passing the examinations of the Pharmaceutical Society he studied at the City of London Guilds, carrying off many prizes, meanwhile gaining practical pharmaceutical experience in the West End of London. At Bethnal Green he took charge of the manufacturing laboratory where he brought with him George Wessendorff, his assistant at Plough Court.

The work of converting the somewhat scattered buildings at Bethnal Green into the nucleus of a factory had not been easy; during part of the period Cornelius II had taken the opportunity of enjoying for his wife and himself a well-earned holiday on the Continent, but he still kept in close touch with Frederick Janson at Bethnal Green, and the correspondence between father and son reveals some of the problems facing the staff there.

Dodd certainly had a mechanical turn of mind and he must have been of the greatest help to Frederick Janson in adapting old machinery and plant from Plough Court to more modern uses, as well as devising new machinery for new processes.

The work of the mechanical engineer in the eighties of the last century in planning apparatus for use in chemical and pharmaceutical laboratories had then hardly begun, and if illustrations of some of Dodd's plant and machinery, when judged in the light of modern achievement, may have an amateurish or even Heath Robinson appearance, it can be said for it that it did the work required of it with reasonable efficiency, if not perhaps in the quickest time or with the minimum of labour.

Dodd and his crew worked well together, and work in the many laboratories under his control went smoothly. A retired workman recalls his habit of pacing through the departments apparently deep in thought, and wearing in all weathers a straw hat worn well down over his face. Punctually at eleven o'clock he would send out to the nearest public house for a pint of beer, then costing threepence. His method of rewarding those members of his staff, who to his knowledge had worked specially well in routine work or had shown initiative and ingenuity in other ways over a period, was to give each a sovereign or, in special cases, even a five-pound note as a bonus. He extracted this from his pocket and gave it on the spot and not in the wage-packet.

At this point some account of the specialities produced in quantity in the Bethnal Green factory will be given, although these may not all necessarily follow the chronological order attempted in other parts of this story.

WILLIAM RALPH DODD, 1856–1917

CHAPTER 12

EARLY SPECIALITIES

AMONGST the earliest tasks undertaken at Bethnal Green, and which had already occupied the technical staff of Plough Court for a number of years, was the making of refined cod-liver oil. Oil made from the livers of the cod had been used as a household remedy in the fishing villages along the northern European coast-line for hundreds of years ; in Iceland, for instance, a mixture of mutton tallow and fish-liver oil was greatly valued for its health-giving properties. In *Life and Manners of the Icelanders*, published in 1563, there is an account of how such oils were made :

> Having taken them (fish) they plucke out the bones, and lay up their bowels and make Fat or Oyle of them.

Dr. Thomas Percival of Manchester, in *Observations on the Medicinal Uses of the Oleum Jecoris Aselli or Cod Liver Oil* (1789), states that the fishermen of the Western Isles of Scotland had for centuries regarded the oil extracted from fish livers as a valuable remedy for rickets and bone affections. They sometimes rubbed it on the affected limbs and sometimes swallowed it ; both methods are still practised.

We get a glimpse of its use as a remedy for painful conditions of the joints in Woodforde's *Diary of a Country Parson* :

> Mr. Thorne sent Nancy over to-day some Cod Liver Oil about a Quarter of a Pint, for her to make use of about her stiff arm and lame knee—she began it this Evening on her arm only—Pray God ! send Thy blessing upon it for her good.

The first recorded clinical trial of cod-liver oil in England was carried out at the Manchester Infirmary by Dr. Kay and

Dr. Robert Darbey. The accounts of this are set forth in a letter from Darbey to Percival, dated February 12th, 1782 :

> For several years after I came to the infirmary, I observed that many poor patients, who were received into the infirmary for the chronic rheumatism, after several weeks' trial of a variety of remedies, were discharged with little or no relief. . . . About ten years since, an accidental circumstance discovered to us a remedy, which has been used with the greatest success, for the above complaint, but is very little known in any county, except Lancashire ; it is the cod, or ling liver oil.

It is on record that the Manchester Infirmary doctors were so pleased with the results they obtained that no less than fifty or sixty gallons were prescribed annually in spite of the fact that the smell and taste were so repulsive that many patients could not stomach it. It should be noted that in the above instances the success of the oil was due to its internal use.

Dr. John Hughes Bennett (1812–1875), an English medical man of some note, was greatly impressed with the medicinal virtues of cod-liver oil of which he had gained his knowledge during the four years he spent in France and Germany from 1837 to 1841. In 1841 he wrote his *Treatise on Cod Liver Oil as a Therapeutic Agent in Certain Forms of Gout, Rheumatism and Scrofula*, a publication which effectively awakened the medical profession of this country to the value of the new agent.

Another advocate for its use about this time for phthisis was John Thomas Barry's friend, Dr. Theophilus Thompson (1807–1860), physician to the hospital for consumption then in Marlborough Street, London. He declared that he had personally derived more benefit from cod-liver oil than from any other medicine.

One of the earliest objections to the internal use of cod-liver oil was its disgusting taste caused by undue exposure to air in the process of manufacture, and to the presence of putrefactive matter.

Donovan, a well-known Dublin surgeon, appears to have been

the first person in the British Isles to prepare cod-liver oil, although on a laboratory scale only, so as to make it palatable. He did so in 1841. His method was to submit the livers of fresh cod to a heat of 192° Fahrenheit :

> When expressed and filtered the oil thus obtained was entirely free from rancidity—its smell was like that of boiled cod—its taste bland and not disagreeable.

For nearly one hundred and ten years Allen & Hanburys have been interested in producing refined cod-liver oil. In 1845 John Thomas Barry, who appears to have had his interest in the process stimulated by Dr. Theophilus Thompson, gave a quotation to Donovan for cod-liver oil ' of a very pale straw colour ' made by his own process. There seems to be no doubt that Barry was a pioneer in the manufacture of cod-liver oil on a commercial scale in this country, and that the Donovan process, or a modification of it, was used by him before 1845. Soon he was regularly supplying surgeons and hospitals with small lots of a few pounds at a time ; in 1851 ten gallons were shipped to a customer in Melbourne, Australia, at seventeen shillings per gallon ; in the same year the Firm sold ninety-two gallons of what was described as Newfoundland oil to a wholesale firm in the City of London. From then onward oil made at Plough Court, and Newfoundland oil, were increasingly exported. In 1860 Cornelius II sent John Tuttle out to Newfoundland to make cod-liver oil at Quidi Vidia. The venture was short-lived because in 1864 medical opinion pronounced the oil from cod caught in Norwegian waters as superior ; thereupon, early in that year, Allen & Hanburys set up the first British cod-liver oil factory in Norway. Situated at Langved on the island of Scholarn, sixteen miles from Aalesund, it was in charge of Henry Spindler, another of the Plough Court laboratory men. In 1884 a second factory was opened at Kjerstad on Lepso Island, in the Söndmor district. The man chosen to take charge of it was William George Bulley, then head of the cod-liver oil department at Plough Court. In after years he liked to recall that as a youth he entered the wholesale department at Old Plough

Court and, as was the custom, slept under the counter. Eventually Bulley—' George ' to his mates—became head of the oil department at Bethnal Green where he wore something of a halo because from Christmas to Easter he was away in Norway. In 1894 a third factory was opened at Kabelvaag on the Lofoten Islands ; in 1897 this was replaced by a fourth at Henningsvar, also in the Lofotens ; the latter continued to operate until 1952.

It is interesting to note that the Norwegian factories of Allen & Hanburys were amongst those visited in 1921 by a Commission sent out by the Medical Research Council, when entire satisfaction was expressed with the oils examined and tested, and with the manufacturing processes employed there.

In the 1876 National Exhibition held in Philadelphia the only medal of the British Section was given to Allen & Hanburys for their exhibit of Norwegian and English cod-liver oil. The following year John Fordred was granted a patent for ' Improvements in the Treatment and Purification of Cod-liver Oil '. In 1880 oil made by this process was placed in the hands of medical men in order that they might test its palatability and food-keeping properties.

At that time only uncleared oil was produced, the stearin being retained in the oil, the general belief being that its presence added to the oil's beneficial properties. It was not long, however, before a demand arose for a cod-liver oil that remained clear and bright at all temperatures above freezing-point, and the *British Pharmacopœia* of 1914 required cod-liver oil to be filtered at around that temperature. This process results in the elimination of the solid stearin or fats. The proportion of stearin varies between a figure as low as nine per cent in the case of certain Norwegian oils, up to a maximum of about fifteen per cent from oils obtained further south. The stearin is as rich in vitamins as is the oil itself and its removal is in the interest of the appearance of the oil alone.

In 1908 the Norwegian cod fisheries temporarily failed and Allen & Hanburys adapted themselves to the new conditions. They imported the fish from various North Sea fishing ports, and began to manufacture and refine the crude oil at Bethnal

Green. Before another year they had a factory of their own at Aberdeen, with depots at various spots on the Moray Firth ; in 1910 they added a factory at Hull, with depots along the East Coast, so that on neither shore of the North Sea could the elusive cod escape their net. The Norwegian fisheries soon recovered and in 1914 yet another factory was started at Finmarken.

After the First World War, William Hawes, who was then assisting Bulley in the supervision of the Firm's cod-liver oil activities, went out to Newfoundland and, for the second time, an Allen & Hanburys factory was established there, at Mosquito Cove, Burin, a fishing village with a population of about three thousand persons. This factory was, however, destroyed by a tidal wave in 1927, and the Firm's interests thereupon ceased in Newfoundland, the British factory in Aberdeen and the Norwegian at Henningsvar being jointly capable of satisfying all its needs.

It is fitting that a brief account of the part played by Allen & Hanburys in first making malt extract by the vacuum process should follow that of cod-liver oil, for the two products when mixed form a well-known pharmaceutical preparation which is still extensively used.

Before 1880 malt extract was a very different and much less attractive product than it is to-day. It was made then by mixing crushed malt with water and evaporating the resulting liquid down to a thick treacle-like consistence. If too much heat was employed for the purpose, or the time taken to do the work was prolonged, the malt sugars became charred and the final product was often dark brown or even black, with a burnt taste, very different from the well-known golden-coloured, pleasant-tasting malt extract of to-day.

About 1878 or 1879 John Fordred was making experiments in order to produce a malted food for infants in a more soluble form than that available at the time. The malted foods on the market usually contained either an extract made by evaporation as described, or ground malt which was probably more objectionable still, as it contained a good deal of insoluble matter from the cuticle or superficial skin of the malt grain ; this was apt to produce intestinal irritation when given to young children.

It occurred to Fordred that it might be possible to make malt extract in a vacuum apparatus in which a lower temperature could be used to evaporate the mixture of crushed malt and water. The experiments he made were very successful and in October, 1879, he secured a patent for 'Improvements in the Manufacture of Nutritive Foods and Confectionery' in which a concentrated malt extract was to be used. This concentrated malt extract was to be made in a vacuum pan at a specified temperature and, so far as can be ascertained, Fordred was the first person in this country to make, on a commercial scale, a malt extract by using a vacuum pan.

Although the new malt extract was first used in making a malted farinaceous food it was soon found to be suitable, in fact ideal, for mixing with such products as cod-liver oil, and, in a more liquid form, with a whole range of medicaments producing such preparations as Bynin Amara, one of the Company's oldest products which is still widely used to-day.

Medicated throat jujubes as they were then called date from 1850, when small batches of various kinds were first made at Plough Court.

Jujubes for throat medication had many advantages over the harder lozenges. Made from gum, sugar and water with the medicament and flavouring added, they were soft and had no sharp corners to cut and irritate the mucous membrane of the mouth and throat.

They had disadvantages also. They did not keep too well, became sticky, dull in colour and uninviting, and if, as was sometimes the case, they contained volatile ingredients, these were apt to disappear on keeping.

The art of making the *paté de jujube*, as the sheet mass was called, originated in France and in the early seventies of the last century Cornelius II set up a small factory at Nîmes, which, in 1876, was transferred first to Lewisham in Kent, and then to Bethnal Green. The jujubes were punched out or cut by hand from sheets of the *paté*, but it occurred to the French manager of the factory that it would be a great improvement if they could be moulded separately.

This was done, and the resulting jujube was made of a shape more suitable for use in the mouth. In 1876 Cornelius II used a patented method for coating these jujubes in such a way that they were impervious to moisture and kept their shape and appearance for long periods. A collection of these 'patent jujubes' was shown at the Paris Exhibition of 1878 and the pharmaceutical press of the period recorded that the temperature of the Exhibition in June averaged 92° F. in the shade, and that 'although the jujubes were not specifically protected, their edges did not lose their sharpness nor their surface its brightness, except in a slight degree'.

The word pastille was given to these medicated jujubes by Dr. Prosser James, Lecturer on Materia Media at the London Hospital and physician to the Royal Hospital for disease of the chest and throat. Dr. James read a paper on medicated lozenges at the Cambridge meeting of the British Medical Association in 1880 and Allen & Hanburys exhibited there a collection of their jujubes made to formulæ supplied by Dr. James. The lecturer suggested that in future these medicated jujubes should be called :

> . . . pastils, an old English word more familiar in the French pastilles and derived from the Latin pastillus which was used by Celus for such a purpose ; pastilli will therefore be an appropriate name in prescriptions.

Thus the name pastille, or pastillus, first came into use as indicating the medicated jujubes made by Allen & Hanburys. Other pastilles than the medicated throat varieties were soon being made, including the popular Glycerine and Black Currant Pastilles which before the Second World War were in such demand that the output from the pastille department at Ware averaged about one ton a day.

Frederick Janson Hanbury in 1876 brought from America the first machine the Firm used for making compressed tablets after a visit to the Centennial Exhibition : six or eight more were subsequently added. In 1903 the *Pharmaceutical Journal* stated that Allen & Hanburys themselves made the first continuous rotary machine which was capable of compressing one thousand tablets per minute : many of these machines were afterwards made and supplied to other wholesale firms.

One of Dodd's most significant achievements was the production of an improved form of food for infants known as the Allenburys Milk Foods : these closely resembled mothers' milk when reconstituted and will be referred to at a later stage in this story.

In June, 1884, a long-cherished dream of Cornelius Hanbury became a reality in the opening of a retail branch establishment in the West End of London.

Even in William Allen's time the growing need for office accommodation in the City meant that families who once lived in the many courts and squares adjacent to Plough Court were gradually moving over the river to south-eastern or south-western districts of what is known to-day as Outer London, their menfolk coming up to business daily in coaches or driving their own conveyances. In addition, districts west of the Marble Arch were being developed and many of the wealthier merchants moved from the dingy City to what was virtually then a pleasant suburban locality.

Many of the surgical and medical specialists and consultants who lived in Finsbury Square had, perforce, to follow their patients and they found fresh quarters in the squares between what is now New Oxford Street and the Euston Road and their continuation westward.

Quite early in his career at Plough Court Cornelius II, enthusiastically supported by his cousin Daniel, pressed for the opening of a branch in the West End of London. His father, Cornelius I, and Daniel Bell Hanbury were agreeable, but John Barry was strongly opposed to the suggestion.

The prospect was dropped for the time and it was not until many years after the death of both Barry and Daniel that Cornelius II was able to secure premises at seven Vere Street,

Cavendish Square, London, where a retail pharmacy was established.

In December, 1893, like so many of the old family firms of the period, Allen & Hanburys passed one of the most significant milestones in its long history and became a limited liability company.

BOOK FOUR: REALIZATION

THE MODERN PERIOD

1894–1954

There is always a new horizon for onward-looking men.
R. L. STEVENSON : *El Dorado*.

CHAPTER 1

RETROSPECT

THIS story has now reached the beginning of the twentieth century ; before proceeding further with it a brief review of the conditions of medicine and pharmacy in the second half of the nineteenth century and the first half of the twentieth century will provide a background against which the activities of Allen & Hanburys, particularly during the later period, may be judged.

One hundred years ago medicine and pharmacy had hardly begun to emerge from the empirical stage ; the physician in those days depended for the treatment of disease almost entirely upon vegetable drugs and a few chemicals, mainly inorganic. Although most of the active principles of the vegetable drugs were already known, few of them were used, preparations of the crude drugs being preferred. Many drugs were in use which are now regarded as valueless. Pharmacy was then a comparatively simple calling.

Although bacteria had been seen under the microscope by Leeuwenhoek, a draper whose hobby was the making of microscopes, late in the seventeenth century, their significance in the causation of disease was not appreciated until Pasteur made his famous discoveries after 1860 ; it was not until 1882 that the organism causing tuberculosis was discovered, followed in 1883 by the finding of the cholera vibrio. By the end of the century most of the disease-producing bacteria had been recognized and the science of bacteriology had been fully developed, largely by Koch. The diseases which we now know to be due to viruses such as small-pox, whooping-cough and measles, remained a mystery until comparatively recently.

Although Edward Jenner had introduced his method of vaccination against small-pox in 1798, this was not followed by immunization against other diseases until Pasteur's work on anthrax and rabies in the eighteen-eighties. Diphtheria anti-toxin followed on Von Behring's discovery in 1890, but has only been really effective and generally applied in recent years. Vaccines and antitoxins have since been produced for the treat-ment of prophylaxis of numerous diseases. In many cases, how-ever, these have been superseded by the antibiotics. The latter are chemical substances produced by moulds or bacteria which interfere with the growth of the organisms which cause disease. They thereby assist the human body to overcome infection.

Recognition that certain diseases were due to a deficiency of the diet is entirely a twentieth-century discovery, though the provision of lemon-juice in the Navy for the prevention of scurvy was made in the eighteenth century, and in the eighteen-eighties the incidence of beriberi in the Japanese Navy had been much reduced by changing the diet from polished to unpolished rice.

Between 1906 and 1912 Sir Frederick Gowland Hopkins laid the experimental foundation of our knowledge of the accessory food factors or vitamins, which has revolutionized the science of nutrition, and has almost exterminated in many parts of the world the scourges of rickets, scurvy and beriberi, formerly so prevalent. Many others have built on this foundation. Numer-ous vitamins have now been isolated, including the active principle of liver, vitamin B_{12}. Some are made synthetically in large quantities.

The ductless glands such as the thyroid, pituitary and supra-renals were long a problem to physiologists. It was known that certain recognized conditions such as myxœdema, cretinism, gigantism, diabetes mellitus, Addison's and Grave's disease were due to dysfunction of these glands. Murray in 1891 cured myxœdema by giving dried thyroid gland by mouth. It was later shown that these glands exert specific activities by secreting substances into the blood-stream which are now known as hormones. This discovery was the foundation of much research to isolate the active principles of these glands. Adrenaline was isolated in 1901 and thyroxine in 1914, both these hormones being subsequently synthesized in the laboratory. For many years it was known that diabetes mellitus was caused by the absence of a secretion from the pancreas. In fact, the active principle was named insulin by Schafer long before it was isolated by Banting and Best at the University of Toronto in 1922. In the early days the dried glands or extracts of the glands were given by the mouth until it was realized that some of the active principles such as insulin were destroyed by the process of digestion and must be administered by injection. The adrenal gland contains a number of different hormones, and preparations of it are used in the treatment of Addison's disease. Similar chemical compounds, having an action similar to the naturally occurring hormones, have been synthesized and are being increasingly widely used.

The amount of disease caused directly by bacteria, viruses and other organisms such as the spirochaete of syphilis, the trypanosomes causing certain tropical diseases and the malarial parasite is still enormous. Ever since Pasteur's time, efforts have been made to find drugs which will destroy these organisms in the body without harmful effects to the tissues. For many years no success was achieved until Ehrlich in 1909 found, after a prolonged search, the drug salvarsan which destroyed the spirochaete of syphilis in the blood. It was twenty-six years before the next real advance came. In 1935 Domagk of Elberfeld showed that a red dye subsequently known as prontosil was of value in the treatment of infections due to streptococci such as erysipelas. Later, it was found that a simpler compound which forms part of the prontosil molecule was equally effective. This compound was known as sulphanilamide and from it has been derived the series of drugs known as 'sulpha' drugs, which are active by mouth against many infections such as pneumonia.

Before this time, the discovery had already been made which was to revolutionize medicine in so many ways, but its importance was not yet apparent. In 1929 Sir Alexander Fleming made his well-known observation of the destruction of certain organisms growing on a culture plate by the growth of an accidental mould, and named the active principle penicillin. Further development did not come until after the beginning of the Second World War when Sir Howard Florey and his team were to prosecute the complex investigation which showed the potentialities of penicillin and resulted in its commercial production on a huge scale for use on war casualties. Penicillin is effective on a limited range of organisms, amongst which might be mentioned streptococci, staphylococci, meningococci and pneumococci. Its discovery had led to an intensive search for other moulds and organisms of all kinds for the production of similar antibiotics. Some of these have proved of great importance, such as streptomycin, which is effective in certain forms of tuberculosis, chloramphenicol, aureomycin, and oxy-tetracyclin which are effective in some conditions where penicillin fails, e.g. chloramphenicol in certain virus diseases.

When we turn to tropical diseases the picture is not quite so encouraging. It is true that effective substitutes for quinine such as mepacrine, chloroquine and paludrine have been used on a large scale for malaria, and newer drugs continue to be introduced from time to time, but the ideal drug for treating malaria has probably yet to be found. It is also true to say that no really satisfactory drug has been found for the diseases caused by trypanosomes, e.g. sleeping sickness.

Although the great operating surgeons of the early nineteenth century were extremely dexterous their activities were confined to parts of the body which were easily accessible.

The introduction of general anaesthesia and the growth of the antiseptic method of Lister removed such limitations. It was in 1847 that Sir James Young Simpson introduced chloroform for women in labour and for many years ether and chloroform were widely used for this purpose. Joseph Lister (later Baron Lister) grasped the importance of Pasteur's discoveries in relation to fermentation, appreciated that suppuration was due to organized living bodies, believed they were introduced to the wound from the air, and experimented with carbolic acid as an antiseptic (1865). In 1867 he published a paper which established his antiseptic method. By this paper he revolutionized surgery. Lister did a vast amount of work on wound dressings and on materials suitable for ligatures.

In 1851 Helmholtz invented the ophthalmoscope for studying the retina of the living eye and so put into the hands of the general physician a new method of discovering diseases affecting other parts of the body. In 1855 the laryngoscope was invented. In the middle of the nineteenth century a microscopic examination of the blood-cells became a routine in certain cases. In 1852 the haemocytometer was invented for estimating the actual numbers of the cells of the blood, and in 1878 Sir William Gowers devised the haemoglobinometer which, with some modifications, is in use to-day.

In 1895 Wilhelm Conrad Röntgen discovered a new type of ray which would penetrate opaque bodies and radiology was born. Using bismuth, afterwards barium, as a meal the diagnosis of gastric ulcer and cancer was possible. In 1922 lipiodol was used to outline the bronchial tree ; this method is now important in the diagnosis of certain lung conditions. From radiology it was but a step to radiotherapy and radium therapy, the use of radium needles for cancer, the radium bomb, and the employment of very high X-ray voltages for deep X-ray therapy.

Before ending this chapter it should be pointed out that some of the success of modern surgery is due to the latest anaesthetics and to the care of the patient before and after operation. Preparation of the patient for operation is now a highly complex matter, involving not only anaesthesia and sedation but the use of drugs which relax the muscles as well. To obtain this relaxation, anaesthetists used to give excessive doses of anaesthetics, but in 1942 in Canada, H. R. Griffith and G. E. Johnson introduced for this purpose an extract of the South American arrow poison, curare. This technique gave better operating conditions for the surgeon, with less danger to the patient from the hazards of both the anaesthetic and the knife. Curare has since been replaced by the pure alkaloid, tubocurarine, which, in 1935, Harold King of the National Institute for Medical Research had isolated from a specimen of the poison. More recently several synthetic relaxants have been introduced, among which are compounds that act in the body for a much shorter time than does tubocurarine. The research laboratories of Allen & Hanburys have been prominently associated with this work. These compounds of brief duration of action, of which succinyl-choline is the most important, have enabled the technique of muscle relaxation to be still more widely applied in anaesthesia.

CHAPTER 2

BIOGRAPHICAL

THIS section of the story is biographical, and occasionally, autobiographical. It is devoted to brief accounts of the activities of the Directors during the sixty years which passed between the formation of the Company in 1893 and the year in which this story was finished, 1954.

In the year 1896, forty-five years after he had entered the Old Plough Court Pharmacy, Cornelius Hanbury II was presented with his portrait [1] subscribed for by members of the Staff at home and abroad. This was painted by Percy Bigland who, three years earlier, had painted Elizabeth Hanbury, [1] the mother of Cornelius, who had recently celebrated her one-hundredth birthday. It added very considerably to the interest of the presentation when the portraits of both mother and son were exhibited together.

Cornelius, when thanking the Staff for their gift, paid a generous tribute to the work of his predecessors in building up the Firm ; incidentally he gave his hearers some idea of the strenuous part he himself had played in some of this work when he said that from the retirement of his cousin Daniel in 1870 until his son Frederick came into the business in 1875, he had never been away from his office for more than three consecutive days at a time.

In 1900 the health of Mrs. Cornelius Hanbury was failing and the following two-and-a-half years were spent by her and Cornelius in foreign travel for the sake of her health and partly for his own. In the meantime Cornelius had given up Dynevor House, Richmond, and had been occupied in looking for a suitable house within easy reach of London, but in the country.

After inspecting some nineteen likely places he eventually

[1] See illustrations facing pp. 150 and 154.

bought the Manor House, Little Berkhampstead, near Hertford, and while the house was being got ready, he and his wife lived with relatives in the neighbourhood. She died in April, 1903, and soon after Cornelius moved into his new house, being joined there by his three unmarried daughters, Charlotte, Eleanor and Edith, whose loving care somewhat mitigated his loneliness.

About this time he wrote in his manuscript *Recollections* :

> I could happily leave business matters in the hands of my co-directors, who are my son, his two sons, and our valued friend, W. R. Dodd, under whose direction the business has been greatly developed in accordance with my earlier desires.

For some time he went up to business three or four times weekly, but two years before his death Cornelius wrote :

> I have greatly enjoyed the quiet life here and am now entirely unfit for action, sight, hearing, and memory for recent things having greatly failed.
>
> This is scarcely surprising as I have now entered my eighty-seventh year, but still enjoy boundless causes for thankfulness in my daily life and bright hopes beyond.

Cornelius Hanbury II died on the eleventh of April, 1916, in his eighty-ninth year.

*   *   *

In the year 1915 during the First World War, the Bicentenary of the founding of the Old Plough Court Pharmacy was cele-brated by a presentation to Frederick Janson Hanbury of his portrait, painted by Percy Bigland.[1] Hanbury had been in the business, either as partner or director, for forty-three years : in 1912 he had been made Vice-Chairman of the Company, as his father's great age made a substitute in the Chair necessary. The story has already been told of his hard work at Bethnal Green in the early years of the Factory there, and in later years with William Ralph Dodd.

But if the time he spent in business was fully occupied, his

[1] See illustration opposite.

FREDERICK JANSON HANBURY, 1851–1938

REGINALD JANSON HANBURY, 1877–1935

FREDERIC WILLIAM GAMBLE, 1872–1948

JOHN NETHERWAY, 1871–1951

holidays were equally strenuous, occupied as they were with the pursuit of two of his favourite subjects, botany and entomology.

With his friend, Henry Trimen, F.R.S., one of the grooms-men at his wedding, Hanbury had, quite early in his career, taken a botanical journey through northern Europe, finally reaching St. Petersburg and Moscow. Trimen, a botanist of repute, the author of a handbook to the flora of Ceylon and the flora of Middlesex, probably persuaded Hanbury to accumulate material for the flora of Kent, which he completed with the help of the late Rev. E. S. Marshall. When preparing this he met Charles Darwin, then living at Downe, in Kent, who was interested in the plants found in the neighbourhood.

Hanbury edited the eighth, ninth, tenth and eleventh editions of the *London Catalogue of British Plants* and published a list of the British *Hieracia* (hawkweeds), the material for which came from collections he had made on frequent visits to Caithness, Sutherland, the Orkney and Shetland Islands, as well as in the mountain regions of Aberdeenshire, Forfar, Cumberland, Wales and Ireland. On these occasions he became acquainted, amongst many others, with Lord Avebury, Sir Mountstewart Grant-Duff, Lord de Tabley and Sir John Hooker.

In March, 1938, the Company sustained a great loss when Frederick Janson Hanbury died at the age of eighty-six years.

Like his father, Cornelius Hanbury, he had retired from the active direction of the Company before his death, his third son, Frederick Capel Hanbury, taking his place as Chairman of the Board. He was described in an obituary notice in *The Times* as 'gardener and botanist', these two descriptions aptly summed up the two chief hobbies of his life. His early love for botany and his rambles on Clapham and Wandsworth Commons in search of specimens to add to his herbarium have already been mentioned.

This herbarium was later greatly enlarged by the addition of the fine herbarium of his friend, Dr. Boswell Syme, which he purchased after Syme's death. The whole collection was eventually presented to the Botanical Department of the Natural History Museum at South Kensington.

His garden at Brockhurst, East Grinstead, Sussex, was, amongst other features, notable for the rock garden which was excavated from the natural sandstone, native to the place and not made from imported rock and stone.

He also specialized in growing orchids, for which he won many prizes ; and he was an authority on native British plants. He was a Fellow of the Royal Entomological Society and of the Linnean Society and held the Victoria Medal of Honour of the Royal Horticultural Society.

He was a staunch Churchman and had been a churchwarden of St. Edmund the King and Martyr in the City of London for fifty-six years, and he had held office in many other Church of England Councils and Assemblies.

He took a great interest in the revival of plain-song and had been on the Committee of the London Gregorian Association.

His first wife died in 1927, and he was survived by his second wife whom he married in 1930. She died in 1939.

He had three daughters and three sons, two of whom became Directors of the Company, Reginald Janson Hanbury and Frederick Capel Hanbury. The former died in 1935 (see page 206). Frederick Capel Hanbury is the present Chairman of the Board of Directors.

*   *   *

At the Bicentenary Celebration in 1915 a presentation was also made to William Ralph Dodd ; this took the form of a silver centrepiece and a cabinet of silver. Frederic William Gamble, the Chairman of the Meeting, spoke of the many services Dodd had rendered to the Company and summarized the feelings of those present when he said :

> When swords are again beaten into ploughshares shall not the ' Plough ' [1] go forward, itself purged with the fire, out of which we look to see truth, justice, and honesty again emerge triumphant.

On December 4th, 1917, the Company sustained a severe loss in the death of Mr. Dodd, who died of typhoid fever after a short illness.

[1] The plough is a trade-mark of the Firm.

His loss was deeply felt by his colleagues, particularly those in the manufacturing departments of the Firm—he had a flair for devising machinery and plant for the many operations required in the expanding business ; several patents under his name are to be found in the records of the Patent Office.

*　　　*　　　*

In 1913 Frederic William Gamble was elected a Director of the Company. He had joined the Staff at the Plough Court Pharmacy in 1895, but a year later he was transferred to the West End Branch of the Firm in Vere Street, being appointed Manager in 1900.

When Gamble decided to enter pharmacy he appears to have had no special inclination for the calling ; his subsequent career, however, shows him to have been a born pharmacist. He was apprenticed in Kensington, London, and in due course he passed both the examinations of the Pharmaceutical Society, winning in 1894 the Society's coveted Bronze Medal.

He was an active member of the London Chemists' Assistants' Association, being at one time its Secretary and Treasurer. His most important early work for pharmacy was in connection with the original Committee appointed to compile and produce the *British Pharmaceutical Codex* : for four years before the publication of the first edition in 1907 practically all his leisure was devoted to his share of the work.

He early associated himself with the British Pharmaceutical Conference in working on its Committees ; in 1923, when the Diamond Jubilee celebration was held in London, he occupied the chair.

He contributed valuable papers to the evening meetings of the Pharmaceutical Society in collaboration with R. R. Bennett and Norman Evers. He was a member of the Board of Examiners of the Pharmaceutical Society for fourteen years.[1]

[1] Although a very kindly-natured man at heart, he gained the reputation with some candidates of being somewhat snappish and brusque. In after years, when engaging a young pharmacist at Bethnal Green, he usually prefaced the conversation by asking, ' Did I examine you ? ' If the reply was ' No,' good relations between the two were at once established.

Gamble was an enthusiastic worker for the better organization of the drug and chemical industries and in 1930 he was the first Chairman of the Wholesale Drug Trade Association, now the Association of British Pharmaceutical Industry.

Gamble's work at Vere Street is mentioned on page 212, as also his early work for pharmacists in helping to compile the first *British Pharmaceutical Codex* in 1907; he served on the Committees which were appointed to prepare the further editions of 1911 and 1923.

Gamble visited Canada on several occasions and during the autumn and winter of 1925 to 1926 he visited the Branches of Allen & Hanburys, Ltd., in China, Australia and South Africa. At the subsequent 'welcome home' he and Mrs. Gamble were presented by the Staff with a silver salver and other gifts in celebration of their silver wedding.

He may be regarded as a link between the old Victorian period of pharmacy and that of the period following the First World War. To his memory it is fair to say that he was equally at home in both.

He died in September, 1948, at the age of seventy-six. His eldest son, Gilbert Gamble, is a Director of the Company.

*   *   *

In July, 1944, Gamble was succeeded as Managing Director by Cyril Wheatley Maplethorpe, who holds that position at the present time. Maplethorpe was born in 1898 and was educated at Hymers College, Hull. For a period towards the end of the First World War he served in the Royal Engineers Anti-gas Establishment and after the war he entered the School of Pharmacy, Bloomsbury Square, London, where he qualified as a Pharmaceutical Chemist in 1922.[1] He worked in the Research Laboratories and Museum of the Society under Professor H. G. Greenish and Dr. T. E. Wallis. He passed the examination of the Institute of Chemistry in the Foods and

---

[1] Like his predecessor, he was awarded the Society's Bronze Medal and the Silver Medal for practical Chemistry and later received the Ransom Research Fellowship.

FREDERICK CAPEL HANBURY

JOHN CAPEL HANBURY

Drugs Branch, being elected an Associate and later a Fellow of the Institute. He was also elected an Associate Member of the Institution of Chemical Engineers.

In 1924 he joined the staff of Allen & Hanburys as a research chemist, a year later being appointed Head of the Pharmaceutical Production Departments at Bethnal Green. In 1932 he was appointed Manager of the Ware Factory on the death of Harry Radford, and in 1943 was elected to the Board and appointed Managing Director in 1944.

Maplethorpe has also been actively associated with outside pharmaceutical affairs, having been co-opted to the Council of the Pharmaceutical Society in 1943 and subsequently re-elected. He has been Chairman of the Council's Educational Committee, of the British Pharmaceutical Codex Revision Committee and of the Committee which issued the first British Veterinary Codex on January 1st, 1954. He is also a member of the Home Office Poisons Board, the Governing Body of the Chelsea Polytechnic and the Council of the School of Pharmacy of the University of London.

*　　　*　　　*

In 1916 John Netherway, F.C.I.S., Secretary of the Company and its Subsidiaries, was elected a director. A native of Devonshire, he was born in 1871 and joined the Firm in 1894. For six years he filled the post of private secretary to the directors and in 1900 he was appointed Secretary of the Company.

Netherway was a man endowed with great dignity and charm, and most people who knew him well think of him as the embodiment of the quiet, cultured city business man of the old school. His latter years were spent in Chislehurst, where he indulged his love of gardening, and his main interests outside his business activities arose from the possession of an exceptionally fine bass voice. He was a lay reader in the Church of England and many who were there will remember the full beauty of the English language as spoken by him at the memorial service to Frederick Janson Hanbury in 1938. He was one of the early members of the Royal Choral Society and sang regularly at the Society's concerts in the Albert Hall. His fine voice was particularly well suited to the bass solo parts in the Gilbert and Sullivan operas in which he delighted to sing and act.

In 1944 he became Vice-Chairman of the Company, but in 1946 in the face of failing health he was obliged to retire from active participation in its affairs. He died in 1951.

*   *   *

Two of the sons of Frederick Janson Hanbury became Directors of the Company, Reginald Janson, the second son, born in 1877, and the third son, Frederick Capel Hanbury, born in 1879.

Reginald was educated at Marlborough and upon leaving school he followed in the footsteps of his grandfather, Cornelius Hanbury II, by becoming a student at St. Bartholomew's Hospital. He completed his hospital training in 1903 and obtained the diploma of M.R.C.S., L.R.C.P. He was elected a Director of the Company in 1912.

From the beginning of his career he had shown a great interest in the surgical side of the business and this was intensified after his visit in 1905 to the Surgical Congress in Brussels. Like his grandfather, Cornelius Hanbury II, he became a Governor of St. Bartholomew's Hospital and duly served on its Finance and Election Committees. He introduced the operation table, afterwards known as the ' Bart's ' Operation Table, to the Hospital and took the greatest interest in its further development to meet the progressive needs of the surgeons using it.

He was an authority on infant feeding and had written much on the subject.

He died in March, 1935, at the comparatively early age of fifty-seven. He had married in 1914 Eliza Margaret Lycett, of Kirkwood, St. Louis, U.S.A., who survives him, with two sons and one daughter. His eldest son, Raymond, entered the service of the Company in 1947.

He is best remembered for his great interest in all matters pertaining to the personal well-being of the members of the Staff and it was through his influence that a well-equipped

First Aid Room, with a qualified staff, was opened at Bethnal Green.

★   ★   ★

Frederick Capel Hanbury, the third son of Frederick Janson, was born in 1879. He was educated at Marlborough, after which he spent several years as an apprentice in various departments of the Firm, visiting in the winter of 1898 the Cod-liver Oil Factory in the Lofotens where he gained a practical experience of manufacturing cod-liver oil and of the conditions under which the fish were caught.

In 1900 he entered the School of Pharmacy at Bloomsbury Square, London, later becoming a pharmaceutical chemist.

In 1902, with his father, he visited the Company's branch houses in Toronto, Canada, and Niagara Falls, U.S.A., making contact with several of the larger pharmaceutical establishments and becoming familiar with the conditions in which the drug business was carried on in those countries.

He was elected a Director of the Company in 1912.

He took over the control of the manufacturing activities carried on at Bethnal Green, and when these were transferred to Ware he made his headquarters there, guiding the development of the Factory from a number of scattered unrelated buildings into a collection of well-defined units arranged on modern lines. He succeeded his father Frederick Janson Hanbury as Chairman of the Company in 1937.

On Midsummer Day, 1950, he was presented with his portrait painted by the eminent artist, James Gunn,[1] A.R.A. : with it was a volume containing the autographs of two thousand members of the Staff, at home and abroad. These gifts were to mark the fifty-three years of service Mr. Hanbury had given to the Company, of which thirty-eight years had been spent as a Director.

The presentation was made in the Sports Pavilion at Ware by Cyril Wheatley Maplethorpe, the Managing Director of the Company, in the presence of several hundreds of visitors which

[1] Facing page 204.

included the Directors and their wives, members of the Staff, both past and present, and visitors from overseas, including the Managing Director of Allen & Hanburys (Africa) Ltd., Graham Gordon McIntyre.

In accepting the portrait and thanking the donors Mr. Hanbury was in reminiscent mood. He spoke of the long history of the Firm, saying that he was connected by marriage with William Allen, who was, he believed, his great-great-step-grandfather ! He well remembered William Ralph Dodd, who taught him and his brother, Reginald Janson, how to catch rats in the old Ware mill mentioned in the Domesday Book ; in after years, on Dodd's death, he succeeded him as Head of the Manufacturing Department at the Bethnal Green Factory. He paid a generous tribute to William Radford, the first Manager of the Ware Factory and his son who followed him and who died in 1932.

He had been associated in the business with his grandfather, Cornelius Hanbury II, his father Frederick Janson and his brother Reginald Janson, William Ralph Dodd, Frederic William Gamble, and John Netherway who had retired in 1946, but who was present on that occasion ; all these had given outstanding help in building up the Firm to its present status.

In closing his speech Mr. Hanbury said that Allen & Hanburys, whilst remaining faithful to traditional pharmacy, were pursuing an actively expanding programme of research, both in the chemical field and in the field of pharmaceutics.

The occasion was a very happy one and will long be remembered by those who were present. The weather was kind and after the presentation in the Pavilion the Company adjourned to two large marquees erected on the sports ground. If there was one regret, it was that owing to catering and other restrictions it was not possible to invite a greater number of visitors.

★   ★   ★

The fifth generation of the Hanbury family is represented on the Board at the present time by F. C. Hanbury's eldest son, John Capel Hanbury, M.A., B.Pharm., F.P.S., F.R.I.C. J. C. Hanbury was born in 1908 and was educated at Downside

CYRIL WHEATLEY MAPLETHORPE

School, Trinity College Cambridge, University College London, and the School of Pharmacy, Bloomsbury Square, London. He joined the Company in 1932 and worked in the Pharmaceutical Production Departments at Bethnal Green until their destruction by bombing in 1940. He was actively concerned in the re-establishment at Ware of these interrupted production activities and the transfer and expansion of the Company's research laboratories.

In 1944 he was appointed to the Board and is at present Vice-Chairman and Technical Director. In that capacity he has been responsible for a marked expansion of chemical research activities, for the establishment of the Pharmacological Department and for an extension of research in the field of pharmaceutics.

He has been actively associated with outside pharmaceutical affairs, being a member of Council of the Association of British Chemical Manufacturers and of the Association of British Pharmaceutical Industry, of which body he was President from 1950 to 1952. In 1948 he was appointed a member of the British Pharmacopœia Commission which prepared the *British Pharmacopœia* of 1953, and he was reappointed to the present Commission which is working on the *Pharmacopœia* due for publication in 1958. With the introduction of the National Health Service in 1948 Mr. Hanbury was appointed to serve on the Standing Pharmaceutical Advisory Committee, from which body he was nominated as a member of the Joint Medical and Pharmaceutical Committee on Prescribing. He has also been actively concerned in the establishment of the Franco-British Pharmaceutical Commission, a body associated with the Cultural Convention between France and Great Britain.

Brief biographies of the other present directors are to be found in Appendix Thirty.

CHAPTER 3

EXPANSION

Victorian prosperity and Victorian civilization alike in their grosser
and their higher aspects were due to a century's immunity from great
wars and from any serious national danger.

Safe behind the shield of the Navy, Englishmen thought of all the
problems of life in terms of peace and security which were in fact the
outcome of temporary and local circumstances, and not part of Nature's
universal order.

G. M. TREVELYAN in *English Social History*.

SURGEONS' instruments have been supplied to hospitals
and surgeons from the time of Silvanus Bevan ; in Appendix Thirty-one will be found a copy of an order for such
articles dated 1794 from Williams and Robinson, New London,
Newfoundland.

In William Allen's time orders for instruments, mostly from
customers overseas, were frequent. In 1812 he wrote to a buyer,
who apparently had ordered some cheap lancets, to the effect
that quality instruments had been sent, although they were
perhaps dearer than those obtained from Sheffield or Birmingham.

Cornelius Hanbury II, as a surgeon, took a great interest in
the development of the surgical instrument business, although
it was not until the early eighties that he installed a small workshop and forge at Bethnal Green for the fashioning of instruments
of a simple type.

More space for the work was soon needed and this was found
in Wesley Street in the West End of London ; in 1904 this
factory became too cramped and a larger one was built along the
north-east side of the Bethnal Green premises. In October, 1906,
a fire partially destroyed this building ; it was eventually re-
erected with the addition of an extra floor.

The bombing of this old building in 1940, including the

THE SURGICAL FACTORY, 1954
Manufacture of Surgical Instruments

THE SURGICAL FACTORY, 1954

forges, afforded an opportunity for building a new forge shop, which to-day affords excellent accommodation for the work of fashioning instruments of which several thousands of patterns are kept. As a result of the bombing more land was obtainable on the east side of the old property and upon this a new building has been erected consisting of a basement and four floors. In spite of the fact that the area of the Bethnal Green Factory used for the manufacture of surgical equipment is now three times what it was before the Second World War, a considerable floor space is in use at Ware for the manufacture of tubular steel furniture, as well as a polishing shop where stainless steel instruments and some stainless steel furniture are polished.

Hitherto only instruments made by forging and subsequent annealing and polishing have been mentioned, but about 1914 the manufacture of operation tables was begun at Bethnal Green, a few years later a model embodying several new features being produced with the help and co-operation of Sir Holburt Waring of St. Bartholomew's Hospital. The design for this table, familiarly known as the ' Bart's ' table, has been constantly perfected, and to-day there are many modifications of the original design available to hospitals and similar institutions in all parts of the world ; eighty per cent of the total output of these tables is for overseas.' Other work carried on in the surgical factory includes the production of autoclaves for the sterilization of dressings, and the fabrication of stainless steel water and instrument sterilizers.

As far back as 1894 it was realized, as it was with Vere Street ten years before, that it was essential to keep in close touch with the surgical specialists, who, like their medical brethren, had moved West, and a large recently built house at 48 Wigmore Street was taken and fitted up as showrooms, and workshops for dealing with the increasing number of special orders for all kinds of surgical appliances, which in many cases had to be fitted to the patient : this could be more conveniently done at Wigmore Street than at Bethnal Green. Here are large and comprehensive stocks of surgical instruments and appliances, as well as displays of aseptic hospital furniture, and the ' Bart's ' operating tables, departments for the preparation and sterilization of ligatures, fitting rooms for patients needing elastic hosiery, deformity apparatus and other special appliances, many of which are made on the premises.

Members of the Staff at Wigmore Street are frequently consulted by surgeons who have ideas for the making of some special instrument to their own particular design ; such collaboration often results in the production of a new type of instrument or the improvement of an old one.

*   *   *

The Branch of Allen & Hanburys at Vere Street next claims our attention for since Frederic William Gamble was appointed Manager there in 1900, it has been regarded as one of the centres of modern pharmaceutical progress in the West End of London. Gamble had a genius for friendly relations with the medical consultants of the neighbourhood and many a pharmaceutical product which eventually became a well-known speciality of the Firm owes its beginning to chats between Gamble and some well-known physician or surgeon.

Chrismol, a refined liquid paraffin, was one of these ; Sauerin, a pure active culture of the Metchnikoff Bulgarian bacillus for making soured milk, was another ; a liquid preparation of the thyroid gland was prepared at the suggestion of the late Sir Victor Horsley and for a time had a considerable vogue, until superseded by other methods of administration.

Gamble was one of the first to develop in West End pharmacy the hypodermic injection method of presenting drugs. Large numbers of ampoules of these injections were prepared from a wide range of drugs, many of which had before that time been given by the mouth only.

The growth of this department of the business was rapid, and the work soon became too big for the somewhat restricted premises at Vere Street. When insulin was introduced in 1923, the filling and sealing of ampoules and vials was soon transferred to a new department at Bethnal Green and, after the Second World War, to Ware.

THE INTERIOR OF THE VERE STREET PHARMACY, 1954

INTERIOR OF 18 WIGMORE STREET 1904

In 1913 Gamble was appointed a Director of the Company and in 1917 left Vere Street for Bethnal Green. He had made Vere Street a valuable link between the medical profession, including hospitals, and the research and manufacturing sections of the Firm at Bethnal Green and Ware.

In recent years Vere Street has become a convenient depot for the Firm's products where urgent supplies of medical requisites can be obtained in the West End of London on Sundays and Bank Holidays, day or night. Also being close to the London termini of the different railway systems, orders by telephone or telegram can be placed on rail within a very short time of their receipt.

As an inquiry office also it enjoys considerable popularity with chemists and members of the medical profession outside the London area and further afield, because of the readiness and ability of the Staff to give information upon subjects not always obtainable elsewhere.

*   *   *

In the 1890's it was becoming evident that the resources of the factory at Bethnal Green were insufficient for the strain imposed upon them by the many manufacturing processes carried on there. What was wanted was a site for a new factory in suitable and healthful surroundings with ample room for expansion and for the laying down of modern manufacturing plant.

In the autumn of 1898, Dodd, in an endeavour to locate a site for a factory, and being an ardent fisherman, followed the footsteps of Izaak Walton and took a fishing holiday along the banks of the pleasant River Lea, or Lee as it is sometimes called, and at last found what he wanted at the little malting town of Ware in Hertfordshire, celebrated topically for its mention in the well-known ballad of John Gilpin [1] and for the Great Bed of Ware.[2]

The site chosen was that occupied by the old corn mills, mentioned in the Domesday Book survey, situated to the west

[1] By William Cowper, 1731–1800.
[2] The Great Bed of Ware, now in the Victoria and Albert Museum. It now measures ten feet nine inches in length and breadth, and seven feet six and a half inches in height.

of the town and close to the track of the old Roman road, Ermine Street, where it crossed the Lea Valley. That part of the factory erected on the site of the corn mills stands in a river meadow, described in old maps as Mill Mead, on an arm of the Lea and close to Ware Lock.

The head of the New River, the artificial water-way, dating from 1609, which to-day ends in the reservoirs of the Metropolitan Water Board at Stoke Newington, North London, is about half a mile upstream. The New River draws its water partly from wells in the neighbouring parish of Great Amwell and from a spring in the Chadwell Meadow in the Parish of Ware, and partly from the Lea itself. The New River Company owned the mills, and from this Company Allen & Hanburys secured a lease of them and the meadow, in all about five acres.

The River Lea has always been of importance in the history of the town as the chief means of communication between the eastern side of Hertfordshire and London, distant some twenty miles or so.

Indeed, in 1665 at the time of the Great Plague, Ware River and Ware Bargees made a name for themselves in history —they continued carrying corn to London all through the period of that dread scourge, helping very largely to save the City from starvation. For this gallant service Charles II granted certain privileges to Ware to be enjoyed for all time.

From this time onwards Ware barges have been entitled to enter the Thames without taking the services of a Lighterman, and Ware bargees, on their return home from a 'voyage', may demand refreshment at an inn at any hour.
(From *The History of Ware*, by Edith Hunt.)

The illustration facing page 215 portrays the Factory as it was in 1950 : it did not, of course, come into existence at once ; indeed, at first, part of the old mill was made to serve the new purposes. The Staff then consisted of six persons, and the manufactured goods could be carried to Bethnal Green in a one-horse van ; now the employees number more than nine hundred, and a fleet of motor vans and trailers has

WARE MILLS, 1895

replaced the van. As soon as there was time and opportunity to consider the needs of the work, the building of the new factory was begun. The Food buildings were the first addition to be made ; then the old mill [1] was pulled down and the lofty Malt buildings erected on its site, west of and across the mill-tail, and the manufacture of malt extract was transferred from Bethnal Green and carried on here.

In 1898 a freehold of eleven acres of meadow known as Buryfield was acquired, facing the mills on the opposite side of the stream and of Priory Street, the road that runs alongside it here and divides the factory ; and on its frontage a large building was erected. Behind it, on the first two hundred feet or so in depth, ground-floor workrooms were erected at the same time and the power station was installed. The manufacture of foods and malted specialities was now transferred to Ware, and in 1900 the Pastilles and Capsules Departments followed. From 1900 to 1910 the growth of the various manufactures and the need for such plant as engineering and wood-working shops, with timber yards, saw mills, etc., caused almost constant building. In the latter year the Buryfield front building was doubled by an extension.

A good idea of the disposition of the various departments just before the Second World War may be gained by the reader if reference is made to the aerial photograph of the factory and its immediate surroundings facing this page. In the foreground can be seen the extensive milk food factory with the malt department occupying almost the exact centre of the picture ; the river is clearly seen flowing beneath part of it.

The line of buildings stretching away towards the Sports Field house pastille manufacture, drying and packing processes, the manufacture of lozenges and granules, crude drug storage, galenical manufacture and the storage of finished galenicals.

In the centre of the picture can be seen a chimney corresponding to one boiler house, adjacent to which is the main power station, where electricity is generated by Diesel engines and also taken in from the high-voltage public supply.

[1] Illustration facing page 214.

There is no need to describe in further detail the Ware Factory of twenty years ago. Later in the story the modern factory will be considered, so different in many ways from its older prototype.

★ ★ ★

The First World War, 1914–1918, brought finally to an end the Victorian era and ushered in a period of strife and uncertainty in national affairs affecting countries, communities, business houses and individuals alike.

During the first months of the war the Company had to overcome many difficulties ; loss of staff both at home and abroad due to the requirements of the fighting Services ; a growing shortage of raw materials ; and a partial switch-over to manufacturing goods of direct importance to the national effort.

On the night of Whit Sunday, May 28th, 1918, in the last air attack on London, thirty-four Gothas, each carrying a load of bombs of some eight hundred pounds in weight, attacked London : seven of these planes were destroyed by the Royal Air Force.

One of them, however, dropped two two-hundred-pound bombs on the south-western part of the factory at Bethnal Green, causing very considerable damage, although fortunately no lives were lost. On the afternoon of Whit Monday a visit was paid to the neighbourhood by the late King George V and Queen Mary, who at some personal risk to themselves inspected the smouldering ruins, and afterwards visited houses close by which had also suffered from the explosion of the two bombs and of another dropped in Corfield Street nearby. A good idea of the damage done to the buildings can be obtained if the reproduction of the drawing of the Factory as it was just prior to 1918 is studied (see illustration facing page 179). The two- and three-storey buildings in the foreground, housing the drug department, were so badly damaged that they were pulled down. The square building in the centre with ' Allen & Hanburys ' along the top, in which lozenges were made, as also the two-storeyed building on the right of it, in which were the offices of the

Directors and behind them the Analytical Laboratory, were wrecked : the bridge shown, which connected the Directors' rooms with the Advertising Department, had to be removed.

The first task facing the Directors was to provide accommodation for the drug department which had suffered so badly ; this had to be found in those departments remaining, which were accordingly rearranged. Premises in Hague Street close by were obtained for the Analytical Department ; and the manufacture of lozenges which was by then assuming big proportions, was transferred to Ware.

Although the time was very inopportune, plans were rapidly pushed forward for buildings to replace those actually destroyed or rendered unsafe, and the troublesome and dangerous task of clearing the site was begun. There were many difficulties to surmount and problems to solve. For one thing suitable labour was not easy to obtain as official priority was not readily granted, in spite of the Government's recognition of the importance of the work carried out by Allen & Hanburys. The large amount of material required for the erection of such an extensive and permanent building as had been planned was also a formidable obstacle. Had the architect been allowed a free hand, a steel-framed building encased in cement and brickwork would have been chosen : this, however, was out of the question on account of the large amount of steel required. Eventually permission was obtained to begin rebuilding, using external brick walls, reinforced concrete internal piers and floors, and a reinforced concrete ' northern-light ' roof.

This work necessarily took some time, and it was not till the end of 1922 that the new building was structurally finished. The final housing of the different departments which, during the interim period, had been moved from one floor to another as the work progressed, was then completed.

*　　　*　　　*

The years following immediately after 1918 were difficult ones for many classes of industry : manufacturing pharmacy was certainly no exception. Although the dislocation of business generally, due to the withdrawal of man-power and the shortage of plant and materials, was not so serious and far-reaching as that experienced directly after the Second World War, 1939–1945, in the case of Allen & Hanburys it was further complicated by the loss of valuable stocks through the partial destruction of the Factory, as well as by the delay and disturbance caused by its rebuilding : these were serious handicaps towards recovery.

But more than recovery was contemplated. Reconstruction was in the air. Better manufacturing methods and control, new classes of products, as well as outlets for their distribution, both at home and abroad, modern methods of costing and marketing, an improved motor transport system, office reorganization ; these were visualized by the Directors and to their development and perfection they devoted much of their time during this period.

New methods required new men, and one of the most noticeable results of the new outlook was the change in the type of personnel engaged as heads of departments and for other positions of responsibility. Many of the older men were getting towards, or had reached, retiring age. They had grown up from boyhood in the employment of the Company and they had given to it faithful and loyal service. For the most part, however, they had little technical or pharmaceutical training and this was becoming increasingly essential to meet the needs of the wholesale druggist. Legislation was requiring that pharmacists should be in charge of the manufacturing and other departments of such a business : the Dangerous Drugs Act of 1923 which affected the manufacturing, wholesale and retail sides of pharmacy alike, necessitated the employment of trained and qualified men for carrying out many of its exacting provisions.

Pharmacists also were appointed to replace the senior unqualified representatives (as these died or retired) ; for the old type of top-hatted, frock-coated ' traveller ' was becoming obsolete. His method of conveyance had been the railway or horse-drawn vehicle and he did not take too kindly to the motor-car. His progress had been slow and he could not easily call on customers off the beaten track. The type of articles carried was also changing, so that a technical knowledge of the products became necessary. This was particularly the case with representatives who called on members of the medical profession and hospitals, where not only knowledge of drugs was required, but of surgical instruments, hospital furniture and equipment as well.

The space devoted to the General Offices on the top floor of the new building enabled the Directors to provide more comfortable working conditions for the office staff and, among other changes, to install newer methods for carrying out work relating to ledger posting and invoicing, some of which hitherto had been done by hand : machines for this purpose had recently been invented for handling the routine of large-scale office work.

The relatively slow and cumbrous system of book-keeping by hand and all that it implied had served its purpose. It was a relic of the long, leisurely Victorian days, sometimes prolonged into nights when the partners themselves posted the ledgers, eventually retiring to rest in the small hours : even in sleep their dreams were liable to be disturbed by an elusive shilling which persistently refused to reveal itself and so enable the accounts to be balanced.[1]

The Quakers were renowned for their book-keeping. William Allen at his school at Rochester, although his classical education there was inconsiderable, was well grounded in the Italian method of book-keeping, which was synonymous with double entry : for instance, the books kept by him personally in which he recorded the accounts of the 'Lindfield Experiment' are still preserved : they bear testimony to his meticulous accuracy and care. Both Cornelius Hanburys in their turn spent a great part of their time in the counting-house.

The mechanization of parts of the new office resulted in the increased use of women in working the ledger posting, adding

---

[1] This actually happened. In a letter of Cornelius Hanbury I to William Allen he bewails the fact that he is a shilling short on the yearly balance and he proposes to go over the figures again.

and order typing machines, and the release of men who had served as ledger clerks ; these were transferred to positions where their experience was of greater service to the Firm.

★   ★   ★

The impact of the Second World War, 1939–1945, upon the business of Allen & Hanburys, whether manufacturing or distributive, was much greater than was the case during the First World War, 1914–1918, but before hostilities began anticipatory arrangements had been perfected so that the supply of certain essential drugs and chemicals to medical men, the hospitals, the Forces, and the civilian population would be safeguarded.

Soon after war was declared certain Statutory Rules and Orders were issued by the Government, which ordained, *inter alia*, that rigid economy was to be exercised in the use of certain scarce drugs, and that many drugs in good supply were to be substituted for others in short supply. The Vegetable Drugs' Committee was also formed for Great Britain and Northern Ireland to carry out, by voluntary effort, the collection locally of many drugs and vegetable substances which, although native to Great Britain, had been imported from Europe and other parts of the world, such as belladonna, digitalis, colchicum, taraxacum, male fern and others.

The diversion to the Forces of members of the staffs of both the Bethnal Green and Ware Factories ; the implications of the Civil Defence Act of April 1939, which made it the duty of the employer to lay down an Air Raid Precaution Scheme and to train personnel for fire fighting, wardens' duties, first aid, decontamination and the like, and, during the autumn of 1940, the increasing frequency of air raids on London and the Home Counties by day as well as by night, all meant loss of time and great difficulty in carrying on the work of both the Bethnal Green and Ware Factories.

On a night in August 1940, three incendiary bombs fell on the roof of the Sundries Department of the Bethnal Green Factory. The resulting small fires were quickly dealt with ; the damage was slight.

The second 'incident', as such were called, on the night of Friday, September 20th, 1940, was a very different matter.

A brilliant moon was shining in a clear sky as the wailing sirens sounded their usual 'alert', telling the citizens of London that enemy aircraft were coming.

Far up on the Factory tower at Bethnal Green the 'spotters' were keeping their nightly vigil. They had already heard the noise of bombing away to the south : it was not until the early hours of the Saturday morning that they reported enemy aircraft approaching in the direction of the Factory : the beams of the searchlights eventually picked up an aeroplane to the north-east.

The firemen on duty were commenting on the absence of any gunfire when the sprinkler alarm bell rang. A brilliant blinding blue flash of light followed immediately to the accompaniment of what those who heard it described as a 'ripping, tearing explosion' caused, as was afterwards found, by a 'D' type of bomb holding about a ton of high explosive striking the roof of the laboratory. These bombs were in the form of a cylinder suspended from a parachute so that they came down comparatively slowly and the whole force of the explosion was expended sideways rather than on making a crater in the ground. Other eye-witnesses actually watched the parachute coming down and a second before the explosion saw a portion of the wall of the printing department fall into the yard as the bomb passed through it diagonally. It was this that had set the alarm bell ringing, although the bomb did not actually explode until it struck the roof of the stockroom a second later.

That night there were about eighty women and children from the small houses in the neighbourhood, sheltering in the basement of the central building, and the first thought of those on duty, firemen, members of the Home Guard, and other services, was for their safety.

A fierce fire, fed by highly inflammable material, was already raging in the nearby manufacturing laboratory : the six-inch sprinkler water mains, severed by the explosion, were discharging huge quantities of water : the refrigerator in the basement had received such a jar that choking ammonia fumes were escaping.

As quickly as possible the occupants of the basement shelters were shepherded to safer quarters. The fire, however, was so close that it was necessary to direct a curtain of water from a hose in such a way as to give them some protection as they left the building.

After the explosive bomb came the incendiaries, for a further attack was made by the same or another aeroplane which dropped a shower of these astride the factory. Some fell on the central building and the printing section of the east block and started further fires.

The Fire Brigade were quickly on the scene, bringing into action a number of trailer-pumps, two-wheeled vehicles then drawn behind London taxis, housing a fire pump driven by a petrol engine and capable of supplying several hoses at the normal working pressure.

In about two hours the fierce blaze had been quelled ; sporadic outbursts continued, however, for two days and kept the firemen busy.

A trick of the German pilots was to return to the scene when the fire-fighting and rescue services were nicely down to their jobs. Sure enough, about four hours afterwards one of them returned and dropped a 'stick' of bombs across the factory. The ragged rain clouds which then overcast the sky and which allowed him to approach without the sirens sounding, interfered with his aim and the bombs landed outside the factory a hundred yards or so away, killing and wounding several people.

It was very fortunate that no lives were lost through the actual bombing of the factory. One of the Firm's firemen was blown over the area railing of the east block. His condition was at first thought to be grave ; he was eventually found to have sustained injuries which necessitated a few days in a local hospital, but it was twelve months before he was able to return to work. The fire brigade officer and another fireman, who were partially buried by debris through the explosion, were not seriously injured, and both were at work again after a few days' rest.

Where everyone showed great courage in the face of terrifying conditions, it might be regarded as invidious to single out any

BETHNAL GREEN FACTORY AFTER THE BOMBING, 1940

special member of the staff on duty that night, but the conduct of the fire brigade officer, in his devotion to duty, his disregard of personal danger and his own injuries and the cool-headed manner in which he handled the situation was worthy of all praise and gained for him an official ' Mention '.

*   *   *

When the staff returned to work on the Monday morning following the bombing they saw the north end of the spacious yard filled to a height of fifteen to twenty feet with twisted girders and wrecked machinery and plant resting on and partly embedded in great heaps of rubble formed partly from the thousands of bottles and containers from the stock room and other departments affected by blast.

The night's work resulted in the total loss of the manufacturing laboratory, which included the pill and tablet sections with plant and machinery, the rail despatch section and the Ware goods' stock room with their large stocks, and the filing department with its many thousands of customers' records. The northern portion of the east block, housing the printing department, was gutted and demolished ; the southern portion used by the advertising department was not habitable and the other departments had lost their roof lights.

The damage to the central building by fire, blast and water was considerable. All floors suffered, the upper ones most. The contents of the central stock room were badly damaged by blast and the offices of the Directors and of the Sales and Costing Departments were wrecked.

The packed drug and insulin departments on the floor above were totally destroyed, as fire following blast had swept right through, burning everything in its track.

On the top floor of the building an incendiary bomb, falling through the northern lights, had landed directly in the library of the Analytical and Research Departments and the valuable collection of scientific works, the result of twenty-five years of careful selection, was completely destroyed, as well as valuable apparatus used in the laboratories.

The damage to the General Office on this floor was also very heavy, office furniture as well as modern office typing and accounting machinery being either totally destroyed or badly damaged.

On the night of November 12th, 1940, the Plough Court premises suffered a blow which was to lead to their eventual evacuation and the severance of a connection which had lasted for two hundred and twenty-eight years. A 500-kilo bomb fell in the building next door and all the lower windows of the premises facing the Court were smashed, as well as many of those on the upper floors. Plaster was stripped from the walls, some ceilings fell, including that of the pharmacy on the ground floor, where a fire broke out just under the clock, destroying some of the mahogany fittings ; many bottles were smashed and some stock destroyed. The retail Dispensary was transferred to Vere Street, the wholesale Dispensary was accommodated at Bethnal Green : the registered office of the Company on the same floor was removed for the time to the first floor of Plough Court, where a temporary home was also found for some section of the General Office. Eventually these sections were moved back to the damaged but habitable ' D ' floor at Bethnal Green, and while this floor with those above it were being rebuilt, the General Office as a whole, with the Sales and other departments, were transferred to a ground-floor building which was built temporarily on the site of the bombed manufacturing laboratory.

In due course the two upper floors of the main building at Bethnal Green had to be renewed and this was carried out in steel work and pre-cast concrete floor units. The cottages on the east side of the railway were so badly damaged that they had to be demolished and Allen & Hanburys bought the site. This eventually gave them a new and better entrance into the factory from Cambridge Heath Road via Birkbeck Street.

On the site of the printing block of buildings, totally demolished in the bombing, was erected a reinforced brick and concrete building which now houses the engineering and surgical raw material and finished stores and offices.

PLOUGH COURT AFTER THE BOMBING, 1940

While the rebuilding of the Bethnal Green premises was proceeding certain of the Head Office staff continued to work in considerable discomfort at Plough Court, but in January 1943 Bethnal Green was ready to receive the last of them and the premises in Plough Court, where the firm had had its home since its establishment in 1715, were left empty and derelict.

* * *

It should add interest to this section of the story to record the experiences of William J. Hawes, the manager of the cod-liver oil department, who had proceeded to Norway as usual immediately after Christmas 1939 for the purpose of carrying out the normal cod-liver oil production programme in that country, during the first few months of 1940. The production season had proceeded with little interruption until April 9th, 1940, when the people of Norway awoke to find most of their principal ports and air-fields occupied by German troops. The ports of Bergen, Trondjhem and Narvik were among those occupied, with the result that Hawes was completely isolated at his post in Henningsvaer.

The course of the war in Norway is now well known and no attempt will be made to record it here except in so far as it affected the Firm's premises and personnel. At the time of the German invasion of Norway in April, 1940, part of the season's production had already been shipped to overseas markets, part was *en route* for Bergen in a coastal vessel and part was still in the factory at Henningsvaer. The Bergen shipment was commandeered by the Germans, who sold the oil for their own purposes, but credited the Firm's account in the Oslo Bank. The remainder of the oil left behind in Henningsvaer was compulsorily requisitioned by the Germans some months later, but again the value of the oil was credited to the Firm's account.

During the summer months there was no contact between Hawes and the outside world and he was in the exasperating position of seeing British naval units coming and going during their operations against the port of Narvik, but was unable to make contact with them and thus make possible his return to

England.   With the end of the Narvik campaign in June, Hawes had to prepare himself to spend the rest of the war isolated in enemy-occupied Norway.

Following the evacuation of the British and Norwegian Forces, the German army gradually extended its occupation of the country and German officials soon established themselves in Svolvaer and Kabelvaag.   An air-raid warning system was instituted and a black-out enforced.   In the meanwhile, efforts had been made from London to make contact with Hawes in order to make certain of his personal safety, and eventually such contact was established through the agency of the Swedish Red Cross.   From Hawes' point of view this was a most unfortunate occurrence.   Henningsvaer itself had never been occupied by the Germans, and although in July officers began to pay frequent visits, on those occasions Hawes would hide or leave the island and by this means he managed to evade capture until November 19th, 1940.   Following the inquiries from the Swedish Red Cross, the German officials became aware for the first time that an Englishman was resident in Henningsvaer.   Hawes' whereabouts and nationality were discovered and the Germans immediately ordered his arrest and imprisonment.   From the time of his imprisonment to his eventual rescue and return to England four months later, the story is told in his own words.

I was notified at 1 p.m. on November 19th, 1940, that I was to be placed under arrest and was to be ready to leave by boat in charge of the Police at three o'clock.   I arrived at Kabelvaag at 4.30 and was taken into the charge room. Here I was questioned regarding my birth, age, nationality, domicile in England, etc., and was examined for any marks or other peculiarities.   My personal clothes and property were taken from me and I was placed in a cell which was to be my home until the middle of February, 1941.   This cell, which was on the ground floor, was approximately 15 ft. long and 6 ft. wide and I had to share this with a convict undergoing punishment for a hideous crime.   This cell had to pass for living room, dining-room, bedroom, bathroom and lavatory.   The door was in the centre of one wall, with the washbasin, etc., just inside and behind the door. The lavatory consisted of a box with a pail inside which was removed each morning at eight o'clock. The furniture consisted of a table fastened to the wall, a chair, a stool and two box-shaped beds, with a mattress and pillow stuffed with wood-wool, and two blankets. The place was warmed by hot water circulation.

My first meal was afternoon tea, consisting of 300 grammes of dark bread, 20 grammes of margarine and a pint of water. The day began at 6 a.m. with the clanging of the prison bell and the putting on of the lights which meant rise and shine, wash, dress, make your bed, sweep and wash the floor, ready for breakfast at 7 a.m., the same as afternoon tea above. Dinner at twelve o'clock consisted mostly of salt herrings and potato, with a plate of pearl barley soup, or as a change, fish soup. Tea at six o'clock was the same as breakfast. The only change was on Sunday when we had a piece of boiled salt beef and potato instead of fish. I might add that as time passed and as I did not drink tea, I was given hot barley water.

The working hours were from 8 a.m. to 12 and from 2 p.m. to 6 p.m., then lights out at 9 p.m. I was not asked to work, but owing to depression and weariness I asked to be allowed to do something to help pass away the dreary hours. I started repairing socks and clothing, then I was given a knife and file and was making legs for rocking horses. I may say that the top floor of the prison was a workshop where they made all sorts of toys, furniture, etc., for sale, and to finish up I made tables for wireless sets.

After Christmas I had a much better time, having got to know the resident jailer and by offering to pay a small amount I was given much better food. In fact at times I was sitting at table with them at meals and often played bridge during the evening. As regards exercise, this was limited to a small yard, 30 ft. long and 6 ft. wide, in which the snow was usually two to three feet deep. Here again I felt that I could not, neither did I wish to, exercise with the other inmates. The jailer, noticing this, gave permission for me to walk in the courtyard at the front of the house, which was much appreciated.

I received three visits from a German official just before my release. He informed me that the factory was let to a Norwegian and that I would be released on parole to get the machinery fitted up again as during the previous summer I had dismantled everything, and that if anything went wrong I should be put back into prison again or maybe worse. However, I had by this time got into such a frame of mind that I ceased to care what happened to me.

So ended my prison life which seemed to me an eternity rather than a period of no more than three to four months.

When I returned to Henningsvaer I found that the factories were producing oil on a small scale and fishing was being carried out with small four-man boats, the large boats having been taken by the Germans. I began to supervise the erection of the plant, etc., delaying things as long as I could, but the Germans came every day to see how the work was proceeding. I had just got the factory going again and production had commenced when, on March 4th, 1941, at about 7 a.m. one of the lads came running in shouting, 'The English are here.' When I looked out I could see the soldiers rushing up from the quay. The original landing had taken place on the far side of the island away from the village and the landing party had climbed over the rocks so that their first contact with the village was made at the Post Office, where immediate steps were taken to sever all communications.

I saw an officer interrogating Mr. ——, the local shipping agent, whose house was on the opposite side of the road to mine and I ran out to join them. I could see that Mr. —— was having a bad time from the interrogating officer and later I was able to vouch for his being a good friend of ours and he was thereafter left alone. At first, however, I was so excited and overwhelmed that I started speaking in Norwegian. The officer did not understand me and after a few minutes I began to speak in English and explained my identity. He was taking no chances, however, and told me that I was his prisoner and put me in charge of a sergeant who stayed with me for the rest of the time until we were aboard the destroyer later in the day.

The officer informed me that he was going to blow up

our factory for a start and I accompanied him while his party placed a bomb on the centrifuge, another on the boiler and a third on the refrigerating machine. (I later discovered that the one on the centrifuge did not explode and was removed by the Germans three days after.)

After the bombs had been placed in our own factory, the demolition party went round most of the other principal oil-producing factories and storage tanks in Henningsvaer and demolished most of these also. Meanwhile food and clothing were being distributed to the people on the island.

At about midday a siren sounded from a destroyer which had been lying off shore and the landing parties all re-assembled at the quay-side, together with the young Norwegians who wished to come to England to enlist in the Norwegian Forces there, and a party of German officials and about two hundred Norwegian 'Quislings' from Svolvaer and Kabelvaag who had been taken prisoner.

We left the quay in landing craft which transferred us to a destroyer off shore. The destroyer then proceeded to sea and we were transferred again to two Dutch passenger ships in which we were to travel home.

In 1946, Mr. Hawes returned to the Lofotens where cod-liver oil production was resumed in the Company's factory, which in the meanwhile had been partially repaired by the Germans.

*   *   *

To return to England. It was obvious that, as far as manufacture and packing were concerned, since all the plant was destroyed, nothing could be restarted in London and anyhow in view of the frequent raids it was not advisable. Also the East End of London had been badly damaged and many employees had lost their homes and had been evacuated from London, so that labour was very short. Luckily, having a factory at Ware, the Company had a certain amount of duplication of plant. It was decided therefore to transfer all manufacturing and packing activities to the Ware works. This was not simple, as the Ware buildings were fully occupied and could not suddenly accommodate additional work and workers, and there was no excess of labour in the Ware district upon which drafts could be made. A call was circulated to the men and women workers of the Bethnal Green Factory for volunteers to go to Ware and a large number came forward within a day or two. The Ware management were faced with finding billets for these people—no easy task in a town whose normal population was probably already trebled by evacuees. However, the difficulty was overcome, partly by the co-operation of the Ware staff, who took in emigrants from Bethnal Green. For the women and girls the Firm opened a house as a hostel and turned the Ware Sports' Pavilion into a club and dining-room.

At the time of the bombing it was realized that one of its most serious features was the loss of the sterile filling rooms and apparatus, where insulin and other parenteral products were packed. Insulin was essential to many people and the Firm's loss included considerable quantities not only of packed but of bulk insulin as well, representing several months' output. This job was given first priority and within ten days of the bombing insulin was being filled at Ware on improvised apparatus and in premises which normally produced 'Sterivac' intravenous solutions.

During this time several of the Ware and Bethnal Green staff had surveyed the Ware Factory and planned where production and packing could be done. All the time the salvage crews in London were shipping down loads of wrecked machinery, apparatus and furniture, which had to be sorted, identified and passed for repair where possible. As practically everything inflammable had been destroyed, complete orders for everything needed for packaging had to be placed with manufacturers. Hundreds of orders had to be made out, mainly from memory since all stock records had gone. The destruction of the Printing Department meant the loss of every original block and design of all labels, together with all paper and cardboard, stocks of printed labels and the printers' type founts. The sudden wreckage had to be searched for days to try and rescue one copy of every piece of printed matter, so that it could be photographed and reproduced ! In many cases packages of the Firm's products had to be procured from wholesalers or retailers to obtain a record.

It was obvious that once the new materials began to come in they could not be housed satisfactorily, so permission was obtained to erect two Nissen buildings at Ware, each one hundred and forty feet long by forty feet wide. These were put up, concrete floors made, and equipped with heating, light and work benches in twelve weeks, and early in January, 1941, the Packed Drug Department was united again under one roof, with repaired machinery and equipment installed.

On a night almost a year after the bombing the two new Nissen buildings containing the Packed Drugs and the adjoining carpenters' and case-making shops were burnt to the ground. All the contents were lost in the fire which burnt fiercely for two or three hours, leaving only the twisted iron framework of the buildings. Whilst the buildings were burning well the sirens sounded and it was quite expected that bombs would be added to the trouble, but happily nothing occurred : this was a very unpleasant experience for those who went through it.

Again a fresh start with these departments had to be made and by January, 1942, four new Nissen buildings were ready to house the rapidly expanding Packed Drug Department and two more were built for case-making shops. As the new buildings were occupied and stocks replaced again, new work began to pour in, such as bottling Ministry of Food Orange Juice at the rate of more than one hundred and fifty thousand bottles per month ; packing Household Milk Powder, Rose Hip Syrup and producing a number of special products for the Services.

Since the close of the war the extension of this department for peace-time requirements, particularly export, has necessitated additional bottle-washing facilities, and these have been met by the installation of washing machines which wash, rinse and dry three thousand five hundred bottles per hour of any size between one-ounce vials and Winchester quarts. Here also researches into filling apparatus have been carried on resulting in improved forms of vacuum fillers capable of filling limpid liquids at a very high rate and viscous liquids, such as Haliborange, at rates much greater than were previously possible.

*   *   *

A visitor to the Ware Factory in 1950, who was familiar with its departments and lay-out in the years immediately preceding the Second World War, could not fail to notice the new large building immediately facing him as he turned left after entering the Factory from Priory Street. This is the building intended originally for the production of penicillin and a visit to this may well begin a short inspection of the modern Ware Factory.

The name Penicillin was given by Professor Sir Alexander Fleming in 1929 to a substance produced by moulds of the genus *Penicillium*.

Readers of this story will be familiar with the accounts which have appeared in the scientific and lay press of the use of this substance, under the control of the Government, during the later years of the Second World War, for the treatment of infections of many kinds and particularly of injuries caused by modern warfare : at the end of the war it was released for use in hospitals and at a later stage, when supplies were more plentiful, it came into general use, although its sale has always been restricted in Great Britain in order to reduce the development of penicillin-resistant strains of bacteria.

With other large manufacturing concerns, Allen & Hanburys were asked by the Government to begin the manufacture of penicillin, and a pilot plant was set up at Ware for this purpose. Penicillin was then made by surface culture, but this method was discontinued, because it was not only less economical than the submerged fermentation method which superseded it, but was wasteful of plant, materials, space and labour. Similarly the small submerged fermentation plants were less economical than very large ones and with the two big plants scheduled for completion in the north of England in 1946, and with the discovery of a new strain of mould, which roughly doubled the prospective output of these plants, even before they were completed, the operation of the comparatively small factory unit

A PHARMACOLOGICAL LABORATORY, WARE

A CHEMISTRY LABORATORY IN EGYPT

became quite unsound. This coincided with the end of the war during which the economics of penicillin had only been a secondary consideration. With the return to what was hoped would have been normal peace-time conditions, sounder business principles prevailed and although the pilot plant, mentioned above, was run for some months and successfully produced a quantity of penicillin, the translation to the larger-scale plant was never completed, and the building was gradually taken over for other purposes.

' P ' building, as it is called, occupies a ground space of approximately twenty thousand square feet. It consists of three floors with a large basement and has a dignified and pleasing exterior. A principal feature of the elevation is the entrance porch surrounded by a long vertical continuous window to the staircase, while the windows of the other parts of the building, in three storeys, are arranged in orderly groups united by long lines of sill, repeated in the plain coping at the upper terminal of the façade.

The interior of this building was planned to be in semi-darkness for the cultivation of the penicillin moulds, but owing to the adaptability of modern interiors to artificial lighting and ventilation little difficulty has been experienced in making full use of the large cubic content of the building.

The ' Sterivac ' Department, now on the ground floor of ' P ' building, was founded in another part of the factory in late 1939 for the production on a commercial scale of intravenous transfusion fluids supplied in ' Sterivac ' containers which, suitably prepared, could also be used for the storage of donor's blood or for its administration.

During the 1914–1918 War little was known of blood transfusion and the first blood transfusion service in the world came into existence in 1921 under the auspices of the British Red Cross. In 1939 Allen & Hanburys designed and perfected in their laboratories the ' Sterivac ' container, a graduated glass flask in which sterile intravenous fluids are transported to all parts of the world.

The ' Sterivac ' business, starting from a modest beginning, has now developed into a large concern. The design of the container has changed little and the range of solutions remains practically the same as at first. This large increase, occasioned partly by the circumstances of the late war, made the re-planning of a new department necessary and in 1947 the present one was set up on the ground floor of ' P ' building. Here the machinery required for washing the containers, for ensuring sterility and freedom from pyrogens, and for the filling of the containers has been set up on a flow-line basis, resulting in an output which is treble that under the old method of filling. Proper arrangements for storage and transport have also been provided, not only for the containers, but for the many transfusion sets and accessories which accompany them.

On another section of the ground floor of ' P ' building is a workshop for polishing and finishing of certain grades of surgical instruments and a smaller one for the making of tubular hospital furniture ; these are extra-mural sections of the Engineering and Surgical Departments, Bethnal Green.

On the ground floor also is a range of offices for Directors and executives.

On the first floor the tablet department, once housed at Bethnal Green but destroyed in the 1940 bombing, has now found a home and has been re-equipped with new machinery to replace that which was destroyed or had become obsolete.

Another department which had previously been housed at Bethnal Green and which has been transferred to Ware is that concerned with the preparation of sterile solutions for injection. Such solutions are normally prepared either in glass ampoules or rubber-capped vials and machines are used which feed the containers singly to a filling station, displace the air, if necessary, with an inert gas, seal and anneal the ampoule neck and collect the ampoules upright in trays ready for examination. Such machines are capable of automatically filling and sealing one thousand or more ampoules an hour and many such machines are in regular use. Adjacent to the Filling Department is a laboratory where the injection solutions are prepared initially in bulk and sterilized. Many solutions, particularly those derived

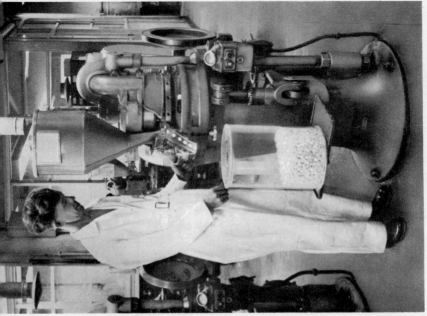

TABLET-MAKING AT WARE

OINTMENT FILLING AT WARE

A CHEMICAL DEVELOPMENT LABORATORY, WARE

from animal glands, are sensitive to heat and must therefore be sterilized by filtration through bacteria-proof filters. Most chemical substances can be sterilized by heat, but some of these also have to be sterilized by filtration.

★   ★   ★

Up to 1940 the preparation of crude drugs and galenicals had been divided between the manufacturing laboratory and the Drug Department at Ware. Following the destruction of the former, a heavy load was placed upon the Drug Department and in 1941 a new building was erected near by to which most of the work concerned with the preparation of glandular extracts and other products of animal origin was transferred. The new building also houses processes involving the preparation of pure chemical substances from drugs of natural origin. Such processes involve the use of large volumes of inflammable solvents and all electrical switches and gear, including the telephones, need to be of flame-proof construction. This building, known as ' X ' building, contains several items of plant which had been originally installed within a few yards of the place where the bomb fell at Bethnal Green, but which have been successfully repaired and brought again into use. Amongst these is one of the first stainless steel vacuum pans ever to be made in this country. In view of the exceptional fire risk in this department, the whole ground floor is fitted with an automatic fire quenching apparatus which in the event of fire discharges carbon dioxide gas in such quantity that any fire would be rapidly extinguished.

The Drug Department to-day is more than the simple result of superimposing the old Bethnal Green laboratory on to the old Drug Department, Ware, and has been laid out more in accord with modern practice and with a great deal of modern machinery, which has replaced some of the old hand techniques. Many old implements are, of course, still in evidence, percolators and copper stills abound and the wooden paddle has not quite disappeared. Modern paste mills have displaced some of the earlier homogenizing devices, and the department has been divided functionally into a section which makes creams and emulsions ; a section concerned with extracts and vacuum pan practice ; a section engaged on the production of tinctures and compound galenicals ; a section on grinding and blending of powders and a new and improved ointment section.

It will be recalled that the technical Library at Bethnal Green suffered considerable damage in the Bethnal Green bombing and a new one has been created at Ware in ' P ' building. A wide range of scientific and technical publications are taken and circulated to the staff, abstracts noted, and of course, recognized text-books and works of reference are available in up-to-date editions for consultations. The Library is in the charge of a Graduate Librarian.

Since the end of the Second World War the Ware factory has become the centre of the chemical and pharmaceutical manufacturing activities of Allen & Hanburys, and in addition has housed the Research, Development and Control Laboratories. Bethnal Green remains the centre for Head Office and General Office activities and also embraces the engineering shops concerned with the manufacture of hospital furniture and surgical instruments, together with the wholesale warehouse from which the Company's products are distributed throughout the world.

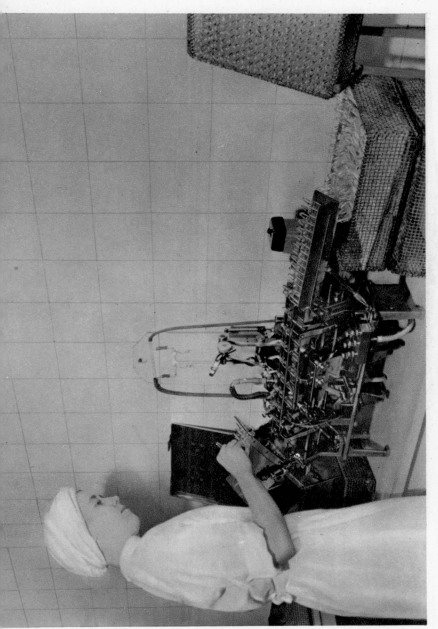

AMPOULE FILLING AT WARE

CHAPTER 4

TRANSPORT

THIS is the story of the various methods of transport used by the Firm from the days of Silvanus Bevan until modern times.

In 1715, the year in which the Firm was founded, pack-horses were still being used for carrying light articles from place to place, mostly in country districts ; it is likely that Silvanus Bevan, who had business connections with the West of England and South Wales, used this form of transport for some part of the journey from Plough Court. The horses travelled in gangs, which sometimes numbered fifty or more ; they formed a single line in which each horse knew his place and kept it with great regularity. The leading horse of the pack train wore a bell (or sometimes a collar of bells) and was known as the ' bell-horse '. The sound of the bells not only guided the horses at the end of the train when it was dark, but also served to warn foot travellers coming in the opposite direction. Generally these were compelled to make way for the pack-horses and to stand to the side since the roadway or path did not afford room for two streams of traffic ! When two pack-horse trains met there were often quarrels between the respective drivers who disputed which team was to step off into the mud and allow the other to pass !

For the carrying of goods for short distances to and from Plough Court the Bevans made use of the services of a messenger or a porter or, as he was sometimes called, a journeyman. When Joseph Jewell applied to Joseph Gurney Bevan for a post as assistant in the laboratory at the Old Plough Court pharmacy he was at the time in the employ of a firm of glass manufacturers in or near the City and his duties included the carrying of fairly heavy loads of sheet glass on his back, using the porter's ' knot ' for greater ease and comfort in carrying.

Incidentally, messengers, porters, and even principals were in those days in danger of robbery, even near their homes or places of business. In the *General Advertiser* of November 24th, 1744, there is a paragraph to the effect that a Mr. ' Beavin ' of Plough Court was stopped near the Old Bedlam by five ruffians who robbed him of about forty shillings and ' stripped off his coat, in the pocket of which was several parcels of physic '. The Mr. ' Beavin ' was probably Timothy Bevan, who in the exercise of his calling as an apothecary would be delivering ' physic ' to patients upon whom he may have previously called during the day, or he may have been delivering medicines prescribed by physicians and collecting his fees for such. ' Bedlam ' was the Bethlem Hospital where lunatics were confined : in 1744 it was situated in Moorfields, at that time open country infested at night by foot-pads and other undesirable persons.

At the beginning of the nineteenth century one of the specified duties of the porter at Plough Court was the delivery of soda water to many of the residential houses in the immediate neighbourhood and this, packed in a case or hamper, would probably be carried on the ' knot '. It was not until the fifties and sixties of the last century that a two-wheeled truck was used for taking goods round the City and sometimes further afield. The late William George Bulley, who entered the Old Plough Court pharmacy as a boy in the warehouse, sleeping under the counter at night, remembered pushing such a vehicle with goods as far as the then West End of London.

By the end of the eighteenth century the business at Plough Court had developed to such an extent that orders for drugs and sundries from surgeons and apothecaries in towns in the Midlands and the north of England were frequent. For the transport of these what were known as ' stage wagons ' were used, roomy, lumbering vehicles, capable of carrying as many as twenty passengers as well as goods. There was little comfort for the former who sat in the straw on the floor or reclined on the merchandise. These ' wagons ' had been in use from the middle of the sixteenth century and carried a heavier class of goods than those carried by the pack-horses. The wheels were broad with heavy iron tyres, there were no springs and the 'wagon' was drawn at a walking pace by six, eight, or even more horses, sometimes with bells on their harness; the animals usually completed the whole journey without being changed.

A little later 'flying wagons', a lighter vehicle, were introduced. On November 16th, 1776, Matthew Pickford, a name still connected with the business of carriers, who had been running 'wagons' for one hundred years before that date, advertised that his 'flying wagons' travelled from Manchester to London in five-and-a-half days—the rate of travel being an average of one-and-a-half miles per hour. The 'wagons' left the Swan and Saracens Head, Market Street Lane, Manchester, on Wednesdays at 5 p.m. and arrived at the Swan with Two Necks, Lad Lane, London, at noon on the following Tuesdays.

Allen & Hanburys' records include many orders from customers outside London who ordered their goods to be sent by these vehicles. A typical one is from High Wycombe:

> Respected friends (then Allen and Howard), please to send the within ordered by 6th. Davy's Wagon and enclose my account.

Another one from John Carter, a surgeon of Maldon, dated September, 1798, reads:

> Please to send me to the Blue Boar, Whitechapel on Friday morning to come by Ward's van on Saturday next, the following. . . .

Another order from Kettering about the same date mentioned goods ordered by 'Wright's waggon'.

In February, 1808, William Allen wrote that certain goods were sent by 'Pickford's Waggon' from the Castle, Wood Street.

The introduction of the stage coach which was primarily intended for carrying passengers only, affected somewhat the business of the 'wagons' as light articles could be conveyed rather more quickly: the mail coaches were quicker still, but were used primarily for the carrying of letters, with passengers as a side-line! The use of wagon transport for heavy goods continued unchecked until the close of the Allen Period ; practically till the beginning of the railways.

With the coming of the railways the owners of some of the 'wagons', notably the one mentioned above, decided to continue their journeys and still serve their customers, collecting and delivering the goods themselves and, if convenient, using the railways as the means of transmission from centre to centre. The goods were sometimes collected and delivered through the local branches of the carrier : sometimes through agents : in some cases even the carriers helped the railways by collecting and delivering their goods for them.

What may be termed the 'carrier' method of sending goods from Plough Court to the outlying districts of London, too far to be reached by a porter with his truck or a messenger with his basket, and to places as far away as Brighton and other South Coast towns, suited the needs of the growing Plough Court business as goods sent one day were usually delivered the next day or the day after.

In 1853 the first underground railway was started in the London area and when opened it afforded an alternative method of delivery of small parcels, although the area served was at first limited. In the meantime the great railways through their heavy goods and lighter passenger services were carrying an increasing tonnage of the merchandise of the country, although there were many districts which in the early years of railway transport were hardly affected and where other methods of transport were necessary. It was not until 1883 that the Parcels Post was introduced and this soon became popular as a means of getting prescriptions, for instance, quickly and safely into the hands of the Firm's retail customers.

Benjamin Thomas Brazier (who is in retirement at Ware) began his career at the Plough Court pharmacy in the eighties of the last century and has given his impressions of those days when there were six assistants on the retail side of the pharmacy and six others employed in dispensing :

Quite a number of prescriptions were sent by Parcels Post packed in tow in special wooden boxes almost every hour, but a crescendo was reached at 6 p.m. as we hurried to post our boxes and letters. Men, women and boys came to the Lombard Street Post Office (next door to the old St. Mary Woolnoth Church) with portmanteaux, boxes and baskets full of letters. The normal slot at the Office was hopeless to cope with such an influx : so it was opened out on hinges to form a big shoot down which you could have fallen with your letters ! Incoming letters were delivered early and by 8.30 a.m. had been scanned and all relating to goods at Bethnal Green were soon on their way by messenger.

The opening of the Bethnal Green Factory and the beginning and development of many of the Firm's specialities implied the necessity for some systematic method of transport to retail chemists. It should be noted that during the eighties and nineties representatives were appointed for calling upon chemists and medical men. This meant regular deliveries of the goods ordered and it was from 1900 onwards that a number of horse vans were used for delivering goods from Bethnal Green. There were, at first, three of these, each having its definite daily journey. One went to the West End, another to the City, and the third covered an area of approximately five miles from Bethnal Green, as well as taking goods to the railway termini and to the Docks.

The year 1896 was a notable one in the history of the Firm as the old Flour Mills at Ware were acquired ; upon this site the present factory was gradually built. The Staff there in the early days was a very small one and the need for transport to carry goods made in the factory to Bethnal Green was not at first very pressing. As the manufacture of goods developed, a contractor was engaged and he used to use two covered wagons each with a pair of horses : the load carried by each van was about thirty hundredweight. He sometimes did the journey overnight, arriving at Bethnal Green in the early morning, where he off-loaded, rested his horses, and returned empty the next night. His fee for the double journey with a load as above was thirty shillings : he usually made two or three journeys per week. He did the journey in all weathers, snow, frost, hail, rain and shine : on some occasions he off-loaded at an inn in Enfield, on to the vehicle of some other carrier.

In the meantime, steam-propelled lorries or wagons were coming more and more into use for carrying goods by road. They were not, altogether, a new form of transport as from the beginning of the nineteenth century vehicles with steam as the motive power, both for passenger and goods, had been on the roads. Legislation, however, during the sixties and seventies had severely restricted their development and it was not until 1896, when the Locomotives on Highways Act became law— one of the provisions of which was the abolition of the man preceding such a vehicle and carrying a red flag—that their use became more general.

The Firm soon began to experiment with steam traction with a six-ton Thorneycroft ; it took five hours for the journey from Ware to Bethnal Green at four miles an hour ! It was not altogether a successful effort, the vehicle was slow and noisy as the wheels were shod with heavy iron tyres which skidded on the roads not then in the condition they are to-day. The driver recalled that he almost got into trouble for taking water from the horse troughs along the road for the boiler of the engine !

At a later date a three-ton Thorneycroft was used which did the journey in three hours each way ; solid rubber tyres were used on the wheels. This was followed by a three-ton Hunslet steam wagon and after that by a six-ton Hunslet.

Motors driven by petrol followed. The first one to be acquired by the Firm was a five-ton De-Dion Bouton. This was a smart-looking car and to add the finishing touch the driver and his mate were fitted out with suitable uniform ! This car did two journeys daily with a five-ton load from Ware to Bethnal Green and back, and was looked upon as a great success.

In 1906 the first motor-car for delivering to retail customers was put into service at Bethnal Green ; the following letter concerning it, written by Reginald Janson Hanbury to the Editor of *The Commercial Motor*, gives some information :

We have pleasure in sending you some particulars with regard to the 16 h.p. Lacre motor van and these will give you an approximate idea of cost, use, etc., we also send you herewith photograph of a van taken by the writer.

The first journey done by the van was in January 1906. It has a 16 h.p. Albion engine fitted to a Lacre chassis and is used for the delivery of goods and collection of empties, the average number of deliveries being about 20 per day. The haulage methods it has replaced are : Rail, C.P. and Co., L.P.D. Co.,[1] and horse and van work, chiefly the first-named, the longest daily journey performed is to Colchester and back, 107 miles : this work was, naturally, not previously done by horses. The cost of running is as follows :—

> Driver's wages, per week 30/–d,
> Driver's assistant, per week, 17/–d,
> Petrol per month, average 100 gallons.
> Lubricating oil per month, average 2½ gallons.
> Uses 1 gallon petrol for every 12 miles.
> Driver's licence.
> Driver's assistant's licence.

(We were pleased to hear from Mr. Hanbury on Monday afternoon last, that the fire at Bethnal Green had not hurt the motor van. It will be satisfactory to his Company's numerous customers to know that the damage was confined to the oil-bottling and hospital-furniture departments, and that the prompt execution of orders will in no way be hindered.—Ed.)

Another interesting allusion to this van appeared in an edition of the same paper several years afterwards, unfortunately the date has not been preserved :

This old-time delivery van was an attraction on London streets in 1906. It was driven by Alec Niven who emigrated to Western Australia and was concerned in the establishment of a well-known Car hire service.

[1] Carter Paterson & Co. ; London Parcel Delivery Company.

A study of the work of this motor, as shown by the log sheet for July, 1908, reveals the following details :

No. of deliveries . . .	472
Hours on road . . .	173
Petrol used	181 gallons
Lubricating oil . . .	23 gallons

The mileage registered is not shown.

During the forty years or so from 1906 until the end of the Second World War a fleet of motors was gradually built up at Bethnal Green, beginning with De-Dion Bouton and Commer cars. Both the First and Second World Wars necessarily affected this form of transport, not only because of shortage of materials with which to supply customers, but because of restrictions affecting the supply of petrol and new vehicles, and the difficulties of renewals of spare parts, etc. Gradually the motor delivery areas have been enlarged and deliveries have been speeded up. The punctuality of this motor service has been commented upon by retail customers who often remark that they can set their clocks by the appearance at their pharmacies of the well-known red and cream motors ! [1]

[1] Red and cream has been the colour design since the days of steam transport.

CHAPTER 5

OVERSEAS ACTIVITIES

AUSTRALIA

IT was during the twenty years between the formation of Allen & Hanburys as a limited company and the First World War (1914–1918) that Frederick Janson and his two sons, Reginald and Capel, turned their attention to a subject which had been in the mind of Cornelius Hanbury II for a considerable number of years, namely the creation of overseas branches of the Firm.

On reading this story so far various allusions to overseas business will have been noted, but these applied to orders received at the Plough Court Pharmacy from customers abroad ; they had been sent in direct to the Firm or through a wholesaler or agent.

The intention of Cornelius was either to build premises in suitable places abroad or to take over existing premises which would prove suitable for carrying on the different activities of the Firm's business, including, if need be, manufacturing.

It was decided that a branch in Australia should be the first of its kind, as a firm in Melbourne had been carrying on a successful agency since 1884, but before considering this, let us go back to the year 1836 when an order was received at the Old Plough Court Pharmacy from Michael Bates of Launceston, Van Diemen's Land (Tasmania).

No details of this order can be traced, but it was accompanied by two bills of twenty-five pounds each on London agents which were accepted by Allen, Hanburys & Barry. There was a note at the foot of the letter stating that the tooth instruments being sent were not quite the same as the ' spring bolt ' type ordered, but those sent were considered more ' eligible ' by the makers, as well as less expensive ! Because the value of the order had already exceeded the fifty pounds sent, and credit at the time to overseas customers was not given, a Sykes hydrometer and a chemical reagents chest were omitted on that occasion.

It is apparent from correspondence relating to further orders that Michael Bates was carrying on a similar type of business to many carried on in the country at the same time, comprising agricultural goods, paints and varnishes, wines and spirits, drugs and chemicals, and dispensing ; in one letter he asks that a paper might be sent out to him regularly showing the markets for, amongst other things, wool and wheat, and the regular despatch of *Bell's Weekly Messenger* was arranged by those at Plough Court.

In June, 1840, Bates asked the Firm to make inquiries about the possibility of sending to Tasmania some quantity of various grass seeds which were required for acclimatizing in that country. Such an inquiry was admittedly quite outside the usual business transactions at Plough Court, but in an endeavour to help the customer John Barry wrote many letters to farmers and seed merchants in this country regarding the best source of supply of such seeds ; and the best methods of packing them. Eventually an order was placed, and after the new season's seeds had been thoroughly dried, they were packed in dry puncheons with instructions that when on board ship they should be kept away from moisture.

The actual order with the prices charged was as follows :

112 lbs. White Clover, 7d. to 8d. a lb.
56 lbs. Saint Foin, say 5 bush, at 4d. a lb.
56 lbs. Smooth Stalked Meadow, 1/6d. a lb.
56 lbs. Rough Stalked Meadow, 1/6d. a lb.
4 Bushels say 80 lbs. Timothy, 6d. a lb.

One very noticeable feature of the correspondence is the length of time which elapsed between the despatch of the goods from London and their receipt in Tasmania. Six and even seven months was the average and the same long delay applied to the letters which were usually carried both ways by the captains of the vessels.

In addition, owing to the small number of boats engaged in the service, or perhaps to the infrequency of their voyages, goods were held up for some weeks before they were shipped. Strong-smelling articles (two instances were spirits of tar and musk) were refused by certain captains of vessels because they would contaminate goods stowed in their vicinity.

In May, 1851, there is a record of the sending of four cases of cod-liver oil to S. J. P. Croad, of Melbourne, once an assistant at the Old Plough Court Pharmacy. This was Newfoundland oil, which apparently the Firm had imported from that country and refined at Plough Court.

During the next thirty years or so regular consignments of articles made or obtained by the Firm were being sent out in increasing numbers to different parts of Australia. It was in 1884 that the firm of Francis Forrest and Co., of South Street, Melbourne, was appointed a special agent in Australasia for the foods and proprietary articles made at that time by Allen & Hanburys.

The success of this agency was due in no small measure to Arthur J. Firkins, who originally came from London and was apprenticed to T. S. Loney, a pharmacist of William Street, Sydney, who himself had been an assistant at the Old Plough Court Pharmacy.

Returning to England, Firkins got in touch with Dodd, at whose suggestion he returned to Australia and became the representative for Allen & Hanburys with Forrest & Co. In this capacity he covered the whole of Australia and New Zealand and once made a special journey on a bicycle from Perth to Coolgardie, where the gold rush was at its height : he paid one pound per night for sleeping on the verandah of a Coolgardie hotel, but he sold his bicycle, for which he had paid thirty pounds, for forty pounds !

Firkins made so many friends on his travels—chemists, doctors, surgeons and hospital staffs—that Cornelius Hanbury formed a Company entitled Allen & Hanburys (Australasia) Ltd., and

Firkins was appointed its first manager. He decided to move from Melbourne and start the new branch in Sydney, then becoming the main shipping port of the continent.

He opened in a small way, with an office staff and surgical showroom in one street and a storeroom in another. The business and the staff grew to such an extent that premises at Forty-seven Bridge Street, Sydney, were found where all the sections could be housed under one roof.

Firkins's great opportunity came in 1909 when the British Medical Association of New South Wales built their headquarters in Elizabeth Street, Sydney, and granted Allen & Hanburys a lease of twenty-one years for showrooms for the display of surgical instruments and hospital furniture and equipment ; this was regarded as one of the finest, if not the finest, show of such goods in the continent.

In the meantime tariff troubles affecting the supply of infants' foods to Australia were developing. A tariff of fifteen per cent upon Allenbury's foods entering the country, as well as upon the wooden cases in which they were packed, was threatened, and although in the first instance relief was obtained from this, it was obvious that unless a factory was built in Australia where the foods could be manufactured, the concession could be short-lived only.

For various reasons the Directors in England did not take this step and the coming of the First World War in 1914 and the stoppage of all supplies from England to Australia precipitated matters still further and the business there came practically to a standstill.

The demolition of the British Medical Association building to make way for improvements in Elizabeth Street was also another blow, but the surgical instrument department was moved to Forty-one Hunter Street, where it remains to-day.

Between the two World Wars the imposing of a heavy duty on medicinal and other goods entering Australia prompted the Directors of the Parent Company in London to close the medicinal proprietary side of the business altogether and transfer it to Harrisons Ramsay Ltd., Agents, of Sydney.

FACTORY AT ST. MARY'S, N.S.W., 1947

FACTORY AT CONGELLA, DURBAN, 1953

SHOWROOMS AT JOHANNESBURG. 1953

During this period the affairs of the Australian Subsidiary Company were in the hands of Charles Moors, but before the end of the Second World War Moors was incapacitated by ill health and a further series of interruptions in the normal flow of trade were encountered during which time R. H. Luker held the fort.

In September, 1945, D. O. Evans, himself a native of Australia, who had been Manager of the Vere Street Branch for several years, undertook a tour of the Australian continent and secured a lease on a suitable factory building at St. Mary's, about twenty-five miles out of Sydney. It was decided to establish at St. Mary's facilities for manufacturing many of the Company's products, and in January, 1947, Evans, assisted by other members of the staff from Bethnal Green and Ware and by Australians recruited locally, commenced manufacturing activities. In 1949 the Company renewed its activities in Melbourne and a Surgical and Pharmaceutical Showroom and Depot was opened in Spring Street, which is close to Collins Street, the 'Harley Street' of Melbourne. Further branches were established in Brisbane and Newcastle, N.S.W. During the same period a pharmaceutically qualified representative was sent from England to New Zealand and the tempo of the Company's activities in that country increased rapidly in association with its agents, Sharland & Company, who have factories and depots in Wellington, Auckland, Christchurch and Dunedin where the University of Otago houses the principal medical school of the dominion.

Having brought about a successful revival of the Australian business Evans returned to England in 1951 and was succeeded by George Percival. Percival became the Managing Director of Allen & Hanburys (Australasia) Ltd. in 1953.

SOUTH AFRICA

' Success is not the child of wishful thinking, it is born of courage, vision, efficient administration, public acceptance of our confidence of the product, fair trading and sincerity of purpose.'

The above statement, taken from a message from the Mayor of Durban, contributed to a souvenir brochure commemorating the opening of a new Allen & Hanburys factory at Congella, Durban, on October 12th, 1950, envisages the spirit in which Cornelius Hanbury and his fellow directors decided fifty years before to open in Cape Town a depot for the supply of the Firm's products.

It is true that William Allen, following the Abolition of Slavery in the British Colonies, had taken an active part with Thomas Clarkson, William Wilberforce and others in the formation of the African Institution in the early days of the nineteenth century, but ' courage and vision ' were certainly required to break new ground in South Africa in 1904, shortly after the end of the second Boer War. It should be borne in mind also that at the beginning of the present century there were only a million Europeans in the country.

' Efficient administration ' was found in the person of African-born Thomas William Tullett, a member of the Parent Company's sales staff, who was entrusted with the task of going to South Africa and of opening a depot in Cape Town. He found premises at 38 Castle Street, where, with a good supply of the Firm's products from London and a small staff, he began supplying retail chemists and certain wholesale distributive firms.

The life of this depot was a comparatively brief one, as shortly after its opening Tullett recommended that another one should be opened in Durban, then rapidly developing, for the reason that the bulk of the Transvaal, Orange Free State, and Natal business was already being conducted more and more from that city, which combined rail and sea facilities for transport with the social amenities of a large seaside town.

A home was found at first for the Durban depot at 38 Field Street ; the Cape Town branch was closed, and Tullett returned to England, his mission accomplished. Before leaving Durban he appointed his brother, John Samuel Tullett, as manager of the depot, and it was not long before the latter began looking for bigger and better premises and these he eventually found in a block of red-brick, iron-roofed warehouses and offices, at

409–411 Smith Street, known by a strange coincidence when the history of number two Plough Court is remembered, as Pope's Buildings. These were purchased by the Parent Company. The African Subsidiary moved into the second half of the building, i.e. 411 Smith Street, and the other half, 409 Smith Street, was let to a leading firm of South African general merchants who, two years later, made way for the owners of the property.

In 1912 J. S. Tullett resigned and Thomas Robert Walton went out from England to reorganize and develop the Company's interests, for by this time a limited company had been formed under the title of Allen & Hanburys (Africa) Ltd. Eventually Walton became the first Managing Director.

Until this time all goods had been imported from London, but under Walton's management a beginning was made with local manufacture, and laboratory and printing equipment were brought from England for that purpose. Walton soon undertook a comprehensive tour of the Union, in the course of which he called upon medical men, hospitals and chemists and rapidly built up the Company's name and reputation and laid a sound foundation for the establishment of a prosperous business in South Africa. Before 1914 pioneering conditions still prevailed throughout most of the Union and travelling conditions were extremely arduous, bearing in mind the great distances to be covered between centres of population and the fact that much travelling had to be carried out in horse-drawn vehicles over very primitive roads. The First World War of 1914–1918 stimulated a rapid expansion of manufacturing activities in Durban and in 1922 another qualified chemist, H. R. Hudson, was sent out from England to assist Walton in the technical control of production and in the establishment of an analytical laboratory. Hudson resigned in 1938 and was succeeded as Chief Chemist by Graham G. McIntyre, who had joined the Company in 1936, and continued in that capacity until 1944, when he was nominated as Walton's successor, being appointed Managing Director to the South African Company on Walton's retirement in 1947.

Thomas Walton had given thirty-five years of efficient and

meritorious service and had built up a sound and flourishing business in that time. He was an outstanding personality, being of a most sociable disposition and a great raconteur. He was well known throughout the length and breadth of the Union in many walks of life besides his own, and he was in addition an exceptionally keen and proficient games player ; he was well able to play a good round of golf or a sound game of tennis even when he had passed eighty years of age.

With the rapid development of the Union during and after the First World War, many new hospitals sprang up and old ones were expanded, and the South African Company's business in surgical instruments and equipment expanded likewise. In 1922 a Surgical Branch was opened in Plein Street, Johannesburg, and both in Durban and in Johannesburg workshops have been built at which certain instruments are manufactured and repair work can be carried out. In 1950 a Surgical and Pharmaceutical Branch was established at 95 Loop Street, Cape Town, not far from where the first depot was opened by Tullett some fifty years before. In the early years of the century the site of the Company's headquarters at Smith Street had been on the outer fringe of the town of Durban, but with the rapid expansion of that city the site became quite unsuitable for a factory and in 1939 Walton acquired three acres of ground at Congella, a few miles outside the city, at which it was planned to build a more suitable modern factory. These plans were inevitably delayed by the Second World War, but in November, 1949, the foundations of the new building were laid and the first part of the new factory was completed by October 12th, 1950, when it was formally opened by Mr. F. Capel Hanbury, the Chairman of the Board of the Parent Company. The occasion was an auspicious one and about two hundred visitors were present, including the Hon. D. G. Shepstone, Administrator of the Province of Natal, the Mayor of Durban and many prominent medical men and pharmacists of the city. The Congella factory had been equipped with much new plant for the manufacture of a wide range of pharmaceutical preparations and in addition to the well-established activities transferred from Smith Street,

SHOWROOMS AT CAPETOWN, 1953

departments for the manufacture of tablets and of sterile products were adequately provided for. Following the opening of the first part of the factory, work proceeded on the main administrative block and this was virtually completed by the beginning of June, 1953, when Popes Buildings in Smith Street were finally evacuated. Three weeks later, however, on the evening of June 30th, a disastrous fire occurred, as a result of which serious and extensive damage was done to the manufacturing sections of the new factory. This grievous misfortune, which was thought to have been due to an electrical fault, came as a severe blow to Mr. McIntyre and his staff, who saw the labours of years apparently dissipated in a matter of minutes. Prodigious efforts were, however, made by all members of the staff, as a result of which much valuable equipment was rapidly salvaged and repaired, and by using undamaged space in the administrative sections of the factory the interruption in the South African Company's business was scarcely noticeable. Within nine months the affected buildings had been fully restored and were in full working order once more.

At this point it is appropriate to refer to the frequent exchanges of visits which now take place between the directors of the Parent Company and the Subsidiary Companies and Branch Offices all over the world. Many such journeys to Australia, Canada, India and South Africa have been followed by visits from the technical and management staff in England and within a few days of the Congella fire C. W. Maplethorpe, W. M. Clayson and the Production Manager from Ware, were on the spot assisting the South African staff in the process of rehabilitation. Conversely, there has been a regular series of visits from the staffs of the Subsidiary Companies to London and Ware, and frequent personal discussion on the Company's problems are now possible in a way never dreamed of before the development of rapid air travel.

CANADA

Frederick Janson Hanbury visited the United States as far back as 1876, but no definite step was taken towards establishing a transatlantic agency till after 1897, when the late William Ralph Dodd attended the first meeting of the British Medical Association at Montreal, and took the occasion to study the opening offered by the United States and Canadian markets for Allen & Hanburys' products. A year later Frederick Janson paid a second visit to Canada and the result was the establishment of two agencies, one at Toronto, the other at New York. The New York agency was closed in 1902 and reopened at Niagara Falls. In the same year he again visited Canada, and it was decided to convert the two agencies into a Subsidiary Company. Toronto became the chief distributing centre, but allowance was made for a development of the American business by the retention of the Niagara Falls Branch, which, however, was later closed.

During the First World War, 1914–1918, a factory for the manufacture of the Allenburys Milk Foods and for Malt products was built at Lindsay, Ontario. Lindsay was the centre of a rich farming district, producing large quantities of good milk ; it was also well situated for the distribution of manufactured goods by rail east and west.

The late Frederic William Gamble visited the Canadian Company on three occasions and was increasingly impressed with the potentialities of the country for the further development and expansion of business in the Company's products, not only in Canada but also in the United States.

In 1927 W. T. Thorn was transferred from the Shanghai Branch to become Managing Director of the Canadian Company, a position which he occupied until 1938. During this period the Malt Extract plant was enlarged and an extensive business in all types of malt products was developed. During the Second World War Malted Milk was supplied in very large quantities to the Canadian Services, but at the end of the war it became apparent that with the dietetic products declining in importance, the future of the Canadian Company lay in the pharmaceutical field and it was clear that Lindsay, situated eighty-five miles up country from Toronto, was too remote for the successful prosecution of a pharmaceutical business. In

August, 1937, G. O. T. Gamble (a son of F. W. Gamble) had been elected to the Canadian Board and acted as resident director until July, 1943, when he was succeeded by D. W. F. Macaulay.

Under Gamble and Macaulay the Canadian Company, in addition to extending its pharmaceutical activities locally, had developed a considerable export business, and in 1950 a new and more suitable factory building was obtained on an industrial site in the north-western outskirts of Toronto, where new pharmaceutical equipment was installed for the manufacture of a number of the Company's newer products.

At the same time Donald MacLaren, a pharmaceutically qualified member of the Parent Company's sales staff, went to Canada as General Manager, becoming Managing Director in the following year. He was followed in 1953 by a surgical specialist who is building up a business in surgical instruments and equipment in line with similar activities in the Parent Company and in the other overseas subsidiaries.

ASIA

It was in the year 1894 that Allen & Hanburys first established business with India on a definite basis by appointing George Reddick of Reddick & Co., East India Merchants, as agent. He had had a long and wide experience of the Indian market and under his guidance many hitherto unknown products of the Firm were introduced, and the foundation laid of substantial business in the future.

The agency was relinquished in 1921 and the first office of the Company in India was opened in Calcutta. A. H. P. Jennings, previously associated with the Shanghai branch of the Company, was placed in charge. The territory covered by the Calcutta Office at that time included India, Burma, Ceylon, Malaya and Siam. No stocks were held by the Company, but regular supplies were shipped direct from home to merchants in all the principal centres. Periodically tours covering the whole of the territory were made, and in spite of many difficulties, sales continued to increase. India was rapidly becoming one of the world's best markets for the Allenburys products.

In 1934 Jennings retired from India and was succeeded by B. W. Clark, senior assistant in Calcutta since 1926. At this time Malaya and Siam were detached from the territory controlled by the Office in India and became an agency in the hands of merchants in Singapore. With the expansion of business in India larger premises were needed, and the steady progress was maintained.

The outbreak of the Second World War in 1939 with its restrictions of supplies and shipping necessitated a change in policy and it was decided to maintain depot stocks in the principal centres. This enabled the Company through its own office and agents to control all available supplies. Strict rationing was introduced and the widest distribution undertaken to combat growing black market and profiteering activities which persisted in spite of Government measures introduced to control them.

The Japanese entry into the War in 1941 was a serious threat to the security of India. The fall of Rangoon and the occupation of Burma brought grave danger to Calcutta. Many firms transferred their offices to inland towns, but the majority of British firms carried on as usual. Japanese naval activity in the Bay of Bengal practically closed the ports of Madras, Calcutta and Chittagong. All shipping was diverted for a time and cargoes for east coast ports were discharged at Cochin, Bombay and Karachi. Because of this state of affairs a branch office was opened in Bombay to control all shipments and forward them to their original destinations.

In spite of many restrictions and difficulties throughout the war years business with India remained at a high level. Since the end of the war economic teething troubles and currency difficulties have necessitated periodic interruptions in the free flow of trade, and the natural desire for some degree of industrialization will necessitate a reorientation of trading relations between India and Great Britain.

With the creation of the State of Pakistan new connections were established in Karachi and Chittagong, where the Company's products, both old and new, continue to play their part in the developing medical services of the new State.

CHINA

Although it was not until 1910 that a branch of the Firm was started in China, considerable business had been carried on there for many years, dating back to the days of Daniel Hanbury, who was the author of a standard work on Chinese Materia Medica : he never visited China, but gained the information he required in correspondence with missionaries, consuls and indeed anyone interested in botanical and pharmacological subjects.

His younger brother, Mr. (afterwards Sir) Thomas Hanbury, was a great traveller and ' China merchant ' and from the travels of the one and the correspondence of the other, important friendships in the country were formed, so that the name of the Firm was familiar to many interested in drugs long before a branch establishment was opened.

In 1910 one small room was rented at 8A Pekin Road, Shanghai, as a sample showroom, followed two years later by a second room ; eventually the whole of the floor was taken. In 1915 more commodious premises were required and offices and warehouse at 40 Canton Road were chosen. Here the staff, beginning with three in number, increased in ten years to sixty ; the stock of drugs carried at the time was probably the largest in China.

In the early days the Chinese Branch was controlled by H. B. Reddick, son of George Reddick of India. In 1924, however, W. T. Thorn took charge of the Branch until he went to Canada three years later. Between the two world wars, as is well known, China went through a period of great political disturbance and frequent civil wars. Business became steadily more difficult to conduct on a satisfactory basis until the Japanese occupation virtually put an end to it.

Since the end of the war there has been a great extension of the Company's business in the Far East and old connections have been renewed and new ones formed in Burma, Siam, Hong Kong, Malaya and Indonesia.

RUSSIA

It is probably not generally known to-day that there is still in existence a Subsidiary Company known as Allen & Hanburys (Russia) Ltd. In 1912 an agency was established in Moscow and in the following year the Subsidiary Company was formed. A flourishing business in chemicals and in some of the Company's dietetic specialities grew up and a factory was built in Moscow and equipped to manufacture many of these products locally. Not unnaturally, these developments were complicated by the outbreak of war in 1914, but the Moscow factory continued in successful production until the outbreak of the Revolution in 1917. At that time the whole of the property of the Company was confiscated by the Soviet Government and has remained in their hands ever since, although it is understood that the Company's name and the factory itself are still in use.

CHAPTER 6

MODERN TIMES

REFERENCE has been made at the beginning of Book Four to the changing trends of medicine and pharmacy during the first half of the twentieth century. It is now appropriate to mention more specifically the manner in which Allen & Hanburys has adapted itself to these changing trends and, in conclusion, to review the present position and policy of the Company.

Prior to about 1880, medicine was concerned primarily in treating and alleviating the symptoms of disease. Since that time the emphasis has been increasingly laid upon a direct attack on the causes of disease and the virtual eradication, at any rate in temperate climates, of such scourges as typhoid and diphtheria. The old and time-honoured inorganic chemicals and drugs of vegetable origin came to be replaced to a large extent by new and potent drugs derived from animal glands, by synthetic organic chemicals and by penicillin and the other antibiotics derived from living organisms. The advent of these newer types of medication necessitated new techniques of administration, and the single-dose tablet taken by the mouth and the hypodermic injection came to replace many of the older mixtures, draughts and powders of earlier days. As early as 1878 a Swiss surgeon had removed the thyroid gland from a woman in the treatment of goitre and it was soon recognized that preparations of the thyroid gland of animals provided a valuable treatment for myxœdema, and by 1893 preparations of the thyroid gland were listed for that purpose.

At about the same time it was discovered that the various glands of the body secreted substances or hormones which had a profound influence on the body, both in sickness and in health. Numerous extracts of these glands were prepared and were used regularly in medicine for many years. It is now appreciated that apart from thyroid, which is active when taken by mouth, the remaining hormones are quickly destroyed in the stomach and are only effective when injected directly into the blood-stream.

It has already been shown how Allen & Hanburys were among the pioneers in the designing of tablet machines and in the preparation of the newer drugs in the form of tablets, and the discovery of the hormones greatly stimulated the development of injectable preparations with which work F. W. Gamble was prominently associated during his period as manager of the Vere Street Branch. In 1921, however, there occurred a momentous and far-reaching event in the discovery by F. G. Banting, J. B. Collip and C. H. Best, workers at Toronto University, of a specific antidiabetic principle in the secretion of the pancreas gland which, when injected hypodermically, had the power of regulating carbohydrate metabolism. This principle was obtained from the group of cells in the pancreas known as the islets of Langerhans, discovered in 1869. This substance they called insulin, the discovery of which has enabled millions of diabetics throughout the world to lead normal and active lives.

On November 4th, 1922, the *British Medical Journal* published a paper entitled ' Insulin and Diabetes ', by J. J. R. Macleod, Professor of Physiology, Toronto University. This paper was described as a general statement of the physiological and therapeutic effects of insulin : it was a summary of the work carried on during 1921 and 1922 by the above and other workers in the Toronto Medical School in the specific treatment of diabetes mellitus : it marked the beginning of the production of insulin in this country.

The originators of the laboratory method of preparing insulin, realizing that the publication of it might be followed by uncontrolled commercial exploitation of the product, with the likelihood of its improper use, offered to apply for patents covering its production and to hand these over to the University of Toronto, provided that body would assume the function of licensing approved manufacturers to produce it and sell it at a reasonable cost. Patents were therefore applied for in Canada, the United States, Great Britain, and other countries, and the University appointed a Committee, partly composed of those who participated in the original investigations and partly members of the Board of Governors to advise with regard to the conditions under which licences should be granted.

The British rights of the Patent were offered, as a free gift, to the Medical Research Council, Hampstead, London, and were gratefully accepted by that body. It was realized that the production of insulin, even on the laboratory scale, was not free from difficulties and risks, and these became greater when its production on a large scale was attempted : the Medical Research Council had to take such steps to protect the method of manufacture so that its commercial production should be carried out in a proper manner and with proper safeguards.

On February 24th, 1923, a statement was published by the Medical Research Council to the effect that insulin was being produced, standardized and used, in the treatment of selected patients at certain hospitals in London, Sheffield and Edinburgh, and that the Council had entered into agreements with certain manufacturing firms for the manufacture of insulin, retaining in the public interest control of the safety and potency of the product and its sale at a fair price. No royalties were payable to the Council under any of these agreements. Later the Council was able to state that rapid progress was being made and that this was due equally to the laboratory investigations of the Medical Research Council and to the experience, skill and enthusiasm which the firms had shown in their co-operation with the Council of that body.

In a statement in the *British Medical Journal* of April 21st, 1923, by the Medical Research Council, the information was given that insulin, at that date, was being supplied from two sources, namely, The British Drug Houses Ltd. of London, in conjunction for this purpose with Allen & Hanburys Ltd. of London, and the firm of Burroughs Wellcome & Company of London : these firms, who undertook the manufacture under an agreement with the Medical Research Council had satisfied all the requirements and tests of the Council for authenticity, standard value, therapeutic activity and sterility of the product sold.

A similar agreement was made with Boots Pure Drug Company Ltd. who also manufactured insulin.

The statement continued that the rapid progress made by the firms mentioned since the end of November, 1922, and the actual achievement of successful and guaranteed supply within a period of little more than four months from the first attempt at large-scale production, had been made in spite of some serious handicaps. The large quantities of alcohol used for extraction brought the manufacture under almost prohibitive restrictions, until certain concessions were made by the Commissioners of Customs and Excise which allowed specially de-natured alcohol to be used duty free. The embargo on the importation of Canadian cattle had greatly reduced the supply of fresh raw pancreas material in this country and a good deal of improvization and initiative had been necessary for the effective organization of the available supply of raw material during recent months. The only limit placed and likely to be placed upon British production was the limitation of raw materials available under suitable conditions.

Owing to the restricted supply in the first instance, authority was given to the above firms to distribute insulin to various large hospitals only and the first British insulin made on a commercial scale was so supplied by Allen & Hanburys Ltd., and The British Drug Houses Ltd., on April 12th, 1923 : Burroughs Wellcome & Company had supplies available about the same time.

It should be noted that insulin, owing to the comparatively small number of doses produced, was at first limited to large hospitals and medical practitioners who undertook to observe certain conditions in its administration : in the *British Medical Journal* of May 26th, 1923, the statement was made that owing to the considerable increase in production by British firms it was no longer necessary to maintain restrictions upon the supply of insulin, which therefore could be obtained through the usual commercial channels.

While negotiations were taking place between the interested firms and the Medical Research Council with a view to the manufacture of insulin on a large scale, discussions also took place between the directors of Allen & Hanburys Ltd. and The British Drug Houses Ltd., with a view to combining the resources of the two Companies in this venture. It will be recalled that the Bethnal Green premises had been extensively damaged in the last air raid of the First World War in May, 1918, and the damaged area had been replaced by a fine modern building in which analytical, research and bacteriological laboratories had been fitted up. These laboratories were exceptionally well suited to the work that was needed in the development of the insulin process, whereas The British Drug Houses were better placed in their Graham Street premises for the erection of a large-scale production unit. In this task they were greatly assisted by Mr. (later Dr.) F. H. Carr, to whom great credit was due for the rapidity with which insulin was produced in quantity. An Agreement was drawn up between the two Companies and the insulin produced by their joint efforts was and still is marketed under the name 'Insulin A.B.' By July, 1923, the A.B. Partnership was producing thirty-thousand doses of insulin a week, a supply which was in excess of the amount immediately required. As a matter of historical interest, it may be noted that the price of a 5-c.c. vial of insulin containing ten doses was, when it was first introduced, 25s. At the present time the same sized vial costs considerably less than a tenth of that figure.

*   *   *

Soon after the discovery of insulin, it was observed that aqueous extracts of mammalian liver contained a substance or substances of value in the treatment of pernicious anaemia. On account of the nausea produced by a large daily intake of fresh liver, extensive researches led to the production of concentrated and palatable aqueous extracts containing the active principle, which extracts were at first administered by mouth, but subsequently came to be further purified so that they were suitable for parenteral injection.

Contrary to the experience with pancreas extract from which biochemists quickly isolated crystalline insulin, the active principle of liver defied isolation for more than twenty years. Ultimately it was in 1948 that the isolation of a pure red-coloured crystalline substance was announced almost simultaneously in Great Britain and the United States. This substance was at first called vitamin B_{12} but was subsequently named cyanocobalamin. It is present in liver only in extremely small quantities, but it was soon discovered that a richer source was to be found in the metabolite liquors produced by the mould *Streptomyces griseus*, which also produces the antibiotic Streptomycin. Cyanocobalamin was later shown to be one of those substances which is widely distributed in animal tissues and the healthy subject derives his essential requirements from minute quantities obtained from a wide variety of foodstuffs. Two liver extracts were originally developed in the Company's research laboratories—Anahepol and Hepolon. The former was a concentrated extract which has been superseded by the introduction of crystalline cyanocobalamin, but hepolon, which is a relatively ' crude ' but injectable extract, contains not only cyanocobalamin but also other factors of particular value in a number of nutritional tropical anaemias.

Other products which were developed at about that time were Pitibulin, an extract of the posterior lobe of the pituitary gland ; Euparatone, an extract of the parathyroid gland, containing the principle associated with calcium metabolism, and a number of products derived from the anterior pituitary, containing the lactogenic, adrenotropic and thyrotropic hormones.

In the early 1930's it had been hoped that the growth-controlling hormone of the parathyroid gland might prove to be of value in the control of cancerous growth. Promising results were obtained in the early stages and the Research Laboratories, in close association with a team of medical men and physiologists, carried out an extensive investigation and production programme of preparations derived from the parathyroid gland. This gland is one of the smallest in the body and a world-wide search was made for supplies of parathyroids to meet what might have been an overwhelming demand. A great quantity of these glands was accumulated from all over the world and extensive clinical trials were carried out on the extracts prepared from them. Unhappily, however, and despite a number of enthusiastic reports, the early promise of the work was not fulfilled, and like so many other ventures in the field of research, the end-result was largely negative.

At about the same time a more successful investigation led to the production of a preparation containing the active principles of the adrenal cortex. A number of processes were published in this and other countries at about that time, but ultimately Allen & Hanburys developed their own process, which resulted in the production of Eucortone, a substance used specifically in the treatment of Addison's disease.

Despite the subsequent discovery and synthesis of a number of these active principles, there are still occasions when a potent extract of the adrenal cortex offers significant advantages over the synthetic steroids and eucortone continues to be widely used and prescribed.

*   *   *

The latter years of the nineteenth century were characterized by remarkable advances in the field of immunization therapy by the use of vaccines and sera. In 1726 Silvanus Bevan in treating a girl of fifteen for smallpox found that she had inoculated herself with the disease which then ran its normal course ; this case was recorded in a letter addressed to the Royal Society.

About eighty years later William Allen also interested himself in the subject of vaccination which had been introduced by Jenner in 1796. Jenner's discovery that it was possible to provide immunity against smallpox in human beings by inoculating them with the serum which develops in the vesicles of cattle suffering from cow-pox, and Pasteur's explanation that vaccination was in reality inoculation with a virus which had been weakened (attenuated) by its passage through the cow, was followed by his production of cultures of low virulence for the treatment of anthrax and particularly hydrophobia.

It was not until 1882, however, that Koch and his co-workers isolated and identified the pathogenic organisms causing tuber-culosis, and the isolation of cholera followed in 1886. From then until 1898 the causative organisms of such diseases as diph-theria, typhoid fever, Malta fever, tetanus, plague, dysentery, bovine abortion and pleuro-pneumonia were brought to light.

On July 1st, 1889, a meeting was held at the Mansion House in the City of London at which was inaugurated the British Institute of Preventive Medicine, which in 1903 was renamed the Lister Institute. The specific purpose of the meeting was to discuss the urgent problem of the incidence in Great Britain of hydrophobia in the light of Pasteur's work in France on immunizing the victims of the bites of rabid dogs with his attenuated virus. The New Institute had objectives similar to those of the Pasteur Institute of Paris and in 1891 it received its Charter. In May, 1895, Cornelius Hanbury entered into an arrangement with the Institute by which Allen & Hanburys became the sole distributing agent for the Institute's products, and the Firm's price list of 1898 describes several products under the heading 'The Treatment of Diphtheria and other diseases by Anti-Toxic Serums'. Pure vaccine lymph for vaccination against smallpox was also described.

*   *   *

At about the same time further revolutionary discoveries were about to be made in the field of nutrition, and a great number of hitherto intractable diseases were found to be due to the absence in the diet of adequate quantities of certain accessory food factors, subsequently termed 'vitamins'. As far back as 1881 a young assistant working in the laboratory of the German chemist Bunge came very near to discovering the vitamins in connection with some experiments he was making on the rearing of young mice, but he did not carry his investigations far enough, and it was not until 1901 that it was proved that from the polishings of rice an extract could be made which was curative to a striking degree in the human disease beriberi. In 1909 Dr. Stepp, a German biochemist, discovered the significance of the fat-soluble vitamins A and D, but it was left to the late Sir Frederick (then Professor) Gowland Hopkins to demonstrate that animals declined in health on a diet lacking the essential vitamins, even when they were eating sufficient protein fat carbohydrate and minerals to supply their requirements in other respects.

Earlier in this narrative it has been described how Allen & Hanburys had been closely linked with the manufacture of cod-liver oil in the mid-nineteenth century. The value of liver oils had been appreciated as a result of practical experience from time immemorial, but at last it was understood how these oils had a value greater than could be accounted for merely by their fat content. Ever since the Industrial Revolution children growing up in big cities had suffered almost as a matter of course from rickets, due to their receiving an inadequate intake of dairy produce, which also contains the vitamins A and D that they need. Once the need for these things was understood, cod-liver oil in its various forms came to be appreciated as a supplementary foodstuff of great value and, as is well known, the disease of rickets which as recently as 1910 was the normal thing amongst industrial populations has to-day become practically non-existent. Later it was discovered that the symptoms of scurvy resulted from a deficiency of vitamin C which is normally present in fresh fruit and vegetables.

Before the beginning of the First World War when F. W. Gamble was at Vere Street he was interested in the treatment of beriberi and prepared a hypodermic injection of the vitamin B complex for the treatment of this disease. When he came to Bethnal Green he considered that the time was ripe for making preparations incorporating the other important vitamins. In the early 1930's investigations showed that many other fish oils contained a far higher proportion of vitamins A and D than cod, and the most useful of these newer oils was halibut-liver oil which may contain anything from fifty to a hundred times as much vitamin A as cod-liver oil, thereby allowing the administration of an equivalent dose in a much smaller volume, to the great benefit of those who find fish oils nauseous. Allen & Hanburys formulated their well-known product ' Haliborange ', combining the vitamin C of the orange-juice with the vitamins A and D of the halibut liver oil in a palatable preparation which is now well known throughout the world.

The appreciation of the important roles of the vitamins in medicine stimulated the biochemists to examine their chemical structure and to-day the majority of the vitamins can be synthesized in the laboratory and administered in precise dosage either by the mouth or by injection.

*   *   *

We have seen how during the last one hundred and fifty years medicine has progressed by a series of positive steps. In 1800 the old empirical drugs were all that were available—mineral salts, crude vegetable materials—the majority of them useless, but a few of them as valuable to-day as they were a thousand years ago. Then we saw the isolation of the active principles present in the drugs which were responsible for their action on the human body. In the mid-nineteenth century came the discovery of the aniline dyes which led in turn to important advances in two different fields, namely that of bacteriology, in which disease-causing organisms could be stained and examined with greater clarity than had previously been possible, while the chemists opened up the vast new science of organic chemistry and began to synthesize a multitude of new substances previously non-existent with which the organisms causing disease could be directly attacked and reduced to impotence. We have seen the development of vaccines and sera which within a few generations achieved the virtual elimination of such universal scourges as smallpox and diphtheria, followed by the isolation of penicillin and the antibiotics, and synthetic drugs, of which the sulpha drugs are typical, both of which interfere with the life cycles of disease-bearing organisms, thereby assisting the body to overcome their attacks. Immense efforts have been made all over the world to isolate and examine a wide variety of the lower fungi and soil organisms, and while it is rash to prophesy in such matters, it is possible that the majority of valuable anti-biotics have by now been discovered. The emphasis to-day therefore lies in the field of synthetic chemistry, and the best hope for the elimination of the many diseases to which a cure is as yet unknown lies as far as we can see in the chemist's laboratory. It is often said that we must all die in our time and if not from one cause, then from another. The almost total elimination of such diseases as diabetes, pernicious anaemia and pneumonia as causes of death means that the mortality figures from cancer and the heart diseases has shown a marked increase. It may perhaps be questioned whether the discoveries of the last hundred years have reduced materially the sum total of human suffering. A good case could be made out to show that they have in fact done that in good measure, but it must be remembered that all we can achieve is to ensure for as many as possible a normal and healthy span of life and a peaceful old age as free as possible from pain and discomfort.

EPILOGUE

THE object of this story has been to record the development from small beginnings of an industrial organization with world-wide ramifications. It is a story of high ideals and their fulfilment ; of honest endeavour and its reward. It is a far cry indeed from the eighteenth-century apothecary's shop of Silvanus Bevan with ' its stuffed crocodile athwart the entrance ', and it will be plainly apparent that an organization of this kind has been built up primarily round the characters and abilities of the people who have controlled its progress generation after generation. The philanthropist will find in it the narrative of far-reaching movements for the betterment of humanity, movements which were closely associated with the historic room over the old pharmacy. The scientist will be interested in the part played by the Partners of the Firm in the advancement of science ; William Allen with his multifarious interests in the experimental sciences of chemistry and physics and his association with many of the most famous chemists and physicists of his day ; Daniel Hanbury who blazed a trail into hitherto unknown regions of the pharmacology of his time and whose too short life was a record of single-minded devotion, rarely paralleled, to the particular section of knowledge he deemed his own.

In passing, he will note that five Fellows of the Royal Society were trained in the old Plough Court Pharmacy and that a sixth, Luke Howard, was associated with it for a short period.

It has become commonplace to observe that within the lifetimes of those now middle aged there has been a greater advance in our understanding of disease and its causes than in the whole previous history of mankind. The people whose story has been chronicled in these pages, partners, directors, scientists and others, have played a not unworthy part in the fight for a better, healthier and happier world. No one can say what the future holds in store, but it is certain that great as have been the advances seen in our generation, the years immediately ahead will see even more remarkable strides forward in man's conquest of his environment.

APPENDICES

INDEX

APPENDICES

No. 1. QUARE, DANIEL, 1649–1724

Britten in his *Old Clocks and Watches and Their Makers*, says, of the first horologists of Tompion's time who can be admitted as his peers, Daniel Quare was perhaps the most notable example. In 1676 he invented and made a repeating movement for watches and in 1680 perfected his design and made repeaters. A clock was made with many of his improvements to the order of William III as well as a repeating watch. The clock which was still going in 1912 is wound only once a year and shows the phases of the moon and the course of the sun. It was designed as a bedroom clock for the King and stood near his bed.

Quare obtained a patent for his portable weather glass in 1695. Six or seven of his instruments, made according to his specifications, are known to exist. It appears to have been the usual long barometer with an arrangement for emptying the contents of the mercury cistern into the tube and keeping it there, when it could be carried in any position.

*   *   *

No. 2. ALEXANDER POPE

Alexander Pope (1688–1744), poet, was born in either May or June, 1688, at number two, Plough Court, Lombard Street. His father was Alexander Pope, who originally lived, and carried on the business of linen-draper, in Broad Street in the Parish of St. Bennet-Fink. After his first wife's death in August 1679, he appears to have removed to the premises at number two, Plough Court. He married as his second wife, Edith, daughter of William Turner of Towthorpe, Yorkshire, in either 1686 or 1687. Of this marriage Alexander Pope was born.

There has always existed doubt as to the reliability of the above statement regarding Pope's birthplace, but the evidence of Spence should settle the question. Joseph Spence was a contemporary and intimate friend of the poet and he preserved notes of his conversations with him somewhat as Boswell did of Dr. Johnson's : these were not published until 1820, long after Spence's death. Under date of 1737–1739 he writes :

> Mr. Pope was born in the City of London, in Lombard Street, at the house which is now one Mr. Morgan's, an apothecary.

But who was Morgan ? Careful research has failed to trace him and there seems no doubt that the name of Morgan was mistaken for Bevan. Paul Bevan stated that he had always understood that Alexander Pope and Joseph Gurney Bevan were born in the same room and that room was the one on the second floor of number two looking on to Plough Court.

J. G. Bevan also remembered that sight-seers often visited Plough Court to gaze on the house where the poet was born.

In volume II, ' *Poetical Works of Alexander Pope* ', *edited by Robert, Carruthers, in four volumes, London, Nathaniel Cooke, Milford House, Strand, 1853*, is an engraving of a view of number two Plough Court presumably as it was in Pope's time. A copy of this appears on the frontispiece.

★　　　★　　　★

No. 3. EIGHTEENTH-CENTURY REMEDIES

Mumia (or mummy) was regarded as a most useful remedy for consumptions, wasting of flesh, ulcers and various corruptions ; in the *London Pharmacopoeia* of 1677 several kinds are specified. There is the factitious, made from bitumen and pitch, the Egyptian, Arabian, and artificial ; the directions for making this last begin : ' Take the carcase of a young man (some say red hair'd) not dying of a disease, etc.' !

Cran. Human (human skull). This was specific in the case of most diseases of the head . . . ' the Triangular Bone in the Temples is the most Specificall against the Epileptic '.

Theriaca Andromachi, to give it its full title, or Venice treacle, as it was popularly called, was reputed to have been invented by Andromachus, the physician to Nero, as an improvement on mithridatum which until then was the great antidote in Roman pharmacy. The new preparation contained vipers and opium ; it was Pliny who alluded to it and probably popularized it as theriaca, and although for some centuries it was made in turn at Constantinople, Cairo, and Genoa, Venice eventually appears to have secured the monopoly of its manufacture for a considerable period. It contained in addition to vipers

276

and opium no less than seventy-five ingredients, including rhubarb, black pepper, cinnamon, ginger, cardamoms, etc. It was used in this country till the end of the eighteenth century and was made in London as well as in certain cities in France, Germany and Italy. According to the records of the Society of Apothecaries for 1721, five hundred pounds of Venice treacle were publicly made and potted in London, and were sealed with the Company's seal ; this was the first occasion when the seal was affixed to any preparations made by the Apothecaries Company.

Lapis, Bezoar, Orient, Occident. Bezoar stones were introduced into European medicines by the Arabs ; the most esteemed variety. These came from Persia and were supposed to be obtained from the intestines of the native wild goat. The stone was a calculus which had formed itself round some nucleus such as hair, or the stone of a fruit such as a date. It was believed that the special virtues of the stone were due to some unknown plant on which the animal fed. In 1714 the price in London varied from about three to five pounds per ounce. It was regarded as a valuable remedy against all kinds of fevers, the stone was often carried about in a gold or silver box as an amulet and in Portugal in times of plague they were hired out at the equivalent of ten shillings per day. Genuine stones were required to be of an olive-greenish tint, to be striated, and to yield a musky odour.

The importance attached to bezoar stones in the eighteenth century and, incidentally, their liability to falsification, is illustrated by a minute of the Society of Apothecaries dated May 25th, 1630, as follows :

The pretended (bezoar) stones sent by the Lord Mayor to be viewed were found to be false and counterfeit and fitt to be destroyed and the whole 'table' (Court) certified the same to the Lord Mayor.

A jury composed partly of druggists and partly of apothecaries was empanelled, and confirmed the verdict of the Court, and the stones were duly burnt.

Viper Sicc. (dried viper). Vipers are stated to be

' Alexipharmick and strongly prevail against poison, plagues and all manner of Infectious Diseases. They were also recommended to be eaten sodden, roasted or raw. The essence appeared to be the best method of exhibiting their virtues.'

★   ★   ★

No. 4. LETTERS FROM SILVANUS BEVAN TO DR. JURIN

Dr. Jurin

The following case being some what remarkable, I request it may be inserted in the Account of Innocculation for Year 1725——

a Daughter of Walter Newberry a Merchant of Philpott Lane ab^t 15 years of age, haveing often importuned her Father to admitt her being inocculated, which he not consenting to, she took the following opportunity to do it herself.

Her Younger Sister being taken ill with the Small Pox, ab^t the beginning of November last (which happened to be a favourable kind) 'twas proposed the Eldest should be removed, which she refused, asured them, she was so far from being afraid of it, that she wished she might have them, & desired she might have Liberty to see her Sister as often as she pleased, she took a Vomitt by way of preparation, in case she should have them the Naturall way, 8 or 9 days haveing passed & finding no approach of it, she resolved to inocculate herself, she went to her Sister's room & persuaded the Nurse to go down to Supper & she took the Bedcloths off the Child, to find out the largest Pock, & finding one in the foot, which would best answer her purpose, she opened it with a Needle, & with the Top of her finger applied the Contents to a Scratch she had before on her Arm, ab^t 2 inches below the Elbow, without applying anything over it, only took care to dry it on, to prevent its being rub'd off.

The part in 3 or 4 days inflamed & by the Time I saw it, it formed the same kind of Ulcer as is Usuall from inocculation, on the Seventh day she was attack'd with a slight fever of which Little Notice was taken, on the eighth day it considerably increasing, I was sent for, & found her under the Usual Symptoms of an aproaching small pox, which I Mentioned to her friends in her hearing, she was very well pleased & then Discovered the Secrett. . . .

. . . on the 9th day there was a small appearance, which proceeded in a regular & kindly Manner, the Ulcer discharged a thick pus, which declined with the pock, since which she enjoys better state of health than before.

By the above account there is little doubt but she had the Desease by Inoculation, the Distance of that time to the apearance corresponding Exactly with those, who have been inoculated, severall of whom I have attended & here I beg leave to make one remark which I have some reason to think, tho I have not observed it so strictly as to vouch it for Truth & therefore do recommend it as worthy the Observation of those who Practise Physick that the Infection received by the common way seldom produces of desease in less Time than when it is given by inocculation, & I have frequently observed in familys were are a Number of Children & one of them have the Desease it is at least 9 or 10 days before any of the rest fall ill.

I am with Respects thy Loveing Friend.

Silvanus Bevan.

*   *   *

No. 5. LODDIDGE STREET

There is an interesting, although brief account, in William Allen's diary, of a visit he paid to this district in company with his cousin, Emily G. Birkbeck, and Anna Hanbury in the afternoon of March 30th, 1822.

> . . . we all went to Loddidge's Nursery, to see the Cammelias which are now in full bloom and very beautiful ! There is quite a forest of them : his hot-houses are, perhaps, the most capacious in the world : one of them is 40 feet high : in this there is a banana tree which reaches to the top.

*   *   *

No. 6. LETTER TO SAMUEL FORTE FROM J. G. BEVAN

London 10th 12th month 1791.

Samuel Forte
  BARBADOES.

Altho' I cannot at this time send thee an Acct. Sales of the Sugar Rece'd by the *Martha*, it may be agreeable to thee to know they were Sold in course and at the markett price of that time for brown Sugar viz—70/-, tho I believe the price has risen since. In my next I hope to send thee amount.

Altho' the present rise of Sugar be very agreeable to the planters I think it will ultimately hurt their interest. Many have no doubt learned to refrain from so dear a purchase of an article that may be done without, and many, probably many more, since the late defeat of the endeavours used to put an end to the Man-trade have renounced the gratification of their palates as almost the only way of obtaining their wishes. Others have been helped on in their aversion of W.I. Sugar, which to make they take to be the most distinctive employment of Slaves, by the late introduction of E. India Sugar, w'ch notwithstanding the high duty, vies at this time in many families with yours, and it seems to me that the very great disproportion of cost with which this Sugar is said to be made by free Men (I have heard 9/- even to 3/4 plus) shews beyond dispute that whilst Planters are connecting the ideas of ruin with the stop of the Slave Trade these are ultimately endangering the prosperity of their Country by not attempting some mode of Culture and manufacture less expensive than the present and that if they much longer oppose the wishes of the friends of the African they may be induced by interest to second them when it cannot be done so much for the advantage of the W. Indies as it might have been.

I do not often diverge in my Letters from Business ; but we have been, tho' personally unknown, pretty old acquaintances I hope not dissatisfied with each other, and this consignment naturally introduced the remarks.

I am with respect thy friend

J. G. Bevan.

* * *

No. 7. MONTEGO BAY ORDER

The orders sent in from the West Indies in those days often contained not only a considerable number of items, amounting in some cases to well over one hundred, but their variety was extraordinary and embraced not only drugs, chemists' sundries and surgeons' instruments, but haberdashery, groceries, footwear, as well as other goods not easily classified.

Space forbids the giving of such an order in full, but a few extracts from one to be shipped to Montego Bay towards the close of the eighteenth century should be amusing :

18 Pairs small women's cotton stockings
    3 threads four in the heels.
6 Pairs neat green Morocco shoes to fitt small women or big
    girls, 2 pairs to be about $\frac{1}{2}$ in. longer than the rest.

6 Pairs common black leathern shoes low and broad heels to
  fitt as the Morocco, not servants' shoes but neat.
5 Yards fine black prunella.
1 Best Green silk umbrella (9 sticks).
1 Man's best black Beaver Hatt 6½ inches.
4 doz. lings (?) of 1sts. Fiddle Strings.
1 doz. best Green hand^le Knives and Forks London Blades with
  Carving Knife and Fork.
1 P^r double jointed temple spectacles, silver frames and green
  shagreen case with glasses for 70 years of age and spare
  lenses for 60 and for 80 years of age to fitt.

The following books—

  Boyse's four last things.
  Jenkin's reasonableness and certainty of the Christian Religion.
  Universal Restitution in Scriptural Doctrine.
  Law's Serious Call.
½ cwt. of Sun raisons and ¼ cwt. Currants.
½ cwt. fine White Biskets in 2 kegs.
½ hundred pickled walnuts in jars.
1 doz. E.I. Mangoes & 1 Quart Mushroom Ketchup & 6 pints
  of best ol: oil.
6 lbs. best mildest
  smoaking Tobacco in Box
  (not in papers).

In addition there was a long list of drugs.

*   *   *

No. 8. QUOTATION FOR HORSES

London 31st. 12th month 1824.
T. G. Whitfield.
  Respected Friend,
    We wrote thee under date 12 month 4th. per duplicate herewith
since which we have received thine dated Sept. 8 being nearly a
duplicate of thy letter dated Aug. 23. In this communication thou
requests that we would ascertain the probable expense of sending out
to Buenos Ayres, a Race Horse and Mare and a draft Horse and Mare.
We have accordingly made some enquiry on the subject and find
from the Ship Brokers that the following will be the terms for the

Freight and provision for the 4 Horses including necessary fittings in the vessel for their reception, viz.

Hay	£30			
Water casks	£14			
Corn	£15			
Fittings	£20			
		£79	0	0
Freight of Hay		30	0	0
,, ,, Water		17	10	0
,, ,, Corn		6	0	0
,, ,, each Horse £50		200	0	0
Total		332	10	0

Exclusive of Insurance.

With respect to the cost of the Horses, everything depends upon their qualities Breed, Age, etc., but from some information which we have received from a person acquainted with their value we are induced to think that such as might suit thee could be procured at an average of about £100 each. Thou wilt observe that the above amount does not include the expense of a groom to go out with the Horses to take care of them which will be indispensably necessary, this, together with unforeseen contingencies, would probably make the total cost little short of £1,000.

* * *

No. 9. EARLY EDUCATION—WILLIAM ALLEN

Quite early in his career he laid down a plan for filling in the gap in his academic education. He writes 'a grand object with me is to perfect myself in the study of medicine also in Latin'. He usually had some work in French on hand and read a portion of it every day. He also made considerable progress in German. In drawing, to which he occasionally devoted some time, he engaged the services of a Master—some few years later he began the study of Algebra with his lifelong friend, John Hodgkin, and when on holiday was 'pretty busily engaged in taking angles and in calculating them which has considerably improved me in trigonometry'.

* * *

No. 10. THOMAS CLARKSON, 1760–1845

Many references will be found in this story to Thomas Clarkson the anti-slavery agitator who was one of William Allen's closest and life-long friends. He was the son of the Rev. John Clarkson, one time headmaster of the Free Grammar School at Wisbech, and entered St. John's College, Cambridge, in 1779 ; in 1784 and 1785 he won the members' prizes for Latin essays open to middle and senior bachelors respectively. The subject for the essay of 1785 was the question *Anne liceat invitos in servitutem dare ?* and the contest for this prize determined the whole course of Clarkson's life.

He translated the essay in order to draw the attention of influential people to the horrors of the Slave Trade. He was introduced to James Phillips, the Quaker bookseller of George Yard, Lombard Street, London, by whom the essay was published in June 1786.

Early in 1833 his eyesight failed him due to the growth of a cataract on each eye. Although he contemplated undergoing an operation, a somewhat formidable ordeal in those days, he thought it best to dedicate what conceivably might be the last letter he would ever write to ' dear William Allen ', bringing to memory their joint labours in ' some of the most interesting subjects that can interest the mind of man '.

The operation was successful and in July 1835 he wrote to Allen sympathizing with him on the death of his third wife Grizell whom Clarkson had known for forty-nine years.[1]

Clarkson survived Allen but two years, in a letter to an unnamed friend of both, he said ' I do not hesitate to say on my part that there never has been any man living, for whom I had so great a regard '.

*   *   *

No. 11. BRYAN HIGGINS

Bryan Higgins, M.D., 1737–1820, was a chemist and physician who gave lectures on the sciences in Greek Street, Soho, London.

An account of the work carried on in the laboratory was published in 1795 under the title of *Minutes of the Society for Philosophical Experiments and Conversations*. The laboratory was well equipped and of considerable size.

[1] See illustration facing page 119.

*   *   *

No. 12. RICHARD PHILLIPS, 1776–1851

Richard Phillips, the son of a well-known printer in George Yard, Lombard Street, was born in 1776. His father was a Quaker and a near neighbour and associate of William Allen. Richard entered the Plough Court Pharmacy as dispenser, and assistant in the laboratory. His elder brother, William, was a mineralogist of good reputation and he and Richard became founder members of the Geological Society.

Richard Phillips started as a chemist and druggist at No. 29 in the Poultry, and in 1811 he published a book in which he criticised the *New London Pharmacopoeia of 1809*. The College of Physicians and the Apothecaries' Society issued a further edition in 1815, *Editio Altera*, and this called forth from Phillips a still more caustic criticism.

Leaving business, he devoted himself to scientific and literary pursuits and was appointed lecturer on chemistry at the London Hospital. He was one of the editors of *The London, Edinburgh and Dublin Philosophical Magazine*. In addition, he was at different times chemical lecturer at the Government Military College at Sandhurst, and also at St. Thomas's Hospital. In 1822 he was elected F.R.S. and in 1824 he became the authorized translator of the 1824 *London Pharmacopoeia* and later the editor and translator of the 1836 and 1851 editions. In 1839 he was appointed Curator of the Museum of Practical Geology, which was then established under the Government in Craig's Court, Charing Cross, and subsequently removed to Jermyn Street : he died on May 11th, 1851, the day before that on which Prince Albert opened it.

*   *   *

No. 13. LECTURES AT GUY'S HOSPITAL

It was on January 10th, 1802, that Dr. Babington called at Plough Court and offered Allen a partnership in his lectures on chemistry at Guy's Hospital. This visit was followed by Astley Cooper, who strongly advised Allen to accept the offer. Obviously such required earnest consideration and after consulting with J. G. Bevan, he agreed to Dr. Babington's suggestion and about a month later he gave his first lecture. He felt, he says, low and anxious, but he got through, much to his satisfaction, although much distressed by the loud plaudits of the students which began and ended the lecture.

On the 16th March, 1814, Allen gave a lecture at the Hospital on Earths and showed iodine for the first time. In December, 1816, the year in which John Keats, the English poet, entered the Hospital as a student, Allen was lecturing both morning and evening and the new theatre was crowded.

In a week's review in his diary he notes

' that the lectures are a great weight upon me and take up much time, yet I get through them satisfactorily and I understand that the pupils are greatly pleased '.

His subjects were always topical : he gave a lecture on the steam engine in 1817.

The lectures were divided into two main sections : physics, which were given in the evenings, and chemistry, which were given in the mornings.

PHYSICS

Subject	No. of lectures
Astronomy	2
Electricity	5
Galvanism	2
Hydraulics	2
Hydrostatics	5
Magnetism	1
Mechanics	10
Optics	5
Pneumatics	5

CHEMISTRY

Subject	No. of lectures
Acids	3
Caloric	6
Combustibles	4
Earths	4
Elements	1
Gases (Oxygen)	3
Gases (Hydrogen)	1
Gases (Azote)	1
Organic Substances	2
Salts	2

There were a few lectures not coming within these categories ;

one of these was on compound engines, clocks, etc. The apparatus used to demonstrate these included :

> Bevan's Crane
> Steam Engine and Circular Saw
> Model of Crank
> Pile Driver
> Windmill, Flint's Model of
> Millwork
> Parts of a Watch.

In the bicentenary number of *Guy's Hospital Gazette*, published in 1926, there is a very appreciative note on William Allen and the work he did at the Hospital. He is alluded to as the Spitalfield's Genius.

*   *   *

No. 14. LETTER TO SIR HUMPHREY DAVY FROM WILLIAM ALLEN

Note : The finances of the Institution were not too satisfactory in 1810, as will be seen from this letter written by Allen to Sir Humphrey Davy.

26 of 7 mo. 1810.

Dear Davy,

It is not pleasant to me, to say much about money matters, but on looking over my accounts I find that the last settlement with the Royal Institution was up to the end of the year 1806, and that beside the amt. for Chemicals there is £105 due to me for 24 lectures begun near the close of 1806 and finished in 1807. If I were to charge interest, which I shall not, there would be due to me

Int. on 1807 and 1808 Accts.	£6. 14. –
do. 3 years on £105	£15. 15. –
	£22. 9. –

So that I may fairly consider myself that sum out of pocket. I just mention this, not with a view that the managers should be urged on the subject, but in hopes that if a favourable opportunity occurred and the state of the funds would permit that thou wouldst just remind them of the claim of

Yours sincerely,
Wm. Allen.

P.S. I leave the settlement of the last 9 lects. delivered this year entirely to the Managers.

★   ★   ★

No. 15. GEOLOGICAL SOCIETY

The Geological Society apparently sprang from the Mineralogical Society. This latter was founded at a meeting held in the Askesian Society's room at Plough Court on April 2nd, 1799. There were present William Allen, W. H. Pepys, Alexander Tilloch, Richard Knight and William Lowry. The number of members was not to exceed twenty. For the present, none were to be admitted members, but such as 'are able and willing to undertake a chemical analysis of a mineral substance'. Mr. W. H. Pepys was chosen as Secretary and Treasurer. At the end of 1800 country members were added. On December 18th, 1806, the Mineralogical Society was incorporated with the Askesian Society

Allen's statement in his diary regarding the Geological Society is as follows :

13th Eleventh month, 1807. Dined at the Freemason's Tavern about 5 o'clock with Davy, Dr. Babington, etc. etc., about eleven in all.—Instituted a Geological Society.

★   ★   ★

No. 16. COPY OF ORIGINAL LETTER FROM J. DALTON TO WILLIAM ALLEN

Manchester. 1st month 30th 1809.

Respected Friend
W. Allen

Being in want of a mercurial apparatus I wish to enquire of thee what the present price of the article is—I should have about 60 lbs. avoir. to fill my trough : please to send me a line as soon as convenient.

(quoted 5/4 to him of 7 of 2mo. 1809)

I have read with great interest your two papers on Carbonic Acid and Respiration and upon the whole am very well pleased with them.

I wrote a paper two or three years ago on Respiration which will perhaps appear in our next volume. The results of my experiments led me to conclude that all the oxygen which disappears is to be found in the carbonic acid. There is one very striking difference in our experiments, the medium of air expired with me loses only 4 or 5 oxygen per cent and gains nearly the same acid. The conclusion you obtain from respiring the same air as long as possible is very remarkable : I cannot make up my mind upon it. You say nothing as to the aqueous vapour exhaled. I find that Hales is spare of the truth in this respect. In the introduction in adverting to the name of those who have distinguished themselves you have somehow or other omitted the most distinguished of all, Crawford. This appeared to me somewhat like a person running over the names of those who have been eminently conspicuous on the subject of astronomy over-looking Newton.

I was glad to see your results on charcoal, so clear and definite. The notion of Diamond being a simple substance and common Charcoal the oxide of Diamond has long been discarded with me. You say nothing absolute on the subject of charcoal absorbing gases, but (?) seem to imply a doubt whether there is any absorption besides water.

From some expts in hand I am inclined to believe that charcoal never absorbs any kind of gas in the manner it has been represented, but only water. Have you made any experiments on this head ? Dr. Henry has just been making some very fine discoveries on the combustion of gases, the results of which will afford me some beautiful illustrations on the theory of their constitution.

I am only beginning the composition of the 2nd part of my elements : I am sorry that in the Progress I find a great many things to be erroneous, which I shall have the labour formally to disprove : such has been the credulity of our most approved writers—— We cannot understand the reason of your circuitous Eudiometer, what is the advantage of first letting nitrous gas into sulphate of iron and then expelling it again, that it may seize the oxygen ? Would it not save three fourths of the time and be in every other respect the same if the two gases were weighed together ? You find 21 per cent oxygen in the air : but if you are rigidly strict in the investigation another integer number somewhat nearer the truth may, I believe, be obtained.

This is of importance in experiments in respiration and combustion.

Hoping to receive a line from thee soon.

With respect thy assured friend.

J. Dalton.

P.S. Thou could not pick up for me a copy of Attwood on motion etc. ?

★   ★   ★

No. 17. BERZELIUS

To Professor Berzelius,
Stockholm.

19 of 12 month 1820.

Esteemed Friend,

The three pots with the substance containing Selenium arrived safe and we purpose to do the best that we can with it pursuant to thy directions. Though we doubt whether purchasers will be found. However, we intend to give public and private notice of it and to inform thee of the results. I have ordered the whole of it to be powdered and sifted and mixed thoroughly that it may be uniform. The accounts my people give of the weight is as follows :—

(Weights are then given showing that 23 lbs. 4 oz. were received in all.)

They tell me that it is somewhat moist and will probably lose weight in sifting etc. Now having undertaken to do the best I can for thee in this business may I ask in return for some information on the subject of your Publick Institutions.

(These enquiries relate to Allen's visits to Stockholm at the end of 1818, when he found time, amongst many other matters, to pay a visit to the ' large and convenient laboratory ' belonging to Berzelius.)

There was no reply to this letter, Berzelius was a busy man and may not have had the information which Allen required. On the 20th of January, 1823, another letter was sent from Plough Court, signed by ' Wm. Allen & Co.'. In it the writer reminded Berzelius of the contents of the former letter and reported that steps had been taken for the disposal of the selenium. An advertisement had been inserted in the Philosophical Journal, Vol. 59, page 221 ; there was still a balance of 12 lbs. of the original consignment in stock and the sum of £11 4s. 3d. for what had been sold would be paid to ' any person thou mayst be pleased to appoint '.

★   ★   ★

APPENDICES

No. 18. A VISIT TO J. G. CHILDREN

This is an account from his diary given in full of a visit William
Allen and a large number of English chemists paid to the large private
laboratory set up at Tunbridge by John George Children, Secretary
to the Royal Society.

1813 Seventh month 2nd. To town at eight o'clock. About
ten set off in a post-chaise with Wilson Lowry and Dr. Thompson
for Tunbridge. We reached Children's about four. There was
a great assemblage of English chemists—Dr. Wollaston, Tenant,
Davy, Hatchett, etc., etc., etc. Thirty-eight of us dined together.
Held a committee which did not break up till between twelve
and one. Children kindly provided lodging for all.

3rd, very busy assisting in preparation for the experiments.
The battery consisted of twenty pieces of copper and zinc plates,
six feet by two feet eight ; breadth of cells, two inches, distance
between each, four and a half inches ; about one part acid to
thirty of water by measure : the acid composed of three parts
nitric, and one part sulphuric : melted iridium—the pure metal
is easier melted than its ore ; we also performed many other
experiments. Set off with my former companions between
three and four o'clock, reached Newington about nine, very
tired.

A paper was read on this battery—printed in the *Philosophical
Transactions of the Royal Society*, 1815—it was the largest made to
that date (1813).

* * *

No. 19. THE DUKE OF KENT'S AFFAIRS

At Luneberg and Geneva the Duke of Kent had, before he was
of age, been coached by a Baron Wagenheim, who practically appro-
priated his pupil's income, allowing him 30s. a week out of £1,000
a year, and, after he was of age, out of £5,000 a year. Ordered to
Gibraltar on military service the Duke had to buy an outfit, transferred suddenly to Canada he had to buy a second, transferred to
the West Indies he had to buy a third, which was sunk in Lake
Champlain ; ordered back to Canada his fourth outfit (costing
£2,000) coming from England was captured by the French, and
another ordered for the same office was also captured ; raised to the
rank of General and transferred to Halifax a still more costly outfit

290

(costing £10,000) was also captured coming from England ; raised to the post of Commander-in-Chief of the Forces in North America, a still more costly outfit (£11,000) was wrecked coming from England. These heavy liabilities were thus incurred before Parliament granted him any income, and neither King nor Ministry would help him out of his embarrassments.

*   *   *

No. 20. TRANSIT INSTRUMENT

He began to prepare tables of the right ascension and declination of the stars from the first to the fourth magnitude with the places of some of the most interesting double stars. These were, in the first instance, arranged for his own amusement, but as they seemed likely to be useful to persons possessing a circular or transit instrument he was induced to publish them. In this little work entitled *A Companion to the Transit Instrument*, the variations in right ascension and declination were given to the end of 1814.

*   *   *

No. 21. COPY OF THE ORIGINAL LETTER FROM S. T. COLERIDGE

10th May, 1814.
2 Queens' Square, Bristol.

Dear Sir,

I take a great liberty which yet, I trust, your humanity will excuse in consideration of the calamitous state of my health ; tho' Heaven's Master be praised, by the skill and kindness of my Physician, who has attended me twice and three times a day for a month past, almost the only relict and sediment of my Disease consists in an excessive irritability of the lower part of the intestinal Canal, whenever the Bile (so long locked up in its ducts by the fatal use of narcotics) or the watery secretions, trickle over it, and which by nervous sympathy affects my knees for the time with an indescribable and intolerable aching, weakness, and feverish restlessness.

Now some years ago you were so good as to procure for me (tho' not in reality for myself) a *Clyster Machine* of most convenient construction for self injection and when last in London, I settled the Bill with your young man. I well remember that *in appearance it was an elegant Cylinder of polished Brass.* You would not only oblige, but *actually and importantly serve me* if you would condescend to drop a line or two at Everalls' and Wilsons', St. James Street, (formerly Savignys') describing *what* it was, and at what place you procured it, in case they should not possess the same—requesting them to send it, as soon as procured, to their correspondent J. and J. Gillet, Cutlers &c., Bristol.

Should you chance to see Thomas or Mrs. Clarkson, be so good as to inform them that I have been for many months *worse than nothing*, but that by the Grace of God, who has answered my fervent and importunate prayers for mercy, and for increase of faith and fortitude, and (instrumentally) by the great prudence, skill and gentleness of my medical attendant I am almost miraculously restored, and (as it were) *emancipated.* Mrs. C. will understand the phrase in respect of me.

I pray, hope, and trust, that our friend, Sir Humphry Davy—will bring back himself safe from his extensive Tour, with *new* stores of practical science and his *old* English Heart of Understanding.

What scenes, dear Sir ! have we not lived through ! What *centuries* of awful Events condensed into twenty years ! I could not help applying to Buonoparte this stanza of an obscure Poet in the reign of Charles the first, (Habington).

' The Tide, which did its banks O'erflow,
' As sent abroad by the angry Sea,
' To level vastest Fabrics low,
' And all old Trophies over-throw,
' Ebbs, like a Thief away ! '

Dr. Young says, ' An undevout astronomer is mad '. I am sure, we may now with equal truth apply this to an endevout Politician.
Excuse this freedom, Dear Sir,
from your obliged humble servant
S. T. Coleridge.

P.S. Should it be in your power conveniently to send down more directly the machine by the Bristol Coach, addressed to me at my friends, Josiah Wade, Esqre, No. 2, Queens' Square, Bristol, with the Bill, the amount shall be remitted with most unfeigned thanks by return of Post——

No envelope was used. There are two sheets and on the outside one is the following :

William Allen Esque,
Plough Court,
Lombard Street,
London.

Post Payd.

★   ★   ★

No. 22. COPY OF LETTER FROM SYDNEY SMITH TO WILLIAM ALLEN ON THE LINDFIELD EXPERIMENT

Foston York July 22
1824.

Dear Sir,

Suppose 3 Divisions A. B. C., an acre Each

A Turnips Potatoes & Garden stuff as these crops are pulled a batch of Winter Tares to come in very early for soiling next year.

B Winter tares—Summer tares, Broad Clover—or as Green Food for soiling.

C Wheat . . . and so on. I suppose the animals to be a pig and a Cow—or two pigs and a Cow. If the acre of Green food would more than suffice then take out of B $\frac{1}{4}$ of an acre of Barley—otherwise Barley must be bought.

There would not be enough Wheat for such a family—but I know not how to play the game better——

When first I became Rector of Foston the poor people had no Gardens. I took 2 acres from the Glebe & divided them into 16 gardens—they pay me a fair rent & pay me very punctually. It enables them to keep a pig and they are supplied with Garden Stuff, they can gather together enough manure for so small a plot of ground. Early in a Summer's Morning or late in a Summer's Evening you may see before and after the hours of agricultural labour the whole population of the hamlet, man, woman & Child toiling in the public Gardens. I often see the best intended Schemes for the assistance of the poor ending in disappointment. I have no doubt (after an experience of some years) of the utility of this Scheme . . . I am quite unacquainted with the Garden Cultivation applied to Grain Crops. . . . The whole resolves itself into a question of Expense.—The Spade & the Rake (expenses apart) are far superior Tools to the plough and the Harrow. They can make Land fine—deeper & with greater accuracy—and in Crops which do not require *all* the power of these Tools—of Course the power may be restrained—and the Land left in as Coarse a State as will suffice for the object . . . I have seen no instances of Land in such quantities as 3 acres allotted to the poor. I have not heard anything upon the Subject—from a general conviction of the impracticable nature of such projects.

It appears to me as irrational as giving them Looms to weave their Clothes or Forges to make their Tools—it sins against the doctrine of dividing Labour—Such schemes are often laid before the public in the first Honeymoon of the Experiment & nothing is told of their subsequent failure . . . Still I am open to Conviction and am very willing to suppose that you have anticipated and answered these objections,—and that you are well acquainted with the low state of talent & morals of the objects you relieve and of the serious obstacles their imperfections will occasion to your Benevolent Schemes . . . I hope observations are not intended to extinguish Charity but to prevent the disappointments of charity and to preserve its spirit . . . If I can be of any use command me. If you come into Yorkshire come & pay me a visit. I shall be very glad to see you. I thank you for your recommendation & remain truly yours

Sydney Smith.

✱   ✱   ✱

No. 23. MARIA EDGEWORTH TO WILLIAM ALLEN

Edgeworth's Town, January 1827.

Dear Sir,

I am gratified and honoured by your sending me an account of your benevolent plans for Ireland, and I heartily wish you and them success.

There can be no doubt that what you call colonization at home, would be preferable to colonization abroad, if it can be carried into effect, because it would, in the first place, save all the risk, expense and suffering of emigration, and would, in the next place, secure to the home country the benefits of increased and improved cultivation and civilization.

Your plans of improved agriculture and economy, appear most feasible and most promising on paper ; but I fear that in attempting to carry them into execution in this country, there would be found obstacles of which you can form no estimate, without a more intimate knowledge of the habits of the peasantry of Ireland, than a *first* visit to this country could afford, or, in short, anything but long residence could give. Their want of habits of punctuality and order, would embarrass you at every step, and prevent your carrying into effect those regular plans in which it is essential that they must join, for their own advantage. Your *dairy plans* for instance, which have succeeded so well in Switzerland, would not do in this country, at least, not without a century's experiments. Paddy would *fall* to disputing with the *dairyman*, would go to law with him for his share of the *common* cow's milk, or for her *trespassing*, or he would pledge his eighth or sixteenth part of *her* for his rent, or his bottle of whisky, and the cow would be pounded and *re-pledged*, and re-pounded and bailed and *canted* : and things impossible for you to foresee, perhaps impossible for your English imagination to conceive, would happen to the cow and the dairyman. In all your attempts to serve my poor dear countrymen, you would find, that whilst you were *demonstrating* to them what would be their greatest advantage, they would be always making out a short cut, not a royal road, but a bog-road to ther own *by*-objects. Paddy would be most grateful, most sincerely, warmly grateful, to you, and would bless your honour, and your honour's honour, with all his heart ; but he would, nevertheless, not scruple on every practicable occasion, to——to——to cheat, I will not say,—that is a coarse word,—but to circumvent you ; at every turn you would find Paddy trying to walk round you, begging your honour's pardon—hat off, bowing to the ground to you—all the while laughing in your face if you found him out, and, if he outwitted you, loving you all the better for being such an innocent.

Seriously, there is no doubt that the Irish people would, like all other people, learn honesty, punctuality, order, and economy, with proper motives and proper training, and in due time, but do not leave *time* out of your account. Very sorry should I be, either in jest or earnest, to discourage any of that enthusiasm of benevolence which animates you in their favour. But, as Paddy himself would say, Sure, it is better to be disappointed in the beginning, than the end. Each failure in attempts to do good in this country, discourages the friends of humanity, and encourages the railers, scoffers, and croakers, and puts us back in hope, perhaps half a century : therefore, think well before you begin, and, begin upon a small scale, which you may extend as you please afterwards.

You may, in some happy instances, find generous, rich, and judicious landlords, who will assist you ; but do not depend upon it, that this will be general, else you will be cruelly disappointed, not in promise, but in performance.

The mixture of agriculture and manufactures, I have no doubt makes the happiest system for the people, and whether this tended most to the riches of a state or not, the balance of comfort and happiness would decide a friend of humanity in its favour.

★   ★   ★

No. 24. THE FLEETWOOD HOUSE BOARDING SCHOOL

The Lindfield boarding school for boys was not the only one in which William Allen was interested. In 1824 with Grizell Birkbeck, Anna Hanbury, Luke Howard, Samuel Gurney and other prominent Quakers, Allen was the moving spirit in starting a girls' boarding school in Fleetwood House, Stoke Newington. This was on a somewhat ambitious scale, the terms were fifty pounds per annum, washing not included, and the subjects to be taught comprehended

English, Writing, Arithmetic, Geography, Astronomy, and the use of the Globes, Ancient and Modern History, Elements of Mathematics, of Physics or Experimental Philosophy, Chemistry, Natural History—the French Language and Needlework.

The parents of the pupils were members of the Society of Friends and the girls wore the plain Quaker dress with the stiff Quaker bonnets which greatly excited the mirth of the pupils of another girls' school in the neighbourhood.

The Head Mistress was Susanna Corder, a Minister of the Society of Friends and a woman of some literary and scholastic attainments ; with Lucy Bradshaw she edited Allen's diary. When the original number of pupils grew from twelve to fifty, she was assisted by mistresses, William Allen taught the sciences and the Italian poet Ugo Foscolo was Italian master for a short period.

The summer holidays extended over six weeks. The great event of the year was the visit to the Annual Meeting of the Society of Friends at Devonshire House, Bishopsgate. The girls were taken to the City in a special conveyance resembling an omnibus, devised by Susanna Corder.

Joseph Pease wrote of the school some amusing doggerel verses ' A yearly Meeting Epistle from Friend Joseph in London to his cousin Anne in the Country '.

Dear Coz, in my last (which I sent by Friend P . . .)
I shewed the advantage as well as renown
That our body of Friends cannot fail to acquire
By the Female Establishment 2 miles from Town.

Where the pupils imbibe such astounding variety
of Stores intellectual—I solemnly vow
Since the earliest days of the Quaker Society
Such achievements by girls were ne'er heard of till now.

No science, no art, in their tribe is a mystery
The path of the earth and the tides of the sea,
Cosmography, Algebra, Chemistry, History,
To those juvenile Blues are a mere A.B.C.

And in languages—oh you'd not credit their skill !
One can scarce name a tongue, Coz, but what they can reason in,
Greek, Hebrew, French, Latin, Italian, at will,
With Irish and Welch for occasional seasoning.

Nay more—if our principles did but permit
I doubt not ev'n fortification and gunnery
Might be added with ease as a kind of tit-bit,
To enliven the studies at N(ewingto)n Nunnery.

'Tis true some reports have transpired of caballing
From the fair inmates dreading they elsewhere must roam
Should Hymen take from the lectures of Allen
The Champion of Colonies settled at home.

The straight path of Truth the dear Girls keep their feet in
And ah ! it would do your heart good Cousin Anne
To see them arriving at G(racehurc)h Street Meeting
All snugly packed up, 25 in a van.

The reference to William Allen is clearly to his forthcoming marriage to Grizell Birkbeck, see page 107.

From *The Chronicles of Fleetwood House*, by A. J. Shirren.

★   ★   ★

No. 25. DISTILLATION OF OIL OF PEPPERMINT

Of the twenty-two items in the cost of this work, the biggest is for the herb at £10 10s. 0d. per ton ; the hire of horses and waggons, including a horse for Luke, 7s. 2d., their corn and hay cost £14 8s. 8d., wood and coal for heating the furnace £15 12s. 6d., beer, bread, cheese and meat, £2 5s. 6d. Unskilled labour was then called attendance and the only item shown is for two men for three weeks and two days, £8 0s. 0d., that is, 4s. per day of twelve hours which was the current rate. When the costs and expenses were totalled a deduction of £2 6s. 0d. was shown for twenty-three loads of dung from the horses at 2s. per load. Accurate costing was evidently known in 1799.

*　　　*　　　*

No. 26. WILLIAM WEST, 1793–1851

William West was born at Wandsworth in 1793 ; his parents were members of the Society of Friends.

He must have entered the laboratory at Plough Court at an early age, as his name is attached to several costings of chemicals and galenicals during and just after the Allen and Howard period. In 1816 he opened a druggist's business in Leeds. For many years he showed his interest in the scientific as well as the commercial side of pharmacy by contributing to the Leeds Philosophical and Literary Society no fewer than twenty-eight papers. He filled the posts of Literary Secretary, Vice-President and President of this Society.

He was also interested in the work of the Leeds Mechanics' Institute and was Vice-President of the Geological and Polytechnic Society of the West Riding of Yorkshire. In 1842 he was elected an Associate of the Institute of Civil Engineers and was awarded the Telford Medal in 1846 for his paper on *Water for Locomotive Engines*. He was elected F.R.S. in 1846.

In addition to the above, he was lecturer on chemistry to the Leeds School of Medicine from 1831 to 1846. His health broke down in 1846 and he died the same year as R. Phillips, 1851.

He was, with John Dalton and Sir David Brewster, one of that little band of promoters or cultivators of science who assembled at York in 1831 when the British Association for the Advancement of Science was discussed. The first meeting was held at Oxford in 1832.

*　　　*　　　*

APPENDICES

No. 27. WILLIAM ALLEN'S ACCOUNT IN HIS
        DIARY OF THE WEDDING OF HIS
        DAUGHTER MARY WITH CORNELIUS
        HANBURY I

1822

Second Month 20th. Rose abt. 7. Had the headache
                    Thermometer, inside   54.
                         out at 7   41.
          Barom: last night,   30—30.
                 this morning,   30—12.
Breakfast. Weather cloudy. I took Mary and Cornelius to town
in the chariot, set them down at the Meeting House and went to
Plough Court to take up Thomas Clarkson and Dan, brought them
to Meeting. My head was rather painful and nervous system a good
deal shaken. The meeting was held in the women's Meeting House.
The company consisted of :

{ Capel Hanbury,
{ Charlotte Hanbury,

{ Cornelius Hanbury,
{ Mary Allen,

{ William Allen,
{ Anna Hanbury,

{ Daniel Bell Hanbury,
{ Jane Hamilton,

{ Daniel Bell,
{ Eleanor Bell,

{ John Hamilton,
{ Katherine Hamilton,

{ Samuel Allen,
{ Phebe Allen,

{ Joseph Allen,
{ Anna Allen,

{ Benjamin Allen,
{ Ann Allen

{ Joseph Fry,
{ Elizabeth J. Fry,

299

{ Samuel Gurney,
Elizabeth Gurney,

{ John Capper,
Katherine Capper,

{ Daniel Bell Junr,
Sarah Capper,

{ Thomas Clarkson,
Grizel Birkbeck,

{ Mary Chapman,
Ellen Chapman,

{ Abel Chapman,
Rebecca Chapman,

these went in this order into meeting and besides these the following were at Thomas Christys.

Mary Stacey. Ann Brewster. Eleanor Hamilton. Peter Bedford. Robert and E. Jermyn. John and Julia Venning. Elizabeth Fry (cousin to E. J. Fry).

The meeting was rather long in gathering but proved very large. I should think that 800 persons were present and among the rest my old Friend Thomas Furley Forster and Dr. Steinkopf, the Secretary of the Bible Society. After a living Testimony from dear Mary Stacey, our precious E. J. Fry was sweetly engaged in supplication, so that I believe most present were tendered. After 11 o'clock dear Cornelius and Mary rose, (I sat quite close to my child), and expressed the usual form of words in taking each other in marriage and in that suitable gravity, distinctness, and feeling, which could but be universally felt. When the Company began to sign, there was a little bustle and some went out but this soon subsided, and even while the signing went on a holy solemnity prevailed and I felt that the burden of the word was coming upon me so that when the company had signed I stood up and had something given me sweetly to communicate. I say sweetly as to my own feelings, and soon after I sat down we retired. The certificate was signed by 280 persons, the dear children are generally beloved. We did not stay long in the room above stairs, but Cornelius, Mary and I went to my dear mother who was very much affected at receiving us under these circumstances—we had a sweet little uniting opportunity. After this took them in the chariot to Clapham the house of our dear and generous Thomas and Rebecca Christy, who with their dear children Rachel and Charlotte had been making great preparations to entertain the marriage company. The weather was gloomy with a cold raw wind and my head and stomach much out of order but having a humble belief that the dear Master was not far off I was nicely supported and things went on very comfortably. I had a long conversation while walking in the garden with Thomas Clarkson. We dined about half past 3. Dear Rebecca had a written List of the order in which all the Company were to be seated at table which was called over,—I sat at Rebecca's left hand, Sister Charlotte at her right, there were 25 at our table and 17 at the table in the next room. Rebecca had contrived to have the same kind of dinner on each table, there was a profusion of good things.

After Tea, when being all collected in the two great rooms above the hall and the folding doors thrown open we had a memorable meeting. Dear E. J. Fry and I sat together. After we had sat about a quarter of an hour I was engaged in exhortation to the younger part of the company and I trust in a good degree of the power. Dear E. J. Fry followed very sweetly and lastly our precious Rebecca with these words addressed to Cornelius and Mary. 'The Lord bless you, we bless you in the Name of the Lord', this vibrated I believe through all hearts. Lastly dear Catherine Capper concluded in a very acceptable manner in supplication. After this the company separated but it was more than ½ past 8 before we got off. I took my children in the carriage, Tom on the box, to Stoke Newington which we reached about 10.

Cousin Birkbeck brought sister, also Katherine and Sarah Capper who lodge with us. Sarah is Bridesmaid. Supper K. and S. Capper. Evening bright star higher. We all felt that this has been a day which the Lord has blessed. The pain in my head pretty much went off.

*   *   *

No. 28. DANIEL HANBURY'S GARDENS

William Hanbury Aggs, 1871–1953, a grandson of Daniel Bell Hanbury who lived at Hollywood, Nightingale Lane, Clapham Common, in the nineties of the last century, could recall the extensive gardens of Number Three which adjoined those of Hollywood. He remembered the large plant of medicinal rhubarb and particularly recalls 'the olive tree which was the first to fruit in this country'.

An inquiry at the Royal Botanic Gardens, Kew, brought the following information :

The catalogue of the Hanbury Herbarium compiled by E. M. Holmes in 1892 for the Museum of the Pharmaceutical Society lists the following :—

Olea Europoea Branchlet bearing fruit ; South Wall at Clapham Common, 10 Jan., 1864.

In Bentley & Trimen, Medicinal Plants, 1880, under figure 172, *Olea Europoea*, this reference is given :

In England it flowers freely enough and under favourable circumstances will even produce fruit, as in the late D. Hanbury's garden at Clapham Common, near London.

The first record of an olive tree to fruit in this country was at Camden House in 1719. *Millers Gardeners Chronicle 7th Edition.*

★   ★   ★

No. 29. THE HANBURY MEMORIAL MEDAL

MEDALLISTS

1881. Friedrich August Flückiger
(died 1894)
1883. John Eliot Howard
(died 1883)
1885. George Dragendorff
(died 1898)
1887. William Dymock
(died 1892)
1889. Gustave Planchon
(died 1900)
1891. Julius Oswald Hesse
(died   )
1893. Johann Micheal Maisch
(died 1893)
1895. August E. Vogl
(died 1909)

1897. John Elishee De Vrij
(died 1898)
1899. Albert Ladenburg
(died 1911)
1901. George Watt (died 1930)
1903. Eugene Collin (died 1919)
1905. Ernst Schmidt (died 1921)
1907. David Hooper
(died 1947)
1909. Alexander Tschirch
(died 1940)
1911. Eugene Leger (died 1939)
1913. Frederick Belding Power
(died 1927)
1915. Edward Morell Holmes
(died 1930)

1917. Henry George Greenish (died 1933)
1922. Emile Perrot
1927. Thomas Anderson Henry
1929. Henry Hurd Rusby (died 1941)
1931. Hermann Thomas (died 1931)
1933. George Barger (died 1939)

1935. Frank Lee Pyman (died 1944)
1937. Richard Wasicky
1939. Thomas Edward Wallis
1941. Harold King
1943. Sir Henry Hallett Dale
1945. Hindrik Haijo Janssonius
1947. Hans Fluck

★　　　★　　　★

No. 30.

On January 1st, 1954, the Directors of the Company were :

Frederick Capel Hanbury, Chairman	(See page 207)
John Capel Hanbury, Vice-Chairman	(,, ,, 208)
Cyril Wheatley Maplethorpe, Managing Director	(,, ,, 204)
Frederick Arthur Axe	(See below)
William Mackman Clayson	(,, ,,)
Francis John Conduit	(,, ,,)
Gilbert Townley Gamble	(,, ,,)
William John Rennie	(,, ,,)

Frederick Arthur Axe was born at Kettering in 1912, qualified as a Chartered Accountant in 1934 and joined the London Office of Price, Waterhouse & Co. He served during the Second World War in the Royal Artillery and left the Army in November 1945 with the rank of Major. He returned to Price, Waterhouse for a few months and in February 1946 joined the Company as Financial Accountant, becoming Chief Accountant four months later. He was appointed to the Board in 1951.

William Mackman Clayson was born in 1902 and was educated at the Laurence Sheriff School, Rugby, and the School of Pharmacy, Bloomsbury Square, London, whence he qualified as a Pharmaceutical Chemist in 1924. He joined the Company in 1928 and for several years was a medical representative. In 1933 he became Assistant to the General Manager and occupied a number of administrative posts until his election to the Board in 1947. In 1948 he was allotted specific responsibility for liaison with the Overseas Subsidiary Companies and is President of Allen & Hanburys Co. Ltd., Toronto, Canada.

Francis John Conduit was born in 1905 and educated at Farnham Grammar School and the Technical College, Portsmouth, where he qualified as a Pharmaceutical Chemist. He joined the Company in 1929, serving first in the capacity of a representative and later as Manager of the Bethnal Green Factory. He was elected to the Board in 1951 and while concerned principally with the home interests of the Company, he has undertaken a number of journeys and negotiations in the United States, Canada and various European countries.

Gilbert Townley Gamble was born in 1903 and is the eldest son of F. W. Gamble. He joined the Company in 1926 and obtained an extensive knowledge of the various aspects of the business by working in turn in the different departments, both at Ware and Bethnal Green. For a time he was concerned with cod-liver oil production both in Norway and at Aberdeen, but in 1930, having a particular interest in engineering and mechanical matters, he entered the Surgical Factory and since that time has made the surgical side of the business his principal concern. He was elected to the Board in 1947 and is a Fellow of the Institute of British Surgical Technicians.

William John Rennie was born in 1901 at Greenock, Scotland, and was articled to a firm of Accountants at Newcastle-upon-Tyne. In 1926 he was admitted an Associate Member of the Institute of Chartered Accountants and the following year joined the staff of Messrs. Deloitte, Plender, Griffiths & Co. In 1931 he was appointed Chief Accountant to the Rhokana Corporation Limited, a position which he held until his appointment as Secretary of Allen & Hanburys in 1945. He was elected to the Board in 1947.

*　　　*　　　*

No. 31. AN ORDER DATED 1794 FROM WILLIAM AND ROBINSON, NEW LONDON, NEWFOUNDLAND

SURGEON'S INSTRUMENTS

2 cases amputating compleat, bedded in mahogany cases, neat.
2 Do Trepauning   do   neatly bedded.
3 Do dissecting   do
1 Do Lithotomy   do   completely bedded and ground.

2 Setts obstetric do
3 Trocars and Canulas in cases.
2 Setts for Fistulas
6 Male Catheters.
6 Female Do in cases
1 doz. Crown Lancets.
6 doz. Common do
6 Lancet Cases completely tipt each to contain 3 Lancets.
6 dozen paper Lancet Cases.
3 Cases Crooked needles, different sizes.
2 Setts Pocket Instruments Complete first quality.
6 half Setts   do   do
2 Ivory Handles spring tooth drawers best kind.
6 Common Tooth Keys.
2 Pewter pint syringes in cases.
1 Sett Cupping or Scarificator.

*   *   *

No. 32

Allen & Hanburys Limited was incorporated on the 29th December, 1893, with an Authorized Capital of £75,000, consisting of 750 Shares of £100 each The Company purchased most of the assets of the business of Allen & Hanburys, of which the Partners were Cornelius Hanbury and Frederick Janson Hanbury. The purchase consideration was £60,000, and it was satisfied by an allotment to the Vendors of £20,000 in Ordinary Shares and £40,000 in Preference Shares. The assets taken over can be summarized as follows :

Fixed Assets	£42,169
Trade Investments	1,550
Current Assets	40,674
	84,393
Current Liabilities	24,393
	£60,000

The Consolidated Balance Sheet of Allen & Hanburys Limited and its Subsidiary Companies as at the 30th June, 1953, gives the following figures :

Fixed Assets	£1,239,143
Trade Investments	1,211
Current Assets	2,730,551
	3,970,905
Current Liabilities, etc. . . .	999,740
	£2,971,165

These Net Assets have been provided by :

Issued Capital	£800,600
Reserves	1,193,865
4% First Mortgage Debenture Stock 1956/71	976,700
	£2,971,165

The Authorized Share Capital, which at the beginning was £75,000, was at the 30th June, 1953, £1,000,000.

A large proportion of the profits earned by the Company have been 'ploughed back', as will be seen from the 'Reserves' figures. It was not possible to finance the expansion of the business entirely by this means, and from time to time new Capital was created, and the whole, or part, of this new Authorized Capital issued as and when the need arose. The conditions of the money market at the relevant times determined the terms of the issues. The classes of Shares at the 30th June, 1953, were :

	£ Authorized	£ Issued	£
Shares of £1 each :			
6% Cumulative 'A' Preference	100,000	100,000	
6% Cumulative 'B' Preference	75,000	75,000	
6% Cumulative 'C' Preference	100,000	100,000	
7% Cumulative Preferred Ordinary	1000,00	100,000	
8% Cumulative 'A' Preferred Ordinary	100,000	100,000	
Ordinary	525,000	325,600	
	£1,000,000	800,600	

These figures give the permanent share capital only. From time to time there was loan capital, such as Debentures, and temporary borrowing from the banks. A consideration of the various steps taken to provide the necessary finance makes an interesting study of one aspect of the Company's progress as it was effected in a period of very important changes in the financial position of this country.

An account of an intermediate capital structure will illustrate the later part of this history of change. At the 30th June, 1939, the Balance Sheet showed the following position :

Fixed Assets	£548,972
Investment in Stocks and Shares .	47,737
Current Assets	443,534
	1,040,243
Current Liabilities	162,475
	£877,768

This was represented by :

Share Capital	£575,000
Reserves	229,783
4% Debenture Stock . . .	72,985
	£877,768

During the years of the Second World War it was impracticable to raise permanent capital although the Company's business was expanding. After the war the Company's participation in the continued progress in the medical and pharmaceutical practice intensified the difficulties on the financial side. The Company's bankers, Barclays Bank Limited, helped materially during this difficult period by providing loan and overdraft facilities.

It was obvious, however, that new permanent capital had to be sought not only from Shareholders but from the general public. In January, 1951, the Directors announced that the necessary sanction had been obtained to an issue of £1,000,000 Debenture Stock. When the invitation to subscribe was sent to the shareholders, customers and general public, the response was a total application for nearly £11,000,000.

Very quickly, there came indications that the growth in the volume of business would entail the raising of further capital. This new capital would have to be equity capital.

In May 1952, 203,500 new Ordinary Shares were issued by way of rights at a price of 40s. each. This method enabled a number of the general public to acquire Ordinary Shares of Allen & Hanburys Limited for the first time.

At the 30th June, 1953, the total number of holders of shares and debentures in Allen & Hanburys Limited was approximately 5,500.

INDEX

INDEX

INDEX

BIBLIOGRAPHY

Lettsom, His Life and Times, by James Johnston Abraham.
William Allen, by Irene M. Ashby.
Memorials, by Christine Majolier Alsop.
Family Fragments respecting R. L. Beck and Rachel Lucas, by William Beck.
The Quakers, Their Story and Their Message, by A. Neave Brayshaw.
History of Pharmacy, by Bell and Redwood.
A Century of Education, 1808–1908, being the Centenary History of the British and Foreign School Society, by H. Bryan Binns.
History of the Society of Apothecaries, by B. R. B. Barrett.
Poetical Works of Alexander Pope, ed. Robert Carruthers, (4 vols.).
A Portraiture of Quakerism, by Thomas Clarkson, (3 vols.).
William Cookworthy, by Theodore Compton.
Morris Letters, ed. J. H. Davies.
History of William Penn, by William Hepworth Dixon.
The Englishman and His Food, by Jack Drummond.
William Allen, His Life and Labours. Eclectic Review.
The Spitalfields Genius, by J. Fayle.
Extracts from the Letters and Writings of the late Joseph Gurney Bevan, ed. Josiah Forster.
Dr. John Fothergill and His Friends, by R. Hingston Fox, M.D.
Royal Dukes, by Roger Fulford.
Pharmacographia, by Flückiger and Hanbury.
Rise of the Tin-plate Industry, by F. W. Gibbs, (Annals of Science).
A History of the Bevan Family, by Audrey Nona Gamble.
The Operative Chemist, by Samuel Frederick Gray.
A Year in Europe, by John Griscom.
Elizabeth Fry's Journeys on the Continent, by Elizabeth Gurney.
Surgeons All, by Harvey Graham.
Minutes of the Society for Philosophical Experiments and Observations, ed. Bryan Higgins.
Science Papers, by Joseph Ince.
History of Ware, by Edith Hunt.
"Records and Recollections, 1761–1821," by James Jenkins. (Typescript.)
The Hanbury Family, by A. A. Locke.
A Quaker Post Bag, by Mrs. Godfrey Locker Lampson.
The History of the Pennsylvania Hospital, 1751–1895, by Thomas G. Morton, M.D., and Frank Woodbury, M.D.
Additional Morris Letters, by Hugh Owen.
Life, by Robert Owen.
Quakers in Science and Industry, by Raistrick.
Memoirs of William Allen, by James Sherman.
Leaves from the Past, Diary of John Allen, by Clement Young Sturge.

BIBLIOGRAPHY

Memories of Jordans, by W. H. Summers.
All available volumes of the *Journals* of the Friends' Historical Society.
Dictionary of National Biography.
Early bound volumes of the *Pharmaceutical Journal*.
Daniel Hanbury's Note Books.
Three-volume Diary of William Allen.

Date Due